ELEMENTS

OF

MATHEMATICAL BIOLOGY

ELEMENTS

of MATHEMATICAL

BIOLOGY

Formerly published under the title Elements of Physical Biology

BY

ALFRED J. LOTKA, M.A., D. Sc.

Dover Publications, Inc., New York

This Dover edition, first published in 1956, is an
unabridged republication of the first edition of the
work originally published by The Williams and
Wilkins Co., Inc., in 1924 under the title *Elements
of Physical Biology*. It includes corrections from
the late Dr. Lotka's notes, and a complete list of
his publications.

Standard Book Number: 486-60346-6
Library of Congress Catalog Card Number: 57-2438

Manufactured in the United States of America
Dover Publications, Inc.
180 Varick Street
New York, N. Y. 10014

DEDICATED
TO THE MEMORY
OF
JOHN HENRY POYNTING

"Voilà un homme qui a fait son mieux pour ennuyer
      deux ou trois cents de ses concitoyens; mais son
intention était bonne: il n'y a pas de quoi détruire
Persépolis."   —Voltaire

PREFACE

The preface is that part of a book which is written last, placed first, and read least. As I approach my concluding task I am moved to reflect why a preface should be written at all. This question, if followed into all the intricacies of which it holds potentiality, should apparently result in a composition new in literature, a Preface to the Preface. Such precedent should not be lightly established, for it suggests a vista of future degenerations after the pattern of Josiah Royce's infinite succession of maps, each containing within itself its own replica on a reduced scale. But without going to such lengths as this, the philosophy of the preface may perhaps briefly be summarized to this effect, that it is the author's subjective introduction to the more objective matter that should follow. Here he may, if this is deemed of any interest, say something regarding the circumstances that gave origin to the work, and the conditions under which it came into being. He may express his feelings as to its alleged purpose, and may follow custom by giving voice to pious wishes as to the function which the product of his presumptive mind may fulfill in an Universe in which no event, however trivial—be it no more than the addition of one more book to the groaning library shelves—is without distant reverberations.

As to origin, the first plan of the work was laid about 1902, in the author's student days in Leipzig. The development of the topic is recorded, in outline, in various publications, of which the first appeared in 1907 in the American Journal of Science. Reference to this and to its various sequels will be found in pertinent places in the text that follows. The last stage of the work, arrangement of the matter in collected form, and filling in the flesh about the skeleton framework elaborated in the journal literature, was carried out at the Johns Hopkins University upon the invitation of the Department of Biometry and Vital Statistics. For the courtesies so extended to him the author wishes here to express his thanks, as well as for the interest shown in the progress of the work by Dr. Raymond Pearl and the members of the Department, notably Drs. W. T. Howard, L. J. Reed and J. R. Miner. Outside the walls of this University I think with very particular appreciation of the never-failing succor in times of mathematical trouble, which I found at the hands of Prof. F. R. Sharpe of Cornell University; also of the patient assistance, upon more than one occasion, from Prof. W. B. Fite of Columbia University. And I gratefully recall encouragement received from Dr. G. K. Burgess, Director of the Bureau of Standards, especially in the earlier stages of the work, when encouragement was most needed.

Acknowledgment has been made in the text for numerous quotations. The somewhat extended excerpts from certain articles published in the Scientific Monthly call for special notice here, and I wish to express my thanks both to the author, Prof. G. W. Martin, and to the Editor of the Monthly, for permission to quote thus at length from its pages. I am similarly indebted to the Editor of Harpers Magazine for permission to reproduce here certain portions of an article from my pen, entitled *"Biassed Evolution"*, which originally appeared in the May issue (1924) of that publication.

Toward the publishers, Messrs. Williams and Wilkins and in particular Mr. C. C. Thomas, I have every occasion to entertain feelings of the most cordial appreciation. Through their courteous attentions the business of bookmaking was made a pleasure.

My greatest debt is acknowledged in the dedication. Whatever merits this book possesses may well be credited to the influence and teaching of Poynting. There is little danger that its faults shall be charged to his account.

As to the topic of the work it seems unnecessary to say many words here, inasmuch as a delineation of this has been made the subject of a special chapter on *The Program of Physical Biology*. Only this explanation it may be well to offer here, that, as proposed in Chapter V, the term *Physical Biology* has been employed to denote the broad application of physical principles and methods in the contemplation of biological *systems*, whereas *Biophysics*, in common parlance, relates rather to the special field of certain physical aspects of the life processes of the *individual*. With this terminology, Physical Biology would comprehend Biophysics within its scope.

The writer cannot in reason expect to have produced a work without blemish. Even an approach to such absolute perfection is the rare privilege of a few. He would, however, be unjustified in addressing the reading public at all if he did not entertain the hope that, despite shortcomings, these pages may bring to the reader new assets, here and there a new piece for his mental furniture, now and again a new perspective, a new comprehensive outlook over a body of facts and relations in themselves perhaps familiar.

The work has been largely one of systematization, and of development of method. Factual material has been introduced essentially for the purpose of illustrating the point of view to be set forth. There seems therefore hardly any occasion for apologetic explanations that anything of the nature of completeness in the presentation of pertinent facts was in nowise aimed at. Indeed, it must be obvious upon most casual reflection that such completeness, in a subject of the amplitude of that here taken in view, could be achieved only in a cyclopedic work of several tiers of volumes.

Considerable care has been taken to cite in detail the sources consulted. It was felt that, on account of the wide dispersal of these citations over a broad field of scientific literature, few readers could be expected to be familiar with all the branches of pertinent library lore, and for this reason a collation of such references should have a value of its own, even apart from the text. At the same time the compilation of anything like a complete bibliography could not be undertaken on the present occasion.

It is hoped that the mathematical mien of certain pages will not deter biologists and others, who may be disposed to look askance at symbols of the art, from acquiring an interest in other portions of the book. Biometricians will, presumably, not shrink on this score; to them, and to physicists, (whom I should greatly wish to number among my readers) I may perhaps confess that I have striven to infuse the mathematical spirit also into those pages on which symbols do not present themselves to the eye. For this I offer no apology.

For the sake of space economy recapitulary paragraphs have, as a rule, not been given a place in the text. An exception has however been made in Chapters XX, XXXIII and XXIV, the last of which, in particular, resumes and amplifies somewhat certain phases of the topics discussed in earlier chapters. The reader who may wish briefly to review the substance of his reading as he proceeds, should find suitable assistance in the rather detailed *Analytical Synopsis of Chapters* that has been placed immediately after the Table of Contents. And finally, a bird's eye survey of the general field covered in this work can be obtained by consulting the Tabular Synopsis at the end.

Here, then, I make my exit from the prefatory stage and commend my work to the tender mercies of the reader; not without some trepidation, for I recall how Voltaire said of one: "Il fit une philosophie comme on fait un bon roman; tout parut vraisemblable, et rien ne fut vrai;" and there comes to mind the language still plainer of de Maupassant—"Depuis qu'ils ont appris à lire et à écrire, la bêtise latente se dégage." I trust that the reader's response to these pages may not be too fervent an Amen to the prayer of *The Sceptical Chymist* "It is to be hoped that these men, finding that they can not longer write impertinently and absurdly . . . . will be reduced either to write nothing, or books that may teach us something . . . . ; and so, ceasing to trouble the world with riddles or impertinencies, we shall either by their books receive an advantage, or by their silence escape an inconvenience."

ALFRED J. LOTKA.

Johns Hopkins University, May, 1924.

CONTENTS

PART I. GENERAL PRINCIPLES

CHAPTER I

CHAPTER II

CHAPTER III

CHAPTER IV

CHAPTER V

PART II. KINETICS

CHAPTER VI

CHAPTER VII

CHAPTER VIII

CHAPTER IX

CHAPTER X

PART III. STATICS

CHAPTER XI

CHAPTER XII

xi

LIST OF ILLUSTRATIONS

LIST OF TABLES

ANALYTICAL SYNOPSIS OF CHAPTERS

PART I. GENERAL PRINCIPLE

succession the same series of events. In an evolving system each day is unlike any other day, 21—Evolution not a mere changeful sequence, 21—Abortive attempts to formulate the direction of evolution, 21—These attempt definition in terms of a single component, 22—Such definitions are foredoomed to failure, a successful definition must be framed in terms of the evolving system as a whole, 22—Evolution is the history of a system in the course of irreversible transformation, 24—Scope of this definition: What it excludes; what it includes 24—The line of division depends on the nature and extent of our knowledge regarding the system, 25—This is in harmony with the fact that problems of evolution are largely problems of probability, 25—All real transformations are irreversible, hence all real history is evolution, 26—What then is gained by the definition? 26—It indicates the direction of evolution as the direction of irreversible transformations, the direction of increasing entropy, 26—Example of pendulum. Irreversible feature introduced by frictional force, 27—Inertia-free or completely damped systems, 28—Accelerations vanish with velocities, 29—Velocities are single-valued functions of configuration, 29.

Chapter III. The Statistical Meaning of Irreversibility. Apparent irreversibility (progressiveness in time) of certain theoretically periodic processes, 30—Their periodicity, with eventual return to initial state, never observed in practice, 30—Explanation of this discrepancy: Macroscopic model illustrative of irreversibility of gaseous diffusion, 30—Return to initial state possible, but exceedingly rare (highly improbable), 31—The model is competent to illustrate also the highly improbable event of return to initial state, 32—Dynamical theory indicates not only occasional but *periodic* return to initial state, 32—A second model illustrates this also, 32—Evolution as passage from less probable to more probable states, 35—Inadequacy of this "principle": it is indefinite in failing to specify the characteristic with respect to which probability is reckoned; and it is incomplete in failing to draw attention to certain energy relations, 35—Irreversibility is relative, depending upon the means naturally available or arbitrarily permitted to operate upon the system, 35—Significance of this in organic world: Macroscopic irreversibility of diffusion processes in nature, 36—Need of a method of mathematical analysis to deal with cases intermediate, in specified degree, between the following two extremes: (a) Wholly indiscriminate (pure chance) operation upon material in bulk. (b) Wholly determinate operation, with nothing left to chance, upon materials discriminated and acted upon in detail, piece by piece, and circumstance by circumstance, 36—This method must take account of degree of perfection of the mechanical and psychic equipment by which each organism reacts upon its environment, 37—Senses as a means of overcoming chance, 37—Physical significance of our subjective sense of forward direction in time, which finds no expression in the differential equations of pure dynamics, 37—This subjective time sense may be related to the influence of initial conditions in dynamics, 38—But the direction of evolution seems related rather to that directedness in time which is characteristic of aperiodic or seemingly aperiodic processes, 38—Inadequacy of thermodynamic method, 39—The linking of evolution with the concepts of thermodynamics and statistical mechanics is instructive as suggesting a conception of the direction of evolution, the direction of increasing entropy, increasing probability, 39—This point of view, however, is inadequate for application to concrete cases of organic evolution, because data are furnished in terms unsuited to the methods of thermodynamics, 39—Neither are existing methods of statistical mechanics, as applied to molecules and the like, helpful; the instrument is ill adapted to the scale of the object, 39—New method needed, that shall accept its problems in terms of biological data, as thermodynamics accepts its problems in terms of physical data; a General Theory of State, an "Allgemeine Zustandslehre" 39.

Chapter IV. Evolution Conceived as a Redistribution. Evolution viewed as a redistribution of matter among the components of a system, 41—System described by statement of mass of each component, and indication of value of certain parameters, 41—Analytical expression of history of system given by relations or equations established between the variables and parameters defining the state of the system, 41—Fundamental equations usually simplest in form of differential equations, 42—Particular form of equations of evolving systems, 42—General form of equations of evolving system, 43—Equations as applied to life-bearing system, 43—Definition of the components arbitrary but conclusions relate to the components as defined, 44—Relation of evolution, as here conceived, to the problem of the origin of species, 44—Inter-group and intra-group evolution, 44—Analytical indication of intra-group evolution, 45—Fundamental equations resemble in form the equations for an inertia-free or completely damped system, 47—Fundamental equations, as here given, may not cover all cases, but are at any rate of very wide scope, 47—Equations interpreted to include possible lag or lead effects, 47—Singular implications of lag and lead effects; possible relation to phenomena of memory and will, 48—Appearance of lag and lead effects in equations may, however, be spurious, 48.

Chapter V. The Program of Physical Biology. Systematization and division of subject, 49—General mechanics of evolution, 49—Macro-mechanics and micro-mechanics, 50—Statistical mechanics as the connecting link, 50—Stoichiometry, the study of mass relations (material transformations), 50—Energetics or Dynamics, the study of the energy transformations, 50—Kinetics and Statics, 51—Equilibrium and steady states, 51—Moving equilibria, 51—Displacement of equilibrium; Le Chatelier's principle, 52—Sociological analogues of forces and "quasi-dynamics" (economics), 52—The term *Physical Biology* to be used to cover the territory indicated in this chapter, 52—Methods of obtaining data, 52—Chart of Program of Physical Biology, 53—Methods of elaborating data, 54.

PART II. KINETICS

Chapter VI. The Fundamental Equations of Kinetics of Evolving Systems. General case, 57—Some implications of the fundamental equations in their general form, 57—Equations of constraint, 58—Elimination of variables. Introduction of constants A, 58—Evolution with parameters P, Q and A constant, 58—Equilibria or steady states, 59—Number and character of

economic systems, 303—Rent as a measure or index of *population pressure* 304—But population pressure exists independently of rent, e.g., in species other than man, 304—Distant analogy of law of population pressure to gas law, 305—Law of urban concentration, 306—Biological background of population pressure, 307—Influence of population density on rate of reproduction (Pearl and Parker), 308—Influence of population density on duration of life (Pearl and Parker), 309—Topographic parameters during period of diffusion, 311— Willis' theory of Age and Area, 311—Climatic parameters, 317—Their laboratory investigation (Pearl and Parker), 319—Parameters of state and the analytical condition for equilibrium, 319—Thermodynamic analogy, 320— Inversion of typical problem of thermodynamics, 321—Systems of Quasi-Dynamics, 321.

PART IV. DYNAMICS

Chapter XXIV. The Energy Transformers of Nature. The fundamental equations of Kinetics do not exhibit any explicit reference to dynamical or energetic relations, 325—*But certain of the components S are energy transformers*, 325—Fundamental characteristics of energy transformers, 325— Cyclic working; output and efficiency, 326—Thermodynamic law of maximum output, 326—Reversible and irreversible processes, 327—Composite and coupled transformers, 327—Accumulators, 328—Chemical accumulators, 328— Growth, 328—Law of growth, 328—Anabions and catabions, 329—Systems of transformers, 329—Plant and animal as coupled transformer, 330—The World Engine, 331—Share of sun's energy that falls to different constituents of world, 331—Share falling to organic circulation, 331—Relation of transformer cycle to circulation of the elements, 334—Influence of limiting factors upon working of world engine, 334—Evolution of the World Engine, 335.

Chapter XXV. Relation of the Transformer to Available Sources. Distributed and localized sources of energy, 336—*Random* and *aimed* collisions, 337 —Negative correlation, 337—The correlating apparatus, 338—Component elements of correlating apparatus: Depictors, Receptors, Elaborators, Adjustors, 339—Receptor-effector circuit begins and ends in environment, 340— Significance of this, 340—Correlating apparatus not peculiar to living organisms, 340—Mechanical imitations of living beings (automatons) 341—Chess as a conventional model of the battlefield of life, 343—The biological contest considered in the light of the chess analogy, 343—Topographic map, centers of mobility and centers of influence as the elements of the game, 343—Zones of influence, 344—Collisions or encounters, 344—Zones of mobility, 345—Analytical statement of problem of organic conflict, 345—The behavior schedule, 346—Specific productivity, 347—Effect of change in zone pattern, (Intraspecies evolution), 348—Biologic relation of economic value, 350—Effect of change in behavior schedule, 350—Rigid or automaton type and elastic or free-choice type of behavior schedule, 350—Relation between ideal and actual organism, 352—Effect of small departure from perfect adjustment, 353—Relation of economic value to physical energy, 354—Economic conversion factors of energy, 355—General or aggregate effect of individual

PART I
GENERAL PRINCIPLES

CHAPTER I

REGARDING DEFINITIONS

Truth comes out of error more readily than out of confusion.
—*Bacon.*

A definition is a purely arbitrary thing. If I choose to define a triangle as a plane figure bounded by four sides and having four angles; and if, also, I define a quadrilateral as a plane figure bounded by three sides and having three angles, I shall run into no logical conflicts; my geometry need in no wise depart from that of Euclid; I shall need to make no changes in existing works on geometry, beyond that of substituting throughout the word triangle for the word quadrilateral, and *vice versa.*

But while a definition is in this sense, from the point of view of logic, a purely arbitrary thing, while my definition of a triangle as a four-sided figure may be *admissible*, it is by no means *expedient.*

Thus the definition of terms, which naturally forms one of the first steps in the systematic treatment of any subject, may present no particular problems of logic, but it does present certain problems of expediency.

In the geometrical example cited, the unusual definitions given, though quite permissible, are inexpedient for simple etymological reasons. Such a choice of terms would be misleading, and, instead of assisting the memory, would impose upon it an unnecessary burden. In this case the application of the principle of expediency is obvious to the point of being grotesque, the example having purposely been chosen to illustrate the principle in drastic fashion.

But the framing of definitions at times involves more subtle considerations of expediency, so subtle in fact, that they may be overlooked, or misunderstood, and a problem which is, in truth, a problem of definition, falsely masquerades as a problem of fact. Certain pseudo-problems of science have owed their origin to a failure to realize this circumstance.[1]

[1] On the other hand, some very fundamental advances of science are, upon critical examination, found to rest essentially upon the establishment of a

The writer of the book of Genesis shows good judgment. Our legendary forebear, the originator of the first biological system of nomenclature, *sees* each creature first, and thereupon names it. We have not always been equally wise. Sometimes we have tried to invert the method; we have found or made a name, and then gaily set forth on an expedition to discover the thing that should answer to that name; we have hunted the Jabberwock. Forgetful of the wisdom of Mephistopheles:

> Denn eben wo Gedanken fehlen
> Da stellt ein Wort zur rechten Zeit sich ein—

we have given way to an inherent bias of the human mind described in characteristic fashion by H. G. Wells[2]:

> . . . . when we have a name we are predisposed—and sometimes it is a very vicious predisposition—to imagine forthwith something answering to the name. . . . . If I say *Wodget* or *Crump*, you find yourself passing over the fact that these are nothings, ... and trying to think what sort of a thing a *Wodget* or a *Crump* may be. You find yourself insensibly, by subtle associations of sound and ideas, giving these blank terms attributes.[3]

So the biologist of the past generation, finding in his native vocabulary the words *animal* and *plant*, forthwith proceeded in an effort to establish precise distinctions between animals and plants, never giving any thought, it would seem, to the fact that these names had already been parceled out generations ago, by "popular" consent, by unscientific persons without any regard to fine distinctions. There is clearly, here, the tacit assumption that because two distinct words are found in the vocabulary, therefore two correspondingly distinct things exist in nature. In point of fact, we know well enough (though we may not at all times have this knowledge clearly in the focus of our consciousness) that in nature many things form finely graded series, with extremes at the two ends, extremes to which

judicious definition. A notable instance of this is the enunciation of the principle of the survival of the fittest, which is essentially of the nature of a definition, since the fit is that which survives. Regarding the epistemological significance of definitions compare A. N. Whitehead and B. Russell, Principia Mathematica 1910, vol. 1, p. 12.

[2] H. G. Wells, First and Last Things, 1908, p. 32.

[3] "Gewöhnlich glaubt der Mensch, wenn er nur Worte hört,
Es müsse sich dabei auch etwas denken lassen."—*Goethe.*

our vocabulary has lent more or less definitely associated names, but with no definite line of demarcation between. Examples of this are innumerable. We speak of objects as being red, orange, yellow, green, blue, violet, etc. There is nothing in nature to correspond to such *staccato* classification of colors: the visible spectrum runs continuously from a wavelength of about 8×10^{-4} mm. (extreme red) to about 4×10^{-4} mm. (extreme violet). Cases therefore must necessarily arise when we are in doubt whether to call a thing blue, or green, for example; and such doubt can be resolved, if at all, only by arbitrary definition. The question is not "what *is* green, and what *is* blue," but, at best, "what shall we agree *to call* green, and what blue."

It lies in the nature of the mechanism by which we enter into possession of our knowledge, that problems of definition of this kind arise. We are equipped with two separate and distinct senses, the one responding to electromagnetic waves ranging from about 4×10^{-4} to 8×10^{-4} mm., light waves; the other to somewhat longer waves otherwise of the same character, heat waves. Accordingly we have two separate terms in our language *light* and *heat*, to denote two phenomena which, objectively considered, are not separated by any line of division, but merge into one another by gradual transition. Here the question might be raised whether an electromagnetic wave of a length of 9×10^{-4} mm. *is* a light wave or a heat wave. The answer is obvious: Call it what you please, it is merely a question of arbitrary definition. We must beware of

> . . . . that false secondary power
> By which we multiply distinctions, then
> Deem that our puny boundaries are things
> That we perceive, and not that we have made.
> —*Wordsworth.*

Definitions in Biology. The attempt to establish a rigorous distinction between "animals" and "plants" may be similarly regarded. Expediency demands that if these terms are appropriated for exact scientific use, their sense, when so used, shall, if possible, be reasonably near akin to the sense commonly associated with these words. The difficulties encountered in seeking to establish a satisfactory line of division between animals and plants were long regarded as difficulties in a problem of fact. It was thought that some biological principle must be sought which divided animals from plants.

The truth is, of course, that we may define "animals" and "plants" any way we please—as for instance by reserving the term plant for an organism possessing cellulose—but whether such definition is "correct" or "satisfactory" is not a question of biological fact, it is a question of expediency. It is not a question whether there is any definable difference between animals as a class and plants as a class, nor what this difference is, but whether it is expedient to retain for purposes of strict scientific classification the popular terms "animals" and "plants," which were not originally founded upon any rigorous examination of facts; and if so, where we should, by definition, draw the line of separation.

When the problem is viewed in this way the difficulty of distinguishing between animals and plants vanishes. In the case of the higher forms of life it is easy to establish biological distinctions that do not conflict with the popularly drawn lines of division. In the case of certain lowly forms of life popular distinctions cannot exist, since these forms are not known to the public except through biological publications. And the biological line of demarcation we can, by definition, draw arbitrarily where we choose, or, better perhaps, we may say that the terms "animal," "plant," do not correspond to any fundamental objective distinction and, though conveniently applied to certain common forms of living matter, are entirely unnecessary[4] and only introduce difficulties of definition and classification when applied to certain simple organisms. What difference does it make whether *we call* Volvox a plant or an animal? Whether it *is* a plant or an animal is merely a matter of definition, not a question of biological fact.

Somewhat similar remarks apply to the narrower divisions into which the biologist divides the world of living organisms. Disputes as to what constitutes a species are fruitless. "A species is a thing described as such." This is simply a matter of definition. If on grounds of expediency one definition is preferable to another, it may be well to urge its general adoption. But its adoption or rejection will neither add nor subtract one jot from our stock of ascertained facts.

It is necessary to guard against the error of disputing about mere words. Not always does this error strut about in such blatant form as in the example quoted by Fechner: S. Sachs, in a book published

[4] R. W. Glaser, Science, 1918, vol. 48, pp. 301–302: "We are justified at present in not classifying viruses either with plants or animals."

in 1850, takes the astronomers to task for their presumptuous speculations: "How do they know that the star they call Uranus *is* Uranus?"

If any one should think that in our day it is no longer necessary to guard against errors of this kind (though less gross, perhaps), let him consider such a question as this: Is not the perennial debate between vitalism and mechanism a quibble about words? Is not the whole situation summed up accurately in the words of L. J. Briggs:[5] "The mechanism of plant processes not at present explainable on a physico-chemical basis would be *termed* by the vitalistic school "vital," by the physico-chemical school "unknown"?

And in searching for the essential characteristics of *life*, those that should finally and conclusively distinguish the living from the non-living, are we not just searching for the thing in nature that should correspond to a word in our vocabulary? Are we not hunting the Jabberwock?

Definitions of Life. The difficulty of giving a precise meaning to the word life has been realized probably by everyone who has ever seriously attempted a definition. Herbert Spencer remarks:

> Classifications are subjective concepts, which have no absolute demarcations in Nature corresponding to them . . . . Consequently, when we attempt to define anything complex . . . . we can scarcely ever avoid including more than we intended, or leaving out something that should be taken in. Thus it happens that on seeking a definition of life, we have great difficulty in finding one that is neither more nor less than sufficient.

Nevertheless he proceeds to establish his definition of life: "The continuous adjustment of internal relations to external relations."[6]

It cannot be said that Spencer has been very happy in this choice of a definition or that he has been at all successful in avoiding the very pitfalls which he himself so clearly points out. For obviously many purely mechanical systems fall under this definition. It would, for example, include a windmill provided with a device automatically turning its arms into the most favorable plane according to the direction of the wind.[7] Indeed, in a sense it is true of every physical

---

[5] L. J. Briggs, Jour. Washington Acad. Sci., 1917, vol. 7, p. 89; compare also E. M. East, Mankind at the Crossroads, 1923, p. 21.

[6] Herbert Spencer, Principles of Biology, section 30.

[7] Compare the following: "No one has yet succeeded in formulating a clean-cut definition of the limits of the reflex either at its lower or its higher extreme, and perhaps no one ever will; for the whole list of behavior types, from machines to men, probably form a closely graded series." C. J. Herrick: The Evolution of Intelligence and Its Organs. Science, 1910, vol. 31, p. 18.

system that it "adjusts its internal relations to external relations."
For this statement simply implies that there is a tendency for the
establishment of equilibrium between a selected portion of a physical
system, and the remainder, the environment.   Thus, for example, if
the system $2H_2 + O_2$ is left to itself in a suitable vessel at 1480°C.[8]
and one atmosphere pressure, the ratio $\dfrac{H_2}{H_2O}$ which we may term an
"internal relation" of the system, assumes the value 0.0002.   If
now the external conditions of temperature and pressure are changed
to 2929°C. and one atmosphere pressure, the internal relation $\dfrac{H_2}{H_2O}$
adjusts itself to the new external condition and acquires the value
0.11.

With better judgment than Herbert Spencer, Sir Edward Schäfer[9]
frankly evades the definition of life.   He remarks:

> The ordinary dictionary definition of life is "the state of living."   Dastre,
> following Claude Bernard, defines it as "the sum total of the phenomena com-
> mon to all living beings."   Both these definitions are, however, of the same
> character as Sidney Smith's definition of an Archdeacon as "a person who
> performs archidiaconal functions."   I am not myself proposing to grapple
> with a task that has proved too great for the intellectual giants of philosophy,
> and I have the less inclination to do so because recent advances in knowledge
> have suggested the probability that the dividing line between animate and
> inanimate matter is less sharp than it has hitherto been regarded, so that the
> difficulty of finding an inclusive definition is correspondingly increased.

It is, indeed, an elementary historical fact that, as knowledge has
advanced, the scope embraced in the term "vital" processes has
continually decreased, since Wöhler took the first cut out of it in
1828 by the synthesis of a "vital product" (urea) in the laboratory;
and the field of known physico-chemical processes going on in
living organisms has correspondingly increased.   For the rest, the
most uncompromising vitalist does not deny that some, at least, of
the processes going on in living matter are physico-chemical.   Even
so fundamentally biological a process as the stimulation of an ovum
to development we have learnt to effect by purely physical means.

Alleged Characteristics of Living Matter.   On the other hand
some of the features commonly ascribed to living matter as its peculiar

[8] W. Nernst, Theoretische Chemie, 1913, p. 713.
[9] E. A. Schaefer, Presidential Address at Dundee Meeting of Brit. Assoc.
Adv. Sci. 1912.

and characteristic attributes seem irrelevant to the point of triviality. This remark applies particularly to the distinction sometimes claimed for living matter, that it grows "from within," as distinguished from crystals, which, in a suitable mother liquor, "grow from without." There may or may not be many and profound differences between a bacterial colony growing in a culture medium, on the one hand, and on the other hand a mass of crystals growing in a supersaturated solution. But whether the growth takes place from within or without is merely an accident of structure. If a droplet of chloroform is brought near to a glass particle coated with shellac, the drop flows around the particle, engulfs it, absorbs the shellac coating and finally rejects the "undigested" glass particle.[10] The droplet thus grows "from within."

In point of fact "growth from within" is the rule and not the exception in chemical systems. For what do we mean by growth? We mean the increase of the mass of one component of a system at the expense of another. It is precisely the same thing as that which occupies the center of attention of the physical chemist, though he does not ordinarily call it growth. In fact, he does not find it necessary to give it any particular name, for, being accustomed to the use of mathematical methods and symbols, he simply writes it $\dfrac{dm}{dt}$, rate of increase of mass with time, or, more often, $\dfrac{d}{dt}\left(\dfrac{m}{v}\right)$, rate of increase of concentration (mass/volume) with time. And in homogenous systems, at least, which (on account of their comparative ease of theoretical and experimental treatment) figure prominently in the physical chemistry of today, growth is necessarily from within.

Some writers (J. Loeb, The Organism as a Whole, 1916, p. 28) have seen a characteristic feature, peculiar to living organisms, as distinguished, for example from crystals growing out of a solution,

---

[10] "Let it be clearly understood that this illustration is here quoted, not as an example of life-like analogies in the world of non-living matter; nor as a veiled suggestion that such a drop of chloroform represents even a modest degree of success in the artificial imitation of life; nor yet again as an argument that the conduct of amoeba can today be fully accounted for on a physico-chemical basis; this example was cited merely to show that "growth from within" cannot be claimed as a distinguishing characteristic of living matter. For further discussion of so-called *simulacra vitae* see McClendon, Physical Chemistry of Vital Phenomena; Burns and Paton, Biophysics, 1921, p. 403.

in the fact that the latter grow by a physical process, the former by chemical processes. Leaving aside the question as to whether there exists any fundamental distinction between physical and chemical processes, at most the point to which attention is drawn by these authors would class living organisms with chemical, as distinguished from physical systems, but would furnish no basis whatever for separating organisms in a class by themselves from other chemical systems. This is not saying that they *are* not in a class by themselves, but only that the distinction suggested fails in effect.

It has similarly been urged, as a distinction between the growth of a crystal and that of an organism, that the former will grow only in a supersaturated solution of its own substance, while the latter extracts from an unsaturated solution the substance needed for its anabolism.

This is really the same distinction in another form. It may distinguish the organism from the growing crystal, but leaves it in one class with any chemically reacting system whatever, since in the case of the latter also there is "growth," i.e., formation of one or more products of reaction, in a system which need not be physically supersaturated in the narrow sense in which the crystallizing solution is. In a wider sense[11] the system may indeed be said to be supersaturated with regard to a chemical substance that is formed within it—but in the same sense a system can probably be said to be supersaturated with regard to the substance of a bacterial colony growing therein.

Neither can we subscribe to the view set forth by J. Loeb (The Organism as a Whole, 1906, p. 29), that the synthesis of *specific* materials from simple compounds of *non-specific* character distinguishes living from non-living matter. In every chemical reaction specific materials are formed. In a mixture of hydrogen, chlorine, and nitrogen, the hydrogen and the chlorine unite, leaving the nitrogen on one side unchanged. This is merely a brutally simple example of a universal fact. Chemical reaction is always selective. And if "complexity" is to be made the characteristic of life processes, then the question immediately arises, what degree of complexity is required to place a given process in the category of life processes?

[11] Namely in the sense that it is metastable, that is, its thermodynamic potential is not at a minimum.

Reproduction. Another characteristic that has been cited by some as exclusively peculiar to living organisms is the power of reproducing their kind. "How, says Driesch in effect, can a mechanism provide for its own reconstitution? No machine known to us is able to construct another like itself, nor can it repair its own parts."[12] Undue emphasis on this alleged distinction between living and non-living machines seems ill advised, for two reasons. In the first place, though it may be true that no man-made engine exists that performs the functions of self-repair and self-reproduction, no one has ever attempted, so far as I know, to demonstrate that no such engine can be built. Anyone who should be disposed to regard this objection as specious should reflect for a moment on the amazing development in technical arts within the last thirty or forty years. Half a century ago one might with equal justice have pronounced flight a fundamental, essentially biological characteristic of birds, incapable of duplication by man-made engines.

But in another, perhaps more significant respect, we must regard as misplaced the emphasis sometimes laid on the power of reproduction in organisms, and its absence in human artefacts. It is based on an exaggerated conception of the part played by the parent in the *making* of the offspring. This probably has its origin in the instance of reproduction that to us is naturally of supreme interest, the reproduction of man. As a mammal, the young human organism grows within the parent body, and seems to us to be in some way *fashioned* by the parent; this conception must be at the basis of the alleged distinction between organic reproduction and the incapacity of non-living engines to reproduce their kind, for without such conception the comparison would lack all parallel. Now, in point of fact, we need but call to mind the familiar hatching of a chick to realize that the part necessarily played by the parent in the formation of the young individual is really very restricted. The process in this case goes on, for the most part, in complete isolation from the parent.[13]

---

[12] H. C. Warren, Jour. Philos., Psychol. and Scientific Method, vol. 13, 1916, p. 36.

[13] Compare E. G. Conklin, Heredity and Environment, 1918, pp. 99,45, 109: "The hen does not produce the egg, but the egg produces the hen and also other eggs. . . . . . We know that the child comes from the germ cells and not from the highly differentiated bodies of the parents, and furthermore that these cells are not made by the parents' bodies but

As for the initiation of cell division of the ovum, we now know that, in some cases at least, this can be effected by ordinary physical means.

Recent development in experimental embryology suggest a more rational view of this process of self-reproduction of the living engine, a view which strips it of at least some of its mystery, and which certainly takes from it any force it might otherwise have had as a basis for distinction between living and non-living matter. If, after the first division of the ovum of a frog, the two cells are separated, each will under suitable conditions develop into a separate and complete, normal organism. These two organisms A and B are, in fact twin brothers or sisters. No one would for a moment entertain the thought that in this case A reproduces B, or *vice versa*. Now suppose that in some way, after the first division, A alone grows into a complete mature organism, while the single cell B remains attached to it, say for six months. At the end of this time it is separated, and stimulated to start its growth into a frog. We would ordinarily describe this state of affairs by saying that A reproduced B as offspring, that B was the child of A. In point of fact it is merely a delayed twin brother or sister of its elder brother or sister A.[14] A had little or nothing to do with the production of B; the latter *grew*, very much in the same way as A grew in its own time. That nature has evolved, in surviving races, this method of *delayed development*, so as to stretch out the totality of living organisms in a long chain, a succession in time, is of course a fact of most fundamental importance, the significance of which will deserve our profound contemplation. One of its consequences has been to render possible a practically infinite number of organisms, built from a finite and quite restricted amount of matter, the same substance being used over and over again, for it is literally true that we live on our forefathers. Had all

these cells have arisen by the division of antecedent germ cells. . . . . Parents do not transmit their characters to their offspring, but these germ cells in the course of long development give rise to adult characters similar to those of the parent."

[14] The perhaps somewhat doubtfully authenticated cases of *fetus in fetu*, "those strange instances in which one might almost say that a man may be pregnant with his brother or sister," add a touch of realism to the discussion here presented. For further data on this singular subject see G. M. Gould and W. L. Pyle, Anomalies and Curiosities of Medicine, 1897, pp. 199 et seq. Compare also in this connection, the phenomenon of pedogenesis; see for example, G. H. Parker, Psyche, 1922, vol. 29, p. 127.

these organisms sought to grow simultaneously, their career would have been stopped by lack of material.

If anyone should object that these reflections leave out of account entirely the rôle of sex in reproduction, with all the complex phenomena of the fusion of gametes, the mingling of chromosomes, and biparental inheritance, the obvious reply is that these phenomena are now known to be less fundamental than they formerly appeared; that reproduction of an organism can very well take place without them; and that therefore they may at most serve to distinguish certain forms of life from non-living matter, but they cannot possibly be made the basis of a distinction between living matter in general and that which we commonly describe as non-living.

Vital Force. If we have cause to hesitate in defining life, still more is it the part of wisdom to be very conservative in the coining and use of such phrases as *vital force, nerve energy,* and the like. Shall we not do well to follow the biblical example, and wait, to name the animal, until it is physically present to our senses? Or, to pass from legend to the world of scientific fact, let us borrow, if we can, the method of the physicist: He discovers that a quantity $\frac{1}{2} mv^2$ possesses certain important properties. *Then,* he proceeds to name it: *Energy,* in particular, *kinetic energy.* But biologists have been disposed sometimes to adopt the reverse procedure: they have named a *vital force,* a *nerve energy,* a *mental energy,* and what not, and now they entertain the pious hope that in due time they may discover these "things." That there is something radically at fault with such terms is evident from the fact that forces and energy are *magnitudes,* and "to define a magnitude and to say how it is measured are one and the same thing."[15] But who has ever told us how to measure vital force[16] and such like?

Physical Chemistry of Structured Systems. In the physical chemistry of today structure, that is to say, geometrical configuration, plays a subordinate rôle. For obvious reasons the theory of chemical reaction in homogeneous, or in heterogeneous systems of comparatively simple form, is more approachable than that of systems which possess intricate structure, resulting in complicated mechanical

[15] Nature, September 25, 1922, p. 405.
[16] G. Bunge, in his Physiologic and Pathologic Chemistry, 1902, p. 1, remarks: "I regard vital force as a convenient resting place where, to quote Kant, 'reason can repose on the pillow of obscure relations.'" Curiously enough this damning admission is made by an advocate of vitalism.

interactions of their parts, in accompaniment of chemical reaction. In technical practise, too, reactions in homogeneous systems (solution, gas) are common, and where there is heterogeneous structure, this is usually of a form very simple as compared with the complex biological structures.

But this comparative absence, from physico-chemical discussion, of reference to structure, to geometrical features, is not due to any inherent characteristic property of chemical systems, as contrasted with the structurally complex organic systems: the reason for the simplicity is to be found in ourselves. It is not a physical phenomenon of the thing observed, but a psychological phenomenon in the observer. Physical chemistry is still a comparatively young science, and naturally the simpler phenomena have been sought out for first attention. This is not because complex physico-chemical structures do not exist, nor even because they are unimportant. On the contrary, it is to be expected that the future will bring important developments in this direction, as followed, for example by Sir William Bayliss in his work *Interfacial Forces in Physiology*.

The rate of formation, the rate of *growth*, of a chemical substance, is a definite function of its environment. In a structureless system the nature and state of this environment is defined in comparatively simple terms (e.g., by stating the concentration of each of the reacting substances).

But in a system possessing structure, the environment of a given portion of the system depends on the structure, the topography of the system, which, in general, will be variable with the time. In particular, the structure may be such that a given substance or complex of substances carries its own immediate environment around with it. The rate of formation (growth) of that substance will then depend largely upon the *mechanical* properties of those portions of the system which accompany this substance or complex in its travels through the system.

The complete discussion of a system of this kind may well fall outside the scope of present day physical chemistry, not because it is inherently foreign to that branch of science, but because no case of this kind, sufficiently simple to invite discussion on a mathematical and physico-chemical basis, has clearly presented itself.[17]

[17] Compare W. M. Bayliss, Physiology, 1915, p. XI, "All that we are justified in stating is that, up to the present, no physico-chemical system has been

Yet there is absolutely nothing in such a case that *in principle* places it outside the pale of physico-chemical science. It is largely as the result of intentional selection of simple conditions that the systems with which the chemist ordinarily deals (outside of biological chemistry) are comparatively structureless.

We can, in fact, even now lay down certain general observations with regard to structured physico-chemical systems.

Let us consider a system of this kind in which local conditions are subject to variation from point to point and from instant to instant. We fix our attention on some one component which requires for its growth certain definite conditions of its immediate environment. If this component is associated with a structure whose geometrical and mechanical properties secure and maintain for it a comparatively constant suitable environment amid the changing conditions of the system, then that component will grow.

Furthermore, the several components will compete with greater or less success for the material available for their growth, in proportion as their structure is more or less perfectly adapted to secure and maintain for them a suitable environment.

The chemical dynamics of such a system, that is to say, the laws governing the distribution of matter among its several components, may evidently assume a fundamentally different character from that to which we are accustomed from our study of ordinary structureless systems. For in these latter the arrangement and rearrangement of matter within the system depends chiefly on chemical coefficients (affinity coefficients), and scarcely at all on geometrical features.

In structured systems, on the other hand, there is the possibility that geometrical and mechanical features may play the dominant rôle. This possibility will present itself particularly in those systems which receive a continuous or periodic supply of free energy, for instance in the form of illumination. Here *the advantage will go to those structures that are adapted to direct available energy into such channels as lead to the maintenance of the environment required for their growth.*[18] But a little reflection shows that this is precisely the princi-

met with having the same properties as those known as vital; in other words, none have, as yet, been prepared of similar complexity and internal coördination.

[18] It should be observed that nothing has been said of *life* in describing the system. The system may or may not comprise living organisms, the argument

ple which governs survival in the struggle for existence among living organisms. Hence we may say:

The laws of the chemical dynamics of a structured system of the kind described will be precisely those laws, or at least a very important section of those laws, which govern the evolution of a system comprising living organisms.

For it is precisely structured systems of the kind considered above that are presented to us in living organisms growing in an "environment."

Application to Biology. The several organisms that make up the earth's living population, together with their environment, constitute one system,[19] which receives a daily supply of available energy from the sun.

Each individual is composed of various chemical substances assembled into a definite structure and capable of growth, i.e., of accretion out of the environment by chemical reaction—provided a suitable medium or environment is offered.

Moreover, each mobile organism carries with it a travelling environment, suitable for the growth of its substance. It maintains this environment by virtue of the peculiar mechanical properties associated with its structure, whereby it is enabled to turn to this use, directly or indirectly, the available energy of the sun's light. And while the travelling environment may not be absolutely constant,

---

remains the same. This suggests that a term, such as *life*, so vague that it defies definition, is perhaps not likely to play an important part in any exact argument; we may, indeed, find it wholly unnecessary. It may, in time, in the literature of exact science, meet with the fate of the word cause: a term of rare and at best incidental occurrence in records of exact investigations.

[19] This fact deserves emphasis. It is customary to discuss the "evolution of a species of organisms." As we proceed we shall see many reasons why we should constantly take in view the evolution, as a whole, of the system [organism plus environment]. It may appear at first sight as if this should prove a more complicated problem than the consideration of the evolution of a part only of the system. But it will become apparent, as we proceed, that the physical laws governing evolution in all probability take on a simpler form when referred to the system as a whole than to any portion thereof.

It is not so much the organism or the species that evolves, but the entire system, species and environment. The two are inseparable.

"The organism, as Uexküll teaches us, must be studied, not as a congeries of anatomical and physiological abstraction, but as a piece of machinery, at work among external conditions." O. C. Glaser, Science, vol. 21, 1910, p. 303.

it is more nearly so than the more remote portions of the system, and keeps within such limits of variation as are compatible with the survival of the organism or its species. A concrete illustration may help to make this point clear: Many aquatic forms of life are constantly bathed in a saline solution—sea water. Their body fluids are accordingly in equilibrium with this environment. Variations in the salinity of their environment, if they exceed certain comparatively narrow bounds, are apt to be fatal to such organisms.

The higher organisms have made themselves (largely) independent of their immediate environment. Their tissues are bathed from within by a fluid (the blood) which they carry around with them, a sort of "internal environment."[20]

The degree of perfection with which this constancy of the internal or traveling environment, independently of the external environment, is developed, increases as we ascend the biologic scale. This is lucidly set forth, for example, by Claude Bernard:[21]

Chez tous les êtres vivants le milieu intérieur qui est un produit de l'organisme, conserve les rapports nécéssaires d'échange avec le milieu éxtérieur; mais à mesure que l'organisme devient plus parfait, le milieu organique se spécifie et s'isole en quelque sorte de plus en plus du milieu ambiant.

It is the peculiar structure and the mechanical properties of the organism that enable it to secure and maintain the required environment (including the milieu intérieur). The higher animals, in particular, are provided with an intricate apparatus, comprising many members, for securing food (internal environment) as well as for warding off hostile influences.

[20] "Étant donné que l'eau de mer a un contact si intime avec les organismes de la mer et que non seulement elle les entoure de ses flots, mais qu'elle traverse leurs branchies et imprègne en partie les corps des invertébrés, il semble assez justifié de la placer dans la même catégorie que les autres liquides physiologiques." S. Palitzsch, Comptes Rendus de Carlsberg, vol. 10, part 1, 1911, p. 93. Compare also the following:

"Not only do the body fluids of the lower forms of marine life correspond exactly with sea water in their composition, but there are at least strong indications that the fluids of the highest animals are really descended from sea water . . . . the same substances are present in both cases, and in both cases sodium chloride largely predominates." L. J. Henderson, The Fitness of the Environment, 1913, pp. 187–188. See also ibid., pp. 116 and 153; H. F. Osborn, The Evolution and Origin of Life, 1917, p. 37; D'Arcy W. Thompson, Growth and Form, 1917, p. 127.

[21] Introduction a l'étude de la médecine expérimentale, 1885, p. 110.

The increasing independence, as we ascend the biological scale, which the organism displays toward its more remote environment, is thus accompanied by a parallel increase in the perfection of the apparatus by which this independence is earned. Here again we may quote Claude Bernard:[22]

A mesure que l'on s'élève dans l'échelle des êtres, ces appareils deviennent plus parfaits et plus compliqués; ils tendent à affranchir complètement l'organisme des influences et des changements survenus dans le milieu extérieur. Chez les animaux invertébrés, au contraire, cette independence vis-à-vis du milieu extérieur n' est que relative.

The Policy of Resignation: Its Parallel in Other Sciences. Whatever may be our ultimate conclusions, we may do well to adopt at least as a temporary expedient the policy of resignation; with Sir Edward Schäfer we may abandon the attempt to define life. Perhaps, in doing this, we are following historical precedents: Geometers have had to resign themselves to the fact that Euclid's parallel axiom cannot be proved. But as the reward of this resignation came the new geometries of Bolyai, Lobatchewski and Riemann. Enlightened inventors have abandoned the attempt to build a perpetual motion machine; but again, resignation is rewarded with the recognition of a fundamental law, the law of conservation of energy. Physicists, following Einstein, have abandoned, for the time being at any rate, the attempt to determine experimentally the earth's absolute motion through space. The reward has been the theory of relativity, one of the greatest events in the history of science.

The whole development of science, especially in recent years, is a record of tearing down barriers between separate fields of knowledge and investigation. Little harm, and perhaps much gain, can come from a frank avowal that we are unable to state clearly the difference between living and non-living matter. This does not in any way commit us to the view that no such difference exists.

For the present, then, we shall adopt the position that the problem is essentially one of definition. The question is not so much "What is life," but rather, "What shall we agree to call life?" And the answer, for the present at any rate, seems to be that it is immaterial how we define life; that the progress of science and our understanding of natural phenomena is quite independent of such a definition.

[22] Ibid.

We shall, wherever convenient, continue to employ the terms life, living organism, merely as a matter of convenience. This use of the terms does not imply or presuppose any precise distinction between living and non-living matter; it merely rests upon the fact that in *most* cases *ordinarily* met there is essentially universal agreement as to whether a portion of matter is to be classed in the first or in the second category. We will adopt the policy of Sir William Bayliss:

> If asked to define *life* I should be inclined to do as Poinsot, the mathematician did, as related by Claude Bernard: "If anyone asked me to define *time*, I should reply: Do you know what it is that you speak of? If he said Yes, I should say, Very well, let us talk about it. If he said No, I should say, Very well, let us talk about something else."

The ideal definition is, undoubtedly, the quantitative definition, one that tells us how to measure the thing defined; or, at the least, one that furnishes a basis for the quantitative treatment of the subject to which it relates. We have already spoken of evolution. Most of what follows will relate directly or indirectly to evolution. It will be well here, while discussing definitions, to establish a definition, a conception, of evolution that shall, as far as may be, have the quantitative stamp.

CHAPTER II

EVOLUTION DEFINED

Nature must be considered as a whole if she is to be understood in detail.
—*Bunge.*

As has been abundantly made plain, the choice of a definition is a matter of expediency. In adopting, for special use in exact science, a term already in general use, we must seek, so far as possible, to embody in our definition the fundamental and essential features of the concept denoted by the term as used popularly and by the best workers, thinkers and writers.[1] In so far as there is divergence in the use of the term, it may be well to frame the definition broadly, so as to cover a wide range of phenomena and lead to a comprehensive view of natural events, corresponding to the essential unity of nature. In this way we shall be most likely to see the facts of nature arraying themselves in a natural order, and to achieve that economy of thought which is secured by a well devised system of classification. Facts which naturally belong together will, then, be found together, in our system, in the same or in neighboring pigeonholes.

Now if we seek to analyze what is in our minds when we speak of the *evolution* of a given system, we find—and on this probably all are agreed—that the fundamental, the central thought, is that of the history of the system. But the concepts of the history and of the evolution of a system, though related, are not identical—if they were, one word would suffice to denote the single concept. The popular and also the scientific conception of evolution contains as an essential feature the element of progress, of development. We would not ordinarily class as evolution the history of such a system as a swinging pendulum, or a celestial body circling in its orbit, *in so far*

[1] Compare Bertrand Russell, Analysis of Mind, 1921, p. 197: "The use of the word comes first, and the meaning is to be distilled out of it by observation and analysis." "In each case the work consists chiefly in making explicit processes which are instinctive," as J. W. N. Sullivan (Aspects of Science, 1923, p. 24) remarks àpropos of certain other matters.

as these motions are purely periodic or cyclic. In the history of such systems the element of progression in time, of development, is lacking. They repeat in endless succession the same series of events. The hand of the clock, like a symbol of perpetual youth, goes through its daily double cycle, making no distinction between yesterday, today and tomorrow. It is the calendar that reminds us we grow older year by year, the calendar that turns a new and different leaf each day. "The book of Nature is the book of Fate. She turns the gigantic pages—leaf after leaf, never returning one. . . . . "[2]

But, to characterize the kind of history we speak of as evolution, it is not enough that each day be *unlike* every other; it is not merely that a system never passes twice through the same state;[3] not merely that a biological species never retraces its steps,[4] or that "when a race has lived its term it comes no more again."[5]

Evolution not a Mere "Changeful Sequence." Such a statement as those cited in the preceding paragraph alone is insufficient to distinguish evolution as a progress from merely a *changeful sequence*; it is insufficient to define the *direction* of evolution.[6] For if the world's events taken in historical order *A, B, C* . . . are a changeful sequence, the same is also true of the inverted series . . . *C, B, A.* Mere unlikeness of two days is insufficient to tell us which is antecedent to the other. To determine this we must know something regarding the character of the unlikeness. In a vague way this character is indicated by the term *progress*, which, as already remarked, is closely associated, in popular conception, with evolution. And the more rigorous scientific disciplines of biology, too, leave us with a not very clearly defined idea of *progression* as one of the fundamental characteristics of those changes which are embraced by the term *evolution*. Such phrases as "the passage from lower to higher forms" which are often used to describe the direction of evolution, are vague, and

[2] Emerson, Conduct of Life, Everyman's Library Edition, 1915, p. 157. Compare also Lee Wilson Dodd's lines:

> " . . . . Nor do the stars retrace
> their glistening snail marks of slow destiny."

[3] J. Perrin, Traité de Chimie Physique, 1903, vol. 1, p. 142.

[4] Petronievics, Science Progress, 1919, p. 406.

[5] Emerson, Conduct of Life, p. 158.

[6] For this reason the characterization of the trend of evolution given by Petronievics, loc. cit., is inadequate.

undoubtedly contain an anthropomorphic element.[7]   At best they give every opportunity for divergence of opinion as to what constitutes a "higher form."   If, on the other hand it is stated that evolution proceeds from simpler to more complex forms, or from less specialized to more specialized forms, then the direction of evolution is but poorly defined, for the rule is at best one with many exceptions.   It should be particularly noted that all these efforts to specify the direction of evolution attempt to do so in terms of a single component of the evolving system.   Such definitions of the direction of evolution are foredoomed to failure.   It is the system as a whole that evolves, and we can hope to establish a definition of the direction of evolution only in terms of the system as a whole.

Evidently, we must seek a more precise indication of the direction of evolution if our definition is to be truly expedient.   We must analyze further the contents of our mind when it contemplates the concept of evolution.   We return to our examples of the pendulum, or of the earth in its orbit.   When frictional resistances are neglibible, or are disregarded, the periodic series of events in the system may be history, but seems hardly worthy of the name evolution.   In actual fact the motion of the pendulum bob gradually dies down, owing to friction and other dissipative forces.   The motion is not strictly periodic.   The pendulum does not, actually, count out similar seconds, unidentified, but marks, by its greater amplitude, an earlier vibration as distinguished from a later.   So also, the earth in its motion is slightly delayed by frictional forces introduced by the tides; it slows down a little as the centuries pass.   The strictly periodic process is changed into one in which successive days differ by a trifle in length.   The process has a definite direction in time.   We feel justified in speaking of the system as "evolving."   Now the thing to mark is that what has imparted to the process its directed character is frictional resistance, dissipative forces, typical *irreversible* effects, to speak in the language of the physicist.

[7] "Evolution is thus almost synonymous with progress, though the latter term is usually confined to processes of development in the moral, as distinguished from the physical world.   Further, this idea, as Mr. Spencer remarks, has rather a subjective value in existence, *as judged by our feelings*" (Encycl. Brit., 9th edition, vol. 8, p. 751).   Compare also Bertrand Russell, Our Knowledge of the Eternal World, 1914, p. 12.   "A process which led from amoeba to man appeared to the philosophers to be obviously a progress—though whether **the** amoeba would agree with this opinion is not known."

Again, consider a typical example of what we are all agreed to speak of as evolution: the history of the earth and its living inhabitants. The readjustments, the re-adaptations of life-forms which have here taken place, were undoubtedly due in part to changes in external conditions, such as climate, geographic distribution of land and sea, etc. In part, also, such changes have gone on and are going on before our eyes independently of any external changes, and under approximately constant conditions. Organic evolution being a slow process, it takes a certain time, when equilibrium or near-equilibrium is disturbed, for a new equilibrium or near-equilibrium to become established. There is therefore a tendency for internal readjustments or changes to *lag* behind the external changes by which they are conditioned. As a special case, if an external change is followed by constant external conditions, internal changes may continue to proceed under constant external conditions.

Now such internal changes in a material system, which *lag* behind the determining external changes, or which go on under constant external conditions, are *typically irreversible processes*.[8]

---

[8] A process is said to take place *reversibly*, if the direction of the change is reversed by a suitable alteration, *however small*, of the (generalized) force applied to produce the change. For example, if two equal weights are suspended from the ends of a string passed over a simple pulley, then, the weights being initially at rest, any weight *however small*, added on one side of the system will produce motion downward on that side, *provided there is no friction at the pulley and no stiffness in the string*. If, on the contrary, a weight, *however small*, is lifted off from the same side of the system, motion will be initiated in the opposite direction. Note that if there is friction at the pulley, these statements are no longer true. It will now require a weight of definite size, perhaps a decigram, or a milligram, to start or reverse the motion.

In the first instance the change is reversible, in the second it is said to be *irreversible*. Note that in this example the circumstance that imparts to the process an irreversible character is the presence of friction, which causes the dissipation of energy, that is to say, its conversion into heat at the temperature of the surroundings.

Again, consider a vessel containing water at a temperature T_1 in a room at temperature T_2. If T_1 is ever so slightly greater than T_2, heat passes from the vessel to the surroundings, and vice versa. When, therefore, T_1 and T_2 are very nearly equal, the passage of heat from the vessel to the surroundings is essentially *reversible*. If there is a material difference between T_1 and T_2, the heat transference is *irreversible*. For example, if the vessel is at 50°C. and the room at 20°C., heat will pass from the vessel to the room. And the direction of this heat transfer will remain unchanged if the temperature of the vessel is

We are thus led, from two slightly different points of view to the following definition of evolution: *Evolution is the history of a system undergoing irreversible changes.*

Scope of Definition. It is worth while at this point to consider briefly what kind of history this definition excludes and what it includes. It has already been noted that we have excluded certain purely mechanical systems of periodic habit, such as the frictionless pendulum and the planet circling in its orbit through empty space, in absence of tidal effects.[9] It is not the case, however, that all purely mechanical systems are excluded, that is to say, all systems in which all energy is either kinetic or potential (configurational), all forces either inertia forces or positional forces. If our knowledge of such a system is *statistical* in character, if we know only averages of certain of the variables defining the state of the system, it may happen that certain changes therein appear to us irreversible, and would accordingly be classed, by our definition, among processes of evolution.[10] This leads to the seemingly embarrassing conclusion that a process is or is not a process of evolution, according to the

reduced 1, 2 or even 10°. Not until the vessel is cooled by more than 30° will the stream of heat be reversed. The passage of heat in such case, from a body at one temperature to another at essentially lower temperature, is *irreversible* in this sense, the sense in which the term is employed by the physicist in discussions of this kind.

In the case in which internal readjustments lag behind changes in external conditions, there is necessarily a finite difference between the applied (generalized) force, and the opposing resistance. Such processes are, therefore, of necessity, irreversible.

From the examples given, it will be seen that during a reversible change a system is at all times (very nearly) in equilibrium. It can therefore be said that a reversible change is one in which the system passes through a continuous succession of equilibria. In fact, the change is strictly reversible only if the difference in the applied (generalized) force and the resistance is infinitesimal, and the change is infinitely slow.

[9] Such tidal effects act as brakes and destroy the exact periodicity of the motion.

[10] The irreversibility also of those changes occurring in a system whose internal adjustments lag behind changes in the applied forces, may be apparent, and may disappear when detailed knowledge of the individual parts of the system takes the place of statistical data. The reason for this is that when the reaction or readjustment is expressed in a statistical way, an average of individual reactions may show a lag, although each individual reaction itself may be immediate.

nature and extent of our knowledge regarding the system. So, for example, the establishment of thermal equilibrium in a body of gas initially at non-uniform temperature is evolution if we merely know its total mass, composition, volume, pressure and initial temperature distribution. But should we be informed of the exact initial state of each molecule, then the process by which thermal equilibrium is established (if this does occur) would be classed, together with the journey of the earth in its orbit, among the cases excluded, as mere history, from our definition.

This, upon reflection is neither as strange, nor as embarrassing as it may at first sight appear. For problems of evolution are in large measure problems of probabilities, statistical problems. Incidentally, this reflection disposes of the rather foolish objection sometimes raised against the theory of evolution, that it ascribes the course of events in an evolving system to *chance*. When we describe a phenomenon as being governed by chance, we do not, of course, mean that there are no definite causes (determining factors) at work; we merely state in these terms that the causes are complex and not known to us in detail.

Practically there is no cause for embarrassment, since we never do know material systems in sufficient detail to compute their state at every instant from the initial state, except in terms of averages. *In principle*, however, it is necessary to make the admission that, in the last analysis, whether we class the history of a system as evolution or not must depend on the extent and detail of our knowledge of that system.[11]

It will thus be seen that the line of division between reversible (purely mechanical) and irreversible (dissipative) processes is not

[11] To be quite exact, evolution, according to this, should be defined in terms of a *point of view*, say about as follows:

Evolution is the history of a system, *regarded as* a progressive change or development, to which its unidirectional character is imparted by irreversible changes going on in the system.

That a point of view is involved is also implied in the following definition given by Karl Pearson:

"A causal *description* of the appearance of successive stages in the history of a system forms a theory of the evolution of that system.

"If the theory be so satisfactory that it resumes in some simple statement the whole range of organic change, we term it the law of evolution," (Grammar of Science, 1900, p. 375).

зо very sharply drawn. Furthermore, the cases excluded are, in point of fact, ideal cases. *Real* processes are always irreversible. Hence, after all, history, real history, is always evolution, and, though in principle the two concepts may be distinct, in practice they coincide in scope.

What then is gained by our definition of evolution?

This is the gain: Having analyzed the submerged implications of the term evolution as commonly used, so as to bring them into the focus of our consciousness, and having recognized that evolution, so understood, is the history of a system in the course of irreversible transformation; we at once recognize also that the law of evolution is the law of irreversible transformations; that the *direction* of evolution (which, we saw, had baffled description or definition in ordinary biological terms), is the direction of irreversible transformations. And this direction the physicist can define or describe in exact terms. For an isolated system, it is the direction of increasing entropy.[12] The law of evolution is, in this sense, the second law of thermodynamics.[13]

[12] More generally, it is the direction of decreasing thermodynamic potential, this potential being variously defined, according to the conditions of transformation.

[13] "The second law (of thermodynamics) is the law of evolution of the world accessible to our observation" (Chwolson, Lehrbuch der Physik, 1905, vol. iii, p. 499; Scientia, 1910, vol. iii, p. 51.

" . . . . the second law of the theory of energy is now generally regarded as essentially a statistical law. So viewed, the second law of energy becomes a principle stated wholly in terms of the theory of probability. It is the law that the physical world tends, in each of its parts, to pass from certain less probable to certain more probable configurations of its moving particles. As thus stated the second principle . . . . becomes a law of evolution" (Josiah Royce, Science, 1914, vol. xxxix, p. 551.)

"Un système isolé ne passe jamais deux fois par le même état.

"Le second principe affirme un ordre nécéssaire dans la succession de deux phenomènes, sans retour possible aux états déjà traversés. C'est pourquoi j'ai cru expressif d' appeler ce principe un principe d'évolution. Il se trouve qu'en proposant ce nom je suis fidèle a la pensée de Clausius, car le mot ἐντροπή, d'où il a tiré entropie, signifie précisément évolution." (J.Perrin, Traité de Chimie Physique, 1903, vol. 1, pp. 142–143.)

"Il est hautement improbable qu'un système isolé passe deux fois par le même état; cela est d'autant plus improbable que la complication du système est plus grande, et pratiquement il serait insensé de se placer dans cette hypothèse d'un retour a l'état initial." (J. Perrin, loc. cit., p. 146).

Simple Mechanical Example. It will be desirable, at this point, to consider, by the aid of a simple example, the manner in which some of the facts considered in the preceding pages find expression in the analytical formulation of the behavior of mechanical systems. Take the example of the simple pendulum. For small vibrations the restoring force, tending to draw back the bob to its lowest position, is easily shown to be $mg\dfrac{x}{l}$, where x is the horizontal displacement, m the mass of the bob, and g the acceleration of gravity. This force is expended upon two items, first, in overcoming the inertia of the bob, and producing an acceleration α. The force so expended is measured by $m\alpha$. Second, a part of the force $mg\dfrac{x}{l}$ is expended in overcoming the resistance of the air. If v is the velocity of the bob, this part of the force is measured (for ordinary velocities) by kv, where k is a constant depending on the shape of the bob, etc. We have then

$$m\alpha + kv = -mg\frac{x}{l} \tag{1}$$

or, since the velocity v is the rate of change of x with time, i.e., $\dfrac{dx}{dt}$, and α is the rate of change of $\dfrac{dx}{dt}$ with time, i.e. $\alpha = \dfrac{dv}{dt} = \dfrac{d^2x}{dt^2}$,

$$m\frac{d^2x}{dt^2} + k\frac{dx}{dt} = -mg\frac{x}{l} \tag{2}$$

Now there are certain general characteristics to be observed in this equation, characteristics which are typical of the equations of motion of mechanical systems. The equation contains the first and second derivatives of x with regard to t and no higher derivatives.

The first derivative is introduced by the frictional force, and disappears if this force is zero, i.e., if the coefficient k in (2) is zero. The equation then takes the simpler form

$$m\frac{d^2x}{dt^2} = -mg\frac{x}{l} \tag{3}$$

Now in this simplified form the equation has the following peculiarity: It is indifferent to the sign of t. For, in differentiating twice in succession with regard to $-t$, the positive sign of the second derivative is restored. This is the analytical symptom, as it were, of the reversibility of the process.[14] It should be noted that this peculiarity disappears at once if the frictional term $k \dfrac{dx}{dt}$ is present, for a single differentiation with regard to $-t$ yields a result with sign opposite to that of differentiation with regard to t. The presence of a frictional force, therefore, imparts to the process an irreversible character, it establishes a distinction between t and $-t$; it singles out one direction in time as a peculiar direction, the forward direction, the direction of progression.

Now, in point of fact, in the equations of motion of all *real* systems the frictional term (viscosity term) $k \dfrac{dx}{dt}$ or its equivalent is present, though it may be small as compared with the inertia term $m \dfrac{d^2x}{dt^2}$. The reversible system, in which this term is wholly absent (zero) is an ideal case, it represents a limit towards which real systems may approach; an abstraction.

Inertia-Free or Completely Damped Systems. There is another such ideal limiting case, another abstraction, which is of much interest because certain important classes of real systems approach it very closely. This is the case in which the inertia term $m \dfrac{d^2x}{dt^2}$ is negligible, so that in the case of the pendulum, for example, the equation representing the history of the system reduces to

$$k \frac{dx}{dt} = - mg \frac{x}{l} \tag{4}$$

The history of such inertia-free systems is typically of the irreversible kind. They have, furthermore, a property illustrated by certain features in the equation (4) above:

It will be observed that if x is zero, then $\dfrac{dx}{dt}$ also is zero, or, as we may put it, the velocity vanishes with the displacement from equilibrium. Moreover, differentiation of (4) gives

$$k \frac{d^2x}{dt^2} = - \frac{mg}{l} \frac{dx}{dt} \tag{5}$$

---

[14] Compare H. Poincaré, Thermodynamique, 1908, p. 441.

from which it is seen that the acceleration also vanishes with the velocity.[15] This implies that when the system is in its equilibrium *position*, it is also actually *at rest*, unlike the pendulum, which swings twice through its equilibrium position in each vibration. The former property, the vanishing of the accelerations with the velocities, so that the equilibrium position is necessarily the position of rest, is characteristic of an important class of systems, including those with which we shall here be chiefly concerned.

Another important characteristic of such systems, which is also exemplified by equation (4), is that the velocity is uniquely determined for every value of x. This is not the case in the motion represented by (3). This latter equation gives, upon integration,

$$\frac{dx}{dt} = \pm \sqrt{C - \frac{g}{l} x^2} \tag{6}$$

so that for every value of x there are two possible values of $\frac{dx}{dt}$.

We have, then, at the one extreme the "purely mechanical" system free from frictional (viscosity) effects, and, in its most typical form, periodic in habit.

As an intermediate link we have systems exhibiting both inertia and frictional effects. Their action may resemble that of a pendulum swinging in air; typically the history of such a system exhibits the phenomenon of *damped* oscillations, a periodicity over which there is superimposed the dying away of the motion. The damping is introduced by the frictional effects.

At the other extreme we have inertia-free, or, as we might say, completely damped systems,[16] typically irreversible in their history.

The system and processes with which we shall largely be concerned here seem to belong essentially to this third type, as will be seen in the development of the theme.

[15] Compare E. Buckingham, Theory of Thermodynamics, 1900, p. 33.

[16] This does not, however, preclude the possibility of oscillations. More will be said on this point later.

CHAPTER III

THE STATISTICAL MEANING OF IRREVERSIBILITY

Supposons que nous voulions placer un grain d'avoine au milieu d'un tas de blé: cella sera facile; supposons que nous voulions ensuite l'y retrouver et l'en retirer; nous ne pourrons pas y parvenir. Tous les phénomènes irréversibles, d'après certains physiciens, seraient construits sur ce modèle.—H. Poincaré.

One point, to which allusion has been made incidentally, calls for comment. Many processes which, viewed in the gross, present the appearance of typically dissipative, irreversible phenomena, have long been suspected, and have in recent years been fully demonstrated to be, in fact, of the reversible type, "purely mechanical" processes, the details of which are merely hidden from our view owing to the diminutive dimensions (and correspondingly immense number) of the units at play. So, for example, consider the case of two vessels *A* and *B* at equal pressures, communicating by a tube that can be closed by means of a turncock. Let the vessel *A* contain 1 gram of nitrogen gas, and let *B* contain 1 gram of oxygen gas, the communication between *A* and *B* being closed. It is a matter of common knowledge that if the stopcock is now opened, the gas from the *A* will flow over into the vessel *B* and *vice versa*, and in a short time an equilibrium is reached in which each vessel contains 0.5 gram of each gas. Now, in point of fact, the molecules of the gas behave (approximately) like a number of elastic spheres, their equations of motion contain no dissipative term, but are of the type (3) (Chapter II). We should therefore expect the system to exhibit periodic motion, we should expect that after a certain lapse of time the initial condition should return, and that all the nitrogen should once more be contained in the vessel *A*, all the oxygen in *B*. In actuality, such a thing is never observed. How is this discrepancy to be explained?

Let us replace the two vessels and the gas molecules by some simple analogues of dimensions readily accessible to our senses, and let us watch a process analogous to the diffusion of the gas from one vessel into the other. We provide ourselves with two boxes or urns.[1]   In one of these, A we place 50 black balls; in the other B, we place 50 white balls.   We shuffle both boxes thoroughly, and then draw blindly a ball from A, and one from B, and we return them to opposite urns.   We continue this as long as desired.   The more lightly drawn curve in figure 1 shows the graphic record of an actual series of drafts of this kind.   The stair-case-like line shows how in successive drafts the number of black balls in box A gradually diminished until at last there remained about 25, one-half of the original number, in box A.   But note that there are fluctuations, sometimes the box contains 26, 27, 28, then again

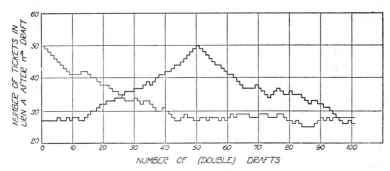

FIG. 1. GRAPH OF MODEL PROCESS ILLUSTRATING THE STATISTICAL MEANING OF IRREVERSIBILITY

The more lightly drawn curve records the number of black tickets remaining in urn A after successive drafts.   The heavier curve records the previous and ensuing history of 50 tickets found in urn A at the end of the fiftieth draft, (Reproduced from A. J. Lotka, Two Models in Statistical Mechanics, Am. Math. Monthly, vol. 31, 1924, p. 122.)

27, 26, etc. of the original balls.   It is nowise *impossible* that, if we continue the drafts for a long time, some time or other all the original 50 black balls will be back in box A; but it *is* highly *improbable* that this should happen within any reasonable time.   Curiously enough, the urn model is competent to illustrate also this highly improbable course of events.   For this purpose, instead of starting with 50 black and 50 white balls, we start with the balls, or in this case more conveniently tickets, all white, and numbered from 1 to 50 in urn A, and from 51 to 100 in urn B.   After a suit-

---

[1] A. J. Lotka, Am. Math. Monthly, March, 1924; Science, 1924, vol. 59, p. 532.

able number of drafts, say 50 double drafts, in which a record is kept of all the numbers drawn, the urns are opened, and the tickets in the second urn are now blackened. The drawing is then continued, for, say, another 50 drafts, recording each time the numbers drawn. The numbers on the tickets enable us to trace the previous history of the 50 black tickets, before they were blackened. In an experiment actually carried out it was found that these 50 black tickets were originally distributed essentially evenly in the two urns. The curve representing the first 50 drafts is an ascending curve, the system passed, during this stage of the process, from more probable to less probable states, as shown in the first, ascending portion of the more heavily drawn curve in figure 1. In the second series of fifty drafts the curve descends in normal fashion, with increasing probability of the successive states of the system. It may seem like a contradiction of terms that what amounts practically to an infinitely improbable series of drafts should be capable of actual realization at will. But if the series of drafts described were extended to great length in both directions, say one million drafts before blackening the tickets, and one million after, it would be seen that the peak on the curve is indeed a very exceptional feature. It is a perfectly safe bet that in two million drafts not more than one such peak, going up to 50 black balls in one urn, would be encountered.

The model described exemplifies among others the fact that in an exceedingly long lapse of time it may some time occur that the system will return to its original state. This is quite in accord with the laws of mechanics; in fact, as already noted, these laws actually demand that every mechanical system of finite dimensions must ultimately return to its initial state, and must do this not once only, but in everlasting reiteration at regular intervals: the motion is periodic. This property also is capable of illustration by a simple model, such as the following: Twenty-six pendulums of periods $T = 0.5, 0.6, \ldots 2.9, 3.0$ seconds are started simultaneously to the left from their equilibrium position, and are then allowed to oscillate undisturbed. Count is then made, at the end of every tenth of a second, of the number of pendulums on the left of the median. In this way the staircase curve figure 2 was obtained (computation here taking the place of actual observation). It will be seen that in the brief fragment of a period covered by the record, this exhibits all the characteristics of a "passage from a less probable to a more probable distribution," though, in point of fact, we know that the system has a perfectly definite period of 7385 years.   The appearance of chance in this wholly determinate mechanical process is brought into still greater prominence if we plot the deviations, from the mean, of the number of pendulums on the left of the median position, at successive counts.   We thus obtain the points indicated by small circles in figure 3.   These group themselves very obviously about a typical Gaussian curve of random distribution, namely one having a standard deviation of $\sqrt{\frac{26}{4}}$; this curve has been drawn in the diagram, and, as will be seen, the agreement is good, considering the smallness of the sample

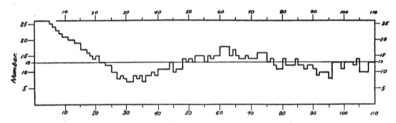

FIG. 2. GRAPH OF SECOND MODEL PROCESS ILLUSTRATING THE STATISTICAL MEANING OF IRREVERSIBILITY

Number of pendulums found on left of median position at successive epochs. (Reproduced from A. J. Lotka, Two Models in Statistical Mechanics, Am. Math. Monthly, vol. 31, 1924, p. 124.)

(412 observations, extending over 41.2 seconds, out of a total period of 7385 years).   Thus for long stretches of time the periodicity of the motion of the system of pendulums is very effectively masked under an aspect of "chance."

These simple models illustrate very clearly how the seeming conflict between the periodicity of all mechanical motions and the apparently one-sided course of events, directed toward one definite end state, is resolved.   The actual process of isothermal gaseous diffusion is, in fact, periodic, but with a period so long that humanly speaking, the return to the initial state never occurs at all.   For all stretches of time that can have any real significance in human thought (and this includes the vast historical ranges of all geology and astronomy), it may therefore be said in a certain sense that evolution proceeds, in all but a vanishingly small class of exceptional cases, from less probable states (e.g., uneven distribution of the 50 black balls in the two urns) to more probable states, tending ultimately toward a most probable state. This statement cannot however be allowed to pass without a word of caution. It is mean-

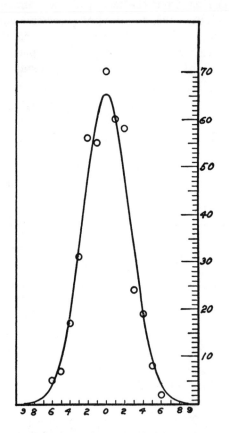

Fig. 3. Frequency Diagram for the Deviations from the Mean Appearing in Figure 2

Abscissae represent deviations from the mean (13) in number of pendulums on left of median; ordinates represent corresponding frequencies, among the observations recorded in figure 2. (Reproduced from A. J. Lotka, Two Models in Statistical Mechanics, Am. Math. Monthly, vol. 31, 1924, p. 125.)

ingless unless the characteristic with regard to which probability is reckoned is explicitly or implicitly indicated. Probability is essentially a matter of classification. An improbable event is one that is a member of a small class, and whether it is so or not depends, clearly, on our system of classification. For this reason the broad statement which has sometimes been made,[2] that the direction of evolution is from less probable to more probable states, is not only inadequate, but is really meaningless. It is indefinite in failing to specify with regard to what characteristic probability is to be reckoned; and it is incomplete in failing to call attention to the fundamentally important connection between the particular probabilities in question and available energy.

Another point, which has not hitherto perhaps received its deserved attention is clearly brought out by the two models described, namely, that irreversibility is a relative term. For, obviously, if we use our visual discrimination in selecting the balls drawn from the boxes (instead of drawing blindly), we can easily bring it about that in short order all the black balls are back in box A. Thus a process may be reversible or not, according to the means that are naturally available or arbitrarily permitted in operating upon the system under consideration; somewhat as the trisection of an angle is or is not an impossible geometric construction, according as we are or are not forbidden the use of instruments other than ruler and compass. In the case of molecular aggregates this fact has long been duly appreciated, having been first pointed out by Clerk Maxwell, who remarked that a demon capable of dealing with individual molecules would be able to cheat the second law of thermodynamics. But it seems to have been pretty generally overlooked that the relative character of irreversibility has an important significance in certain natural processes taking place on a macroscopic scale. In point of fact this is a matter whose importance in the world of living organisms can hardly be rated too high. For there are certain diffusive processes going on in nature which, from the standpoint of thermodynamics, are not of the irreversible type; but which might as well be, so far as any benefit derived from their reversibility by the organism (and, in particular, by man) is concerned. If I should be the fortunate

[2] See for example, J. Royce, Science, 1914, vol. 34, p. 551.

possessor of a pound of gold dust, and some malicious person should take it and scatter it far and wide, so that it became hopelessly diluted with dust and refuse, it would be a small comfort to me to know that it were merely mechanically commingled with such foreign matters, that it had not irreversibly undergone solution or chemical transformation, and that therefore it could *theoretically* be recovered without the expenditure of work. In *practice* its recovery might entail the expenditure of far more energy than if the gold were present in reasonably concentrated solution. The point is that in practice I am restricted to operations in bulk upon reasonably large quantities, in reasonably concentrated form, otherwise the theoretical ideal of recovery without work is very far from being attained. And *with this restriction placed upon my operations*, certain processes acquire an irreversibility which they do not possess apart from that restriction. The illustration of the pound of gold has the advantage of simplicity and cogency. But if by any chance it has conveyed the impression that only in peculiar and far-fetched cases does this kind of irreversibility enter into play, then it is an unfortunate example indeed, for nothing could be farther from the truth. The fact is that nature abounds in just such dissipative processes as the scattering to the four winds, to utter inutility, of materials of the highest importance to life; and one of the central problems which the organism has to solve in the struggle for existence, is the reconcentration, into his immediate environment and into his body, of valuable materials that have become scattered by agencies beyond his control. It is not the least of the triumphs which have made man the lord of creation, that he has learnt, beyond all comparison more effectively than any of his competitors, to carry out this process of reconcentration to satisfy his needs. So a fleet of ships, year by year, bear a burden of saltpeter from Chile to all civilized countries, to balance the losses from our depleted fields. So, in his most recent technical achievement, man has learnt to draw from the air a supply that will continue unfailing, long after the Chilean nitre beds are exhausted.

The fact is, in dealing with the physics of such macroscopically irreversible effects, it will ultimately be necessary to develop a method of mathematical analysis that shall be competent to distinguish and handle not only the extremes—the case of a primitive organism that can deal only in the gross, without intelligent or other discrimination, with the matter and situations presented to it; and an ideally perfect organism, that should expend just the minimum of effort, directed with absolute precision toward the attainment of its ends. A method must be devised that shall duly take account of, and use as a fundamental datum for its deductions, the particular character, the particular degree of perfection of the mechanical and psychic equipment or organization by which each organism reacts more or less selectively upon its environment. We shall have occasion to refer to this matter again in greater detail in a later section. But here it is well to note that our two models are suggestive also with regard to this aspect of the subject. For it appears at first sight as if there were a fundamental difference in character between the first and the second model, since it is essential for the operation of the urn model that the drawing be done *blindly*, so as to give *chance* a part in the process, as we would say; whereas the pendulum model we operate with our eyes open, apparently in full consciousness of what is going on. Chance seems to play no part here, the system is mechanically determinate.

But there is a blindness which is not of the eye, and there is a vision that surpasses optical vision. The same struggle for existence which has developed in man the organ of sight, to depict for him the external world, to furnish him with a map on which to base his plan of campaign, has also, in latter days, developed his internal vision, whereby he extends his world-picture beyond the powers of the bodily eye. It is immaterial by which process his map is drawn—its function is the same; whether I peep into the urn and manipulate the drafts by the light of my eyes; or whether, in the light of my knowledge of mechanics, I adjust the pendulums to equal lengths and phases; or again, whether, in the more serious affairs of life I employ these same faculties to diverse ends, the effect is the same: In greater measure or less these organs and faculties emancipate me from the bonds of the fortuitous and make me a controller of events. Their function is to substitute choice for chance, to introduce aimed collisions in place of random encounters.

Origin of Subjective Sense of Direction-in-Time. The failure of the differential equations of dynamics to discriminate between t and $-t$ raises the question as to the physical significance and origin of our subjective conviction of a fundamental difference between the forward and the backward direction in time,—a conviction that is intimately bound up with the concept of evolution, for, whatever may ultimately be found to be the law of evolution, it is plain that no trend of any kind can be defined or even described without reference to a favored direction in time.

One view which suggests itself is that this conviction is our subjective appreciation of the trend from less probable to more probable states recognized in statistical mechanics. But this does not seem very satisfying, for we somehow feel that our conviction must rest on something more fundamental than this somewhat accidental circumstance, which, as the models described clearly show, is fundamentally incompetent to distinguish between the forward and the backward direction in time. For the peak in figure 1, for example, may indifferently be traversed from left to right or *vice versa*, it presents the same general character in either sense.

Another alternative is to suppose that the differential equations of dynamics, as formulated by us today, are either an incorrect, or else an incomplete statement of facts. The latter view is, indeed, upon reflection, found to have a certain warrant. For the *differential* equations of motion alone do not fully determine the actual course of events; this depends further on the value of certain arbitrary constants of integration; or, to speak in terms of physical entities, upon the initial velocities of the particle of which the system is composed. Strictly speaking it is only when the initial velocities are zero, that the equations of motion, considered in their totality, are indifferent to the substitution $t' = -t$. From this point of view our sense of the forward direction in time would appear as our subjective appreciation of the fact that, once a material system has been started on a certain course, with certain initial velocities, there then remains no further freedom; its history must continue to unfold in the direction determined by the initial velocities.

It seems, however, that it is not with this perfectly general type of irreversibility of the course of events that we are chiefly concerned in the study of evolution. The concept of evolution, according to the analysis which has been made of it in preceding pages, applies principally, if not exclusively, to systems that outwardly at least affect the aperiodic habit, systems that do not return periodically to their initial state, but show a definite trend, whereby yesterday and tomorrow are never alike, and differ moreover in some definite and characteristic fashion, even though we may not be fully competent, at the present epoch of science, to specify exactly wherein lies the characteristic difference.[3]

Inadequacy of Thermodynamic Method. Our reflections so far have linked the fundamental problem of the direction, the trend of evolution, with the disciplines of thermodynamics and statistical mechanics. From this point of view the direction of evolution is identified with the direction of the unfolding of irreversible processes, the direction of increase of entropy (in thermodynamics) or of increasing probability (in statistical mechanics).

A certain mental satisfaction may be derived from this conclusion. It gives us, in principle at least, an answer to our question "Quo vadis?" But *practically* the answer is very inadequate. If the conclusions, the methods of thermodynamics, or of statistical mechanics, are to be applied to a concrete case, the data of the problem must be presented in a very particular form. So long as we deal with volumes, pressures, temperatures, etc., our thermodynamics serve us well. But the variables in terms of which we find it convenient to define the state of biological (life-bearing) systems are other than these. We may have little doubt that the principles of thermodynamics or of statistical mechanics do actually control the processes occurring in systems in the course of organic evolution. But if we seek to make concrete application we find that the systems under consideration are far too complicated to yield fruitfully to thermodynamic reasoning; and such phases of statistical mechanics as relate to aggregation of atoms or molecules, seem no better adapted for the task. To attempt application of these methods to the prime problems of organic evolution is much like attempting to study the habits of an elephant by means of a microscope. It is not that the substance of the elephant is inherently unfitted to be viewed with the microscope; the instrument is ill adapted to the scale of the object and of the investigation.

It would seem, then, that what is needed is an altogether new instrument; one that shall envisage the units of a biological population as the established statistical mechanics envisage molecules, atoms and electrons; that shall deal with such average effects as

[3] Perhaps the objective interpretation of our subjective sense of direction in time must be sought in quantum mechanics. Cf. A. J. Lotka, loc. cit., p, 126, and, W. S. Franklin, Science, 1924, vol. 60, p. 258.

population density, population pressure, and the like, after the manner in which thermodynamics deal with the average effects of gas concentration, gas pressures, etc.; that shall accept its problems in terms of common biological data, as thermodynamics accepts problems stated in terms of physical data; and that shall give the answer to the problem in the terms in which it was presented. What is needed, in brief, is something of the nature of what has been termed "Allgemeine Zustandslehre,"[4] a general method or Theory of State.

It is somewhat along these lines that the system now to be sketched is conceived.

[4] A term introduced by J. R. Rydberg, quoted by C. Benedicks, Zeitschr. f. phys. Chemie, 1922, vol. 100, p. 42.

CHAPTER IV

EVOLUTION CONCEIVED AS A REDISTRIBUTION

Toutes ces choses ne peuvent se determiner surement que par des mesures précises que nous chercherons plus tard; mais auparavant il fallait au moins sentir le besoin de les chercher.—*J. B. Biot.*

It now behooves us to establish, with respect to the problem of evolution, a viewpoint, a perspective, a method of approach, which has hitherto received its principal development and application outside the boundaries of biological science. Such prior development and applications, however extraneous to our chief line of interest here, may well serve us in our present interrogations, since we shall be in a position to profit by the precedents established in methods, in conclusions, and, most particularly, in habit of thought.

This perspective is that which contemplates an evolving system as an aggregation of numbered or measured components of several specified kinds, and which observes and enregisters the history of that system as a record of progressive changes taking place in the distribution, among those components, of the material of which the system is built up.

It is thus that physical chemistry views the progressive changes in a system comprising several chemical species, that is to say elements, compounds, phases, etc. It describes the system by enumerating these components, by stating their character and extent (mass); and by further indicating the values of certain quantities or parameters, such as volume or pressure, temperature, etc., which, together with the masses of the components, are found experimentally to be both necessary and sufficient, for the purposes in view, to define the state of the system. With the instantaneous state of the system thus defined, physical chemistry investigates by observation and by deductive reasoning (theory) the history, the evolution of the system, and gives analytical expression to that history, by establishing relations, or equations, between the variables defining these states (after the manner set forth above), and the time.

It is commonly found that these fundamental equations assume the simplest, the most perspicuous form, when they are written relative to rates of change of the state of the system, rather than relative to this state itself. That is to say, it is found that the expressions for the rate of increase in mass, the velocity of growth, of the several components, are simpler, more primitive in form, than the expressions giving directly the mass of each component as a function of the time. In the language of the calculus, the differential equations display a certain simplicity in form, and are therefore, in the handling of the theory at least, taken as the starting point, from which the equations relating to the progressive states themselves, as functions of the time, are then derived by integration.[1]

So, for example, a simple system may be defined as comprising 4 gram-molecules of hydrogen, 2 gram-molecules of oxygen, and 100 gram-molecules of steam, at one atmosphere pressure, and at 1800°C. The fundamental relation expressing the law of evolution, the historical pattern, of the system, is in this case given by the law of mass action:

$$\frac{1}{v}\frac{dm_1}{dt} = k_1 \frac{m_2^2 m_3}{v^3} - k_2 \frac{m_1^2}{v^2} \tag{1}$$

where v is the volume, m_1 is the mass of steam, m_2 the mass of hydrogen, and m_3, the mass of oxygen (all expressed in gram-molecules). The coefficients k_1, k_2, are functions of the temperature, or, for a given temperature, are characteristic constants of the reaction.

We are not, here, interested in the particular form of the law of mass action. What does interest us is the general form of the equation (1). It states that the rate of increase in mass, the velocity of growth of one component, steam (mass m_1), is a function of the masses m_2, m_3, of the other components, as well as of the mass m_1 itself, and, besides, of the parameters v (volume) and T (temperature), the latter being contained in the coefficients k_1, k_2. This statement, in its more general form, is written, according to established notation[2]

---

[1] In experimental observation usually (though not always) the reverse attitude is adopted.

[2] For the benefit of the non-mathematical reader it may here be explained that equation (2) is merely a short-hand expression, so to speak, of the simple statement: The rate of increase of mass with time $\frac{dm}{dt}$ of the component S_1 is a *function* of, or is determined by, the masses m_1, m_2, m_3, of the components S_1, S_2, S_3, as well as by the volume v and the temperature T. Precisely similar is the construction to be placed on the equations (3).

$$\frac{dm_1}{dt} = F\ (m_1,\ m_2,\ m_3;\ v,\ T) \tag{2}$$

Now it is this habit of thought, expressed in equation (2), that is to be transplanted into the contemplation of problems of evolution in general, and organic evolution in particular; this point of view, this perspective, which regards evolution as a process of redistribution of matter among the several components of a system, under specified conditions.[3]

Having thus passed from the specific to the general—from the case of physico-chemical systems to a general formulation—we now retrace our steps to the particular, but in a new direction. We now contemplate the kind of systems that form the object of study of the biological sciences.

With the outlook gained in our preceding reflections we envisage the life-bearing system, in the progress of evolution, as an assembly of a number of components: Biological species; collections or aggregations of certain inorganic materials such as water, oxygen, carbon dioxide, nitrogen, free and in various combinations, phosphorus, sulphur, etc.

These components are placed in various relations of mutual interaction under specific conditions of area, topography, climate, etc. Under these conditions each may grow, decay, or maintain equilibrium. In general the rate of growth $\frac{dX}{dt}$ of any one of these components will depend upon, will be a function of, the abundance in which it and each of the others is presented; this rate of growth will also be a function of the topography,[4] climate, etc. If these latter features are defined in terms of a set of parameters $P_1\,P_2\,.\,.\,.\,\ P_j$, we may write, in the same sense as equation (2)

[3] Compare F. B. Jevons, "Evolution," Macmillan, 1902, Chapter VI, p. 72.

[4] Terrestial species have an essentially two-dimensional distribution, so that area functions here in a manner somewhat analogous to that in which volume enters into physico-chemical relations. Aquatic life, with its three-dimensional sphere of activity, is enacted in systems whose extension is described in terms of volume. More detailed topographic parameters may be required to define in sufficient completeness the configuration, the structure of these systems. The absence of such detail from the more familiar formulations of chemical dynamics is due to the purely accidental circumstance that the systems commonly dealt with in that branch of science are either homogeneous, or of comparatively simple heterogeneous structure.

$$\frac{dX_1}{dt} = F_1 (X_1, X_2, \ldots X_n; P_1, P_2, \ldots P_j)$$

$$\frac{dX_2}{dt} = F_2 (X_1, X_2, \ldots X_n; P_1, P_2, \ldots P_j) \qquad (3)$$

$$\frac{dX_n}{dt} = F_n (X_1, X_2, \ldots X_n; P_1, P_2, \ldots P_j)$$

In general there will be n such equations, one for each of the n components.

The purport of these equations (3) remains uncertain so long as the components (e.g., biological species, etc.) $S_1 \; S_2 \; . \; . \; . \; S_n$ are undefined. What definitions we may adopt for these is, in accordance with the principles discussed anteriorly, a matter for arbitrary disposition; though we may be guided in our choice by considerations of expediency. These may advise different policies from case to case, according to the particular phase of the problem taken in view. The conclusions reached will, of course, depend upon the particular definitions chosen. This is as it should be; the conclusions apply to the components *as defined*, and, in general, to no other. This seems clear enough, but if any further exposition is needed, it will be found in examples shortly to be considered.

Intra-Group Evolution. While the precise definition of the components $S_1 \; S_2 \; . \; . \; . \; S_n$ may, and indeed must, be held over for determination as each separate phase of the general problem is singled out for treatment, yet there is one class of cases regarding which it is appropriate to set forth certain reflections at this juncture.

It may have been observed that so far nothing has been said regarding one aspect of organic evolution which, in the history of the subject in the past, and in the minds and writings of its exponents and students today, occupies a dominating position—namely, the relation of evolution to the modification of species with the passage of time, and, in particular, to the origin of new species.

Now a biological species, however defined, is not a homogenous group. It comprises portions (individuals) varying more or less widely with regard to numerous features, such as stature, weight, etc.

If our description of the distribution of matter in the system is to be at all exhaustive, we shall need to know, not only the extent (total mass) of each species, but also its constitution, as expressed by the frequency, the relative abundance, of each statistical type within the species. In the case of man, for example, we may wish to know the fraction F (56) of the total population whose height is comprised within the limits 56 and 57 inches at a given instant. And in observing the evolution of the system of which this population forms part, we shall be interested, not only in the growth (or decay) of the population as a whole, but also in the rate of change of the abundance (frequency) of each statistical type. This phase of the problem does not differ essentially, in character, from that first considered: it is essentially a question of distribution and changes in distribution of mass in the system among its several components; only now we have fixed our attention on a different set of components, components defined in a different way, on a finer scale. In the first instance we had taken in view the distribution and changes in distribution of the matter of the system *among* the several major groups or species; now we are considering the distribution *within* each such group. This division of the general problem of organic evolution into two aspects has certain practical advantages, and it will be convenient to have names to designate the two separate aspects or domains of evolution. We shall accordingly speak of *inter-group* evolution on the one hand, when referring to changes in the distribution of the matter of the system among several component groups; and we shall speak of *intra-group* evolution when referring to changes in the distribution of matter within the group, among its statistical types, however defined.

It is possible to set up equations relating to intra-group evolution, similar in general character to those set forth above relative to inter-group evolution. However, this phase of the problem is probably treated more satisfactorily in other ways, of which some examples will arise in due course.[5]

It is nevertheless, desirable, to indicate in the system of equations (3) the incidence of intra-group evolution.

Conveniently this may be done by writing the ith equation, for example, in more detailed form:

$$\frac{dX_1}{dt} = F_1 (X_1, X_2, \ldots X_n; P_1, P_2, \ldots P_j; Q_1, Q_2, \ldots Q_k) \qquad (4)$$

---

[5] See Chapter IX, p. 122; Chapter XIII, p. 170; Chapter XXV, pp. 348 et seq.

where $Q_1, Q_2, \ldots Q_k$ are parameters defining the character of several components (e.g., biological species) S; such definition may take the form of a set of characteristic frequency functions, or some other form. These parameters will, in general, be functions of the time, that is to say, each component may, in general, be variable in character through the occurrence of intra-group evolution. Whether this variability is limited, or constrained to follow a certain course (orthogenesis), whether variations take place in continuously graded series or *per saltum*, or in any or all of these ways, are questions which will not be discussed at this point. At present all that need be said is that the origination of a new species in any of these ways falls within the scheme of our description of evolution as a change in the distribution of matter among the components of the system.[6]

It may be remarked, in passing, that in general a complete definition of the system may require an infinite number of parameters P and Q; this does not necessarily cause any undue complication in practise, since in many cases certain of the parameters P, Q either remain constant, or change so slowly that, in discussing changes in the variables X, we may treat these parameters as if they were constant.

The parameters Q, defining the character of the species, are in general functions of the time, as has already been remarked. In this respect organic evolution exhibits a very important distinction as compared with chemical evolution, i.e., the evolution of a system in the course of chemical transformation. In such a system the character of the components is usually fixed once for all. Water is H_2O for all time, unlike a species of organism which is subject to change in character. One important result of this is that, so far as we know, organic evolution is a process *without end*, for there seems to be no limit to the variety of forms of living matter, as there is no limit to the variety of geometric configurations and mechanical systems that can be formed from a given portion of matter. Chemical evolution, on the contrary, terminates, under constant condition, in a definite equilibrium, determined once for all, by those conditions.

[6] This is not a new *definition* of evolution, it is a *conception* of evolution wholly compatible with the definition that has been laid down in preceding pages.

It will be observed that the fundamental equations (3) resemble in form the equation (4) of Chapter II, which was given as a typical example of the equation for an *inertia-free* or *completely damped* system. The velocities $\dfrac{dX}{dt}$ are single-valued functions F of the variables X. It is the single-valued character of the functions F that gives the system its stamp as an inertia-free or completely damped system; a system in the course of typically irreversible transformation.

It is not maintained that these equations cover all cases that may be brought within the purview of the present study; nor shall we, in all cases, be tied down to the scope of these equations. They are, however, of very broad scope, and, upon reflection, will be found to cover at least a large and significant portion of the field of our interests here.

To one point, however, it may be well to draw attention. To read these equations in their broadest interpretation we must be prepared to consider cases in which the phenomenon of *lag* or *lead* enters. Perhaps the terms lag and lead require explanation. In some cases the course of events today depends on certain features in the state of the world at a previous date. So, for example, the number of persons of age 50 in the year 1924 depends (among other things) on the birthrate in the year 1874. Or, to quote another instance, the number of new cases of scarlet fever today depends on the number of infections a week ago. There is thus a *lag* in the appearance of the observable effect in the system. In other cases there may be a lead. The price of land on Church Street today may suffer an increase or perhaps decrease because it becomes known that in a year's time a railway station is to be built nearby.

Since effects of this kind must be contemplated as a possibility, we must be prepared to read our equations in the following sense: The rate of increase $\dfrac{dX}{dt}$ of the mass of the component S_i at the present instant, is a function of the masses X_1, X_2, etc., at some other instant of time, say X_1 at $(t - p_1)$, X_2 at $(t - p_2)$, etc., where some of the p's may be negative (corresponding to a *lead*).

We must be prepared to consider our equations in this interpretation. Illustrative examples will not be offered here, as the mathematical treatment of these cases is somewhat troublesome. The interested reader will find an illustration in the author's monograph on the Ross Malaria equations, Am. Jour. Hygiene, vol. 3, January Supplement, 1923. Only a reflection of general character shall find its place here. It is characteristic of systems whose history is defined by equations thus involving a *lag*, that, in general, the course of events at a given instant is dependent upon the *previous history* of the system over a certain finite range of time. The consequences of this feature are somewhat singular. If the world's events followed a system of equations of this kind, we might have two worlds, in every respect identical today, but each with a different past, and, in consequence each with a different future. And a similar reflection necessarily applies in the case of lead.

This conclusion is perhaps not in harmony with a mechanistic conception of the universe. But the phenomena of *memory* and of *will* are of precisely such character as to introduce lags and leads into the world's equation, and we may be well advised to keep our minds open as to the possible effects of this circumstance upon the course of events.

It should be observed, that the appearance of a lag or lead in our equation may be spurious. It may be due to a species of mathematical shorthand. It is easier to describe a person as having become infected with scarlet fever three days ago, than to describe precisely his present state today ensuant upon that infection. Hence we may prefer to, or, for lack of detailed knowledge we may be forced to write our equations in terms of $(t - p)$, although, if all the facts were known, we could, were we so disposed, write them in terms of t. And the same reflection applies to the appearance of a lead in our equations. Whether, with complete knowledge of all circumstances bearing on the situation, there should still remain a residuum of influences that could find expression only in terms of a lag or lead, this, perhaps, is fundamentally the nature of the problem of the influence of consciousness upon the course of the world's history.

CHAPTER V

The Program of Physical Biology

.... It will be the function of this new branch of science to investigate biological phenomena as regards their physical aspects, just as Physical Chemistry has treated the physical aspects of chemical phenomena. Because this field has not yet been systematically explored .... the individual data of *Physical Biology* appear, as yet, as more or less disconnected facts, or as regularities for which no proper place is found in the existing scheme of present-day science; and the investigations of isolated problems in this field are as yet carried on as something of a scientific hobby by amateurs, with the result that they are guided by chance rather than by plan. . . . and are often totally lacking in any fundamental guiding principles or connecting theory. As results gathered in this disconnected fashion accumulate, the need of their unification into a harmonious whole, into a distinct discipline of science, becomes more and more acutely felt. Such unification necessarily involves the working out of a viewpoint that shall make the several facts and relations fall in line naturally in an orderly system; in other words, what is needed is a labor of organisation. In the course of this, new and unforeseen problems will inevitably arise, and a fruitful field of scientific endeavor should thus be opened for the investigator.—*Porstmann.*

A first use to which we may with advantage put the results of the preceding analysis, is to systematise the subject here treated; there will thus be gained a general plan of work and a division of the topic into natural sections, upon which the arrangement of the succeeding chapters will, in the main, be based.

Physical Biology,[1] as here conceived and discussed, is essentially a branch of the greater discipline of the *General Mechanics of Evolution,* the mechanics of systems undergoing irreversible changes in the distribution of matter among the several components of such system.

[1] In introducing the term *Physical Biology* the writer would suggest that the term *Biophysics* be employed (as hitherto) to denote that branch of science which treats of the physics of individual life processes, as exhibited in the individual organism (e.g., conduction of an impulse along nerve or muscle); and that the term Physical Biology be reserved to denote the broader field of the application of physical principles in the study of life-bearing systems as a whole. Physical biology would, in this terminology, include biophysics as a subordinate province.

For a summary statement of what might be termed the program of biophysics see A. Forbes, *Science,* 1920, vol. 52, p. 331.

It so happens that many of the components that play an important rôle in nature, both organic and inorganic, are built up of large numbers of individuals, themselves very small as compared with the aggregations which they form. Accordingly the study of systems of this kind can be taken up in two separate aspects, namely, first with the attention centered upon the phenomena displayed by the component aggregates in bulk; we may speak of this as the *Bulk Mechanics* or *Macro-Mechanics* of the evolving system. And, secondly, the study of such systems may be conducted with the attention centered primarily upon the phenomena displayed by the individuals of which the aggregates are composed. This branch of the subject may suitably be termed the *Micro-Mechanics* of the evolving system. It is evident that between these two branches or aspects of the general discipline there is an inherent relation, arising from the fact that the bulk effects observed are of the nature of a statistical manifestation or resultant of the detail working of the micro-individuals. The study of this inherent connection is, accordingly, the special concern of a separate branch which we may speak of as *Statistical Mechanics*. This terminology is in part coincident with accepted usage, but in part must be understood to refer to an expansion of the subject beyond the bounds hitherto covered, whereby its scope shall be extended so as to include the statistical treatment of the dynamical problems presented by aggregates of living organisms; that is to say, aggregates of energy transformers possessing certain significant special properties.

Each of the branches of the mechanics of evolution enumerated so far naturally splits up into two subdivisions, according as we devote our attention to the material changes or to the energy changes involved. By an extension of prior usage in physical chemistry we may employ the term *Stoichiometry* to denote that branch of the science which concerns itself with the *material* transformations, with the relations between the *masses* of the components. The discussion of this branch presents itself as the more elementary task, and will therefore be taken up first; after this has been disposed of we shall be better prepared to discuss the second aspect, the *Energetics* or *Dynamics* of Evolution.

Taking now a survey of the stoichiometry of systems in evolutionary transformation, we can hardly find a better guide, for the organization of this subject, than the fundamental equations

$$\frac{dX_i}{dt} = F_i (X_1, X_2, \ldots X_n; P, Q)$$

which we may speak of as the fundamental equations of the *Kinetics* of Evolution, since they furnish expressions for the *velocities* of transformation and exhibit the relations between these velocities and the masses of the several components, as well as the parameters P, Q.

The very form of these equations suggests, as the first and most elementary problem, the treatment of the case of evolution under constant conditions, as defined by constant P's and Q's. This will, accordingly, be the course here adopted, treating first the general case of n variables X_1, X_2, $\ldots$ X_n, and then some special cases in which the number of variables is restricted to 1, 2 and 3.

The perfectly general case, of evolution under conditions of wholly unrestrained variability of the P's and Q's, is mathematically uninviting (though not wholly intractable), and is also of minor interest in practice. Little will therefore be said of this. Certain special types of changes in the P's and Q's (e.g., *slow* changes) will find a place in the next subdivision of the general subject, the *Statics* of evolving systems. This branch is, in a sense, a special division of the Kinetics of Evolution, namely that which concerns itself with systems in which the velocities of transformation are zero, so that there is *Equilibrium*, or, to be more exact, a *Steady State*. This, of course, implies, strictly speaking, constancy of the parameters P, Q. But something very much like equilibrium presents itself in certain cases when these parameters change *slowly*. There may then arise what has been termed a *Moving Equilibrium*. In view of the important rôle which such moving equilibria play in nature, their discussion must form a part of the program of Physical Biology.

A second special problem of evolution under changing conditions (changing parameters P) that lends itself to treatment with comparative ease, is that which concerns itself with *initial* and *end* states (equilibria), as influenced by changing conditions, without demanding any information regarding the intermediate steps passed through by the evolving system. So, in physical chemistry, we may enquire what will be the effect, upon equilibrium, of a change in pressure or in temperature. Similar questions may be raised regarding equilibria or steady states in life-bearing systems, and the matter calls for at least passing notice. This leads to the consideration of the *Principle of Le Chatelier* and, as a natural sequel of the train of thought thus started, to the examination of relations which may exist between certain of the parameters *P*, somewhat as, in physical chemistry, significant relations exist between pressure and volume, for example. It is found that some, at any rate, of the parameters *P* present analogy to the intensity and the capacity factors of an energy; out of this have arisen in the past sporadic efforts to establish systems of social dynamics and the like, which, however, have been based upon an acceptance as *identity* of what is only *analogy*. Those who have followed this road have been led, not so much perhaps to erroneous conclusions, as to blind alleys, to barren fields. True progress can be expected only by retracing one's steps from such tentative excursions and striking out in a new direction; forsaking the way of *quasi-dynamics*, and breaking a trail toward a system of true *dynamics*, both of the individual (micro-dynamics) and of the system as a whole (macro-dynamics).

Of intra-species evolution, as expressed in changes in the parameters *Q* that define the character of the several species, little will be said here. The reasons and justification for this step-fatherly treatment of so important an aspect of our topic have been set forth in the preceding text. A discussion of at least one phase of intra-species evolution, falling under the head of dynamics, will, however, be presented when dealing with that phase of the subject; and we shall briefly note, in due course, some aspects of intra-species evolution, as discussed more particularly by J. B. S. Haldane.

These, in broad outline, are some of the principal land-marks in the territory ultimately to be covered by *Physical Biology*, and to be given a preliminary survey here. In concentrated form the lay of the land, as set forth above, is sketched in the diagram or scheme table 1, which should be found helpful both in presenting to the eye the salient features of the field of investigation, and also in furnishing a logical basis for the systematic arrangement of the subject in the ensuing chapters.

It remains, in this chapter, to enumerate the methods by which Physical Biology may be expected to develop. For the *gathering* of data two methods are available: observation in natural condi-

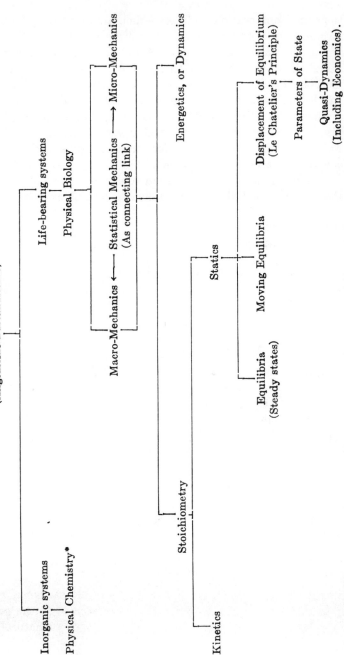

The program of physical biology

Mechanics of Evolution
(Allgemeine Zustandslehre)

Inorganic systems
Physical Chemistry*

Life-bearing systems
Physical Biology

Macro-Mechanics ⟶ Statistical Mechanics ⟶ Micro-Mechanics
(As connecting link)

Energetics, or Dynamics

Stoichiometry

Kinetics

Statics

Equilibria
(Steady states)

Moving Equilibria

Displacement of Equilibrium
(Le Chatelier's Principle)

Parameters of State

Quasi-Dynamics
(Including Economics).

*This term may here be taken to include the treatment of physical *Change of State* (evaporation, fusion, etc.).

tions, and observation under experimental (laboratory) conditions. Examples of both these methods will be noted.

For the *elaboration* of data, the establishment of regularities (laws), there is available in this field, as everywhere in science, the method of *induction*, aided, if need be, by statistical technique. In this volume, however, emphasis will be laid upon *deductive* methods of mathematical analysis, as applied either to data furnished by observation, or to "unknown" quantities, blanks, as it were, in our formulae, ready for numerical substitution whenever concrete data become available.

The principal subdivisions of our topic, and the relations between them, as outlined above, are summarised graphically in table 1.

PART II
KINETICS

CHAPTER VI

THE FUNDAMENTAL EQUATIONS OF KINETICS OF EVOLVING SYSTEMS

L'emploi des signes mathématiques est chose naturelle toutes les fois qu'il s'agit de discuter des relations entre des grandeurs.—*A. Cournot.*

General Case. We now proceed to the systematic study of the subject in accordance with the general plan laid down in the preceding survey of the Program of Physical Biology. According to this schedule (table 1) we approach first of all the section of Macromechanics (that is to say, the mechanics of evolving systems regarded as built up of component species in the gross), without carrying the analysis down to the finer details of individual organisms. And, of the field of Macromechanics, we shall here take up the section of Stoichiometry, that is to say, we shall for the present confine our attention to the relations between the masses involved, leaving aside for a later section the associated energy changes. Of the general field of Stoichiometry the first division to be taken up, according to our schedule, is the Kinetics of Evolution, and we shall here begin with a brief consideration of the Fundamental Equations in their general form

$$\frac{dX_i}{dt} = F_i (X_1, X_2, \ldots X_n; P, Q) \tag{1}$$

One phase of the general problem before us must evidently be the study (by observation, experiment, or any other method available) of the character or form of the functions F which tell us how the growth of each component is dependent upon the other components and the parameters P and Q. It might be supposed, indeed, that until this phase of the problem had received consideration, the system of equations (1), would be at best a barren expression of facts. But this is a misconception. Without knowing anything regarding the precise form of these functions, a good deal of information of considerable interest can be derived from these equations; and before proceeding to the consideration of concrete

57

cases, in which something is known regarding the particular form of the functions F, it is proper, at this point, to extract from the fundamental equations (1) all the information that we can.

This requires a little mathematical manipulation of comparatively simple character.

The variables X, the masses of the several components of the system, are not, in general, wholly independent. They are subject to certain constraining relations. For example, for any self-contained system, we shall have an equation of the form

$$X_1 + X_2 + \ldots + X_n = \Sigma X = A = \text{const.} \tag{2}$$

expressing the constancy of the total mass of the system; and a similar equation holds separately for every chemical element.[1] These equations prohibit certain changes of mass in the system. They are analogous to equations introduced in mechanical problems by the geometric constraints that limit possible displacements (as in the case of a ball rolling down an inclined surface, and prevented, by the resistance of the surface, from falling vertically). They are commonly spoken of as equations of constraint.

Equations of constraint such as

$$\Sigma X = A = \text{const.}$$

will in general enable us to eliminate certain of the variables X, expressing them in terms of the other X's and of certain constants A. If, by the aid of m such equations of constraint, m variables have been eliminated, the system of equations (1) can be reduced to a simpler one, of identical form, but containing only $(n - m)$ variables and the same number of equations.

In all that follows we shall assume that this has been done, that we now read equations (1) in this sense: the n variables $X_1 X_2 \ldots X_n$ are those left over after eliminating as many of the X's as the equations of constraint permit. The functions F will in general, after this elimination, contain constants A introduced by the equations of constraint.

We shall now, except where otherwise stated, restrict our considerations to the case in which the parameters P and Q and A are either constant, or change so slowly that we may disregard

---

[1] Except in those rare cases in which radioactive or other atomic disintegrations occur.

their variation. This means that we restrict ourselves to the consideration of simple inter-group evolution under constant conditions.

With this understanding, the first point we may observe about the system of equations (1) is that they define certain conditions of *equilibrium*, or, to be more precise, of *steady states*. For such a state ensues whenever all the velocities $\dfrac{dX}{dt}$ vanish, that is to say, according to (1) whenever

$$F_1 = F_2 = \ldots = F_n = O \tag{3}$$

We thus have n equations between the n variables $X_1, X_2, \ldots X_n$, which, in general, determine certain values

$$\left.\begin{array}{l} X_1 = C_1 \\ X_2 = C_2 \\ \cdot \ \cdot \ \cdot \ \cdot \ \cdot \\ X_n = C_n \end{array}\right\} \tag{4}$$

such that when masses of the several components have these values, they persist in these values; the system is at rest, as regards changes in the distribution of matter among its components $S_1, S_2, \ldots S_n$.

In general there will be a number of such possible equilibria, some of which will be stable, some unstable. The determination of their number and character is a technical point in the theory of equations, for the general treatment of which the reader must be referred to the pertinent literature (see, for example, Picard, Traité d'Analyse, vol. 1, 1891, pp. 83, 123; vol. 2, 1893, pp. 183, 193, 196, footnote).

To give a touch of concreteness to the discussion at this stage a very simple example may be given to illustrate how several equilibria may occur in a life-bearing system. A perfectly screened dwelling may be kept indefinitely free from flies. This is a condition of equilibrium, but of unstable equilibrium; for if only a few flies gain access, presently these will breed, and the room will become inhabited by a population of flies whose number will depend on the amount of food present, on the measures taken to combat the pest, etc. Unless these measures are very active, the flies will not be wholly exterminated, but the population will attain some approximately steady number (for a given season). There are, then, in this case, two possible equilibria; one with a zero population of flies, the other with some positive number of fly population.

The equilibria in nature, involving countless species, are of course much more complicated in character, but the general principle is the same; and we must expect that in general a variety of different equilibria are possible, some unstable and some stable.

For the further discussion of the equations (1) it is now desirable to express these relations, not in terms of the masses X, but in terms of the excess x_i of each mass X_i over its corresponding equilibrium value,

$$x_i = X_i - C_i \qquad (5)$$

The equation (1) then takes the form

$$\frac{dx_i}{dt} = f_i (x_1, x_2, \ldots x_n) \qquad (6)$$

the parameters P, Q being omitted, for the sake of brevity. Expanding the right hand member by Taylor's theorem we obtain the system of equations

$$\left.\begin{aligned}
\frac{dx_1}{dt} &= a_{11}x_1 + a_{12}x_2 + \ldots + a_{1n}x_n + a_{111}x^2_1 + a_{112}x_1x_2 + a_{122}x^2_2 + \ldots \\
\frac{dx_2}{dt} &= a_{21}x_1 + a_{22}x_2 + \ldots + a_{2n}x_n + a_{211}x_1^2 + a_{212}x_1x_2 + a_{222}x^2_2 + \ldots \\
&\quad \cdots \cdots \cdots \cdots \cdots \cdots \cdots \cdots \cdots \cdots \\
\frac{dx_n}{dt} &= a_{n1}x_1 + a_{n2}x_2 + \ldots + a_{nn}x_n + a_{n11}x^2_1 + a_{n12}x_1x_2 + a_{n22}x^2_2 + \ldots
\end{aligned}\right\} \qquad (7)$$

A general solution of this system of equation is

$$\left.\begin{aligned}
x_1 &= G_{1,1}e^{\lambda_1 t} + G_{1,2}e^{\lambda_2 t} + \ldots + G_{1,n}e^{\lambda_n t} + G_{1,11}e^{2\lambda_1 t} + \ldots \\
x_2 &= G_{2,1}e^{\lambda_1 t} + G_{2,2}e^{\lambda_2 t} + \ldots + G_{2,n}e^{\lambda_n t} + G_{2,11}e^{2\lambda_1 t} + \ldots \\
&\quad \cdots \cdots \cdots \cdots \cdots \cdots \cdots \cdots \cdots \cdots \\
x_n &= G_{n,1}e^{\lambda_1 t} + G_{n,2}e^{\lambda_2 t} + \ldots + G_{n,n}e^{\lambda_n t} + G_{n,11}e^{2\lambda_1 t} + \ldots
\end{aligned}\right\} \qquad (8)$$

where the G's are constants, of which n are arbitrary, and $\lambda_1, \lambda_2 \ldots \lambda_n$ are the n roots of the equation[2] for λ

$$\begin{vmatrix}
a_{11} - \lambda & a_{12} & \ldots & a_{1n} \\
a_{21} & a_{22} - \lambda & \ldots & a_{2n} \\
\cdots & \cdots & \cdots & \cdots \\
a_{n1} & a_{n2} & \ldots & a_{nn} - \lambda
\end{vmatrix} = D(\lambda) = 0 \qquad (9)$$

[2] This equation is commonly spoken of as the *characteristic* equation. For greater detail see A. J. Lotka, Proc. Am. Acad. Sci., vol. 55, 1920, pp. 137–153.

It is seen by inspection of the solution (8) that if all the λ's are real and negative, x_1, x_2, . . . x_n all approach zero as t increases toward infinity, since $e^{-\infty} = 0$. But according to (5), as the x's approach zero, the X's approach their equilibrium values C. In this case, obviously, equilibrium is stable, since, by allowing sufficient time to elapse, we can always make the system approach as near as we please to $X_i = C_i$, for all values of the subscript i. Precisely similar conclusions hold if some or all of the λ's are complex, and the real parts of all the λ's are negative.

If all the roots λ are real (and negative),[3] each term in the solution (8) diminishes continually and approaches zero asymptotically as t approaches infinity.

If all the constants G are of the same sign, the sum of the series also will, evidently, have a similar type of approach to equilibrium.

If some of the G's are positive, others negative, there may be a species of irregular oscillations, the mass X of the component rising sometimes above its equilibrium value C, sometimes falling below it. Ultimately, however, the equilibrium is approached from one side only, since ultimately the term containing the numerically smallest λ will predominate over all other terms.

If some of the roots λ are complex, the solution will contain truly oscillatory terms, since the exponential function, for complex exponents, assumes the trigonometric form

$$e^{(a+ib)t} = e^{at} (\cos bt + i \sin bt) \tag{10}$$

In this case there will be regular oscillations about the equilibrium position; in general these oscillations will be damped, that is to say, their amplitude will diminish, so that equilibrium is approached more and more closely, but always with oscillation—the equilibrium is approached from both sides at once, so to speak, the oscillations persisting forever, though on a diminishing and ultimately vanishing scale.

These conclusions are the analytical confirmation and extension of an inference drawn by Herbert Spencer[4] on qualitative grounds:

[3] The analytical condition that the real parts of all the roots λ shall be negative is given by Hurwitz, Math. Ann., vol. 46, 1895, p. 521. See also Blondel, Ann. de Physique, 1919, pp. 117, 153. It might be noted here that a necessary though by no means sufficient condition, evidently is that the absolute term in $D(\lambda)$, that is to say $D(0)$, shall be positive when n is even, and negative when n is odd; for this absolute term is equal to the product of all the roots λ.

[4] Herbert Spencer, First Principles, Chapter 22, Section 173.

Every species of plant and animal is perpetually undergoing a rhythmical variation in number—now from abundance of food and absence of enemies rising above its average, and then by a consequent scarcity of food and abundance of enemies being depressed below its average . . . . amid these oscillations produced by their conflict, lies that average number of the species at which its expansive tendency is in equilibrium with surrounding repressive tendencies. Nor can it be questioned that this balancing of the preservative and destructive forces which we see going on in every race must necessarily go on. Since increase of numbers cannot but continue until increase of mortality stops it; and decrease of number cannot but continue until it is either arrested by fertility or extinguishes the race entirely.

It will be observed, however, that our analysis enables us to be considerably more specific in distinguishing several modes of approach to equilibrium, and in indicating the particular conditions under which each occurs. A point that here deserves particular emphasis is that, in order to make these distinctions and indications, it is by no means necessary to have a complete knowledge, or even very extensive information regarding the functions F. Only the coefficients of the first (linear) terms in the Taylor expansion of these functions enters into the determinant $D(\lambda)$, and only these need therefore be known to draw the requisite conclusions regarding the stability and mode of approach of equilibrium. Furthermore, Spencer's commentary relates specifically to the case of species related to each other in certain particular ways (food, enemies, etc.); the analysis here given is framed on perfectly general lines and covers any sort of interrelation, interdependence of the components S_1, S_2 . . . S_n. Certain particular interrelations will be duly considered in the course of the further development of the theme. Here it may be well to draw attention once for all to the fact that there is nothing whatever to restrict the application of the principles and methods set forth to systems in *organic* evolution. Indeed, a typical example to which these reflections apply is the case of a chain of elements in the course of radioactive transformation.[5]

It will be seen later, in considering a concrete example, that the equilibrium equation (12) may yield zero or negative roots for C. A zero root is simply interpreted; if the equilibrium to which it relates is a stable one, this means that the species in question will

[5] A. J. Lotka, Proc. Am. Acad. Sci., vol. 55, 1920, p. 148; Proc. Natl. Acad. Sci., vol. 7, 1921, p. 168; Phil. Mag., August, 1912, p. 353.

become extinct[6]. It is unfit, is unadapted ultimately[7] to survive *under the existing conditions*[8] (as defined by the parameters P, etc.).

A *negative* value of C may also signify that the species is incapable of survival under the existing conditions. Masses cannot assume negative values. As soon as any component passes through zero it ceases to function in the system, whose history is henceforth represented by a new set of equations in which this component does not appear.

These conclusions must in one respect be accepted with a certain caution. Since there may be several equilibria, a species may be incapable of existence in the neighborhood of one such equilibrium, but might nevertheless succeed in maintaining itself in the neighborhood of another equilibrium. Whether such cases occur in practise may be left an open question. Our analysis suggests this possibility.

[6] This conclusion does not apply, of course, if the equilibrium with $X = O$ is unstable, as in the example of a fly population cited above.

[7] It may, however, persist for a time, and, it may be, for a long time. An instance in point is furnished, outside the field of organic evolution, by a chain of elements in radioactive transformation. Although here the ultimate equilibrium is one with a single survivor, namely the last link in the chain, yet for millions of years the several products exist side by side in constant ratio though in slowly diminishing amount. At the head of such a chain is always found a "parent substance" which is the longest-lived in the chain. This is not accident. It is easily shown that if at some prior period this substance was preceded by a more rapidly decaying pre-parent, this latter must have disappeared in the course of the ages. It is totally unfit, unadapted, even for a temporary equilibrium, under present conditions. (See A. J. Lotka, Phil. Mag., August, 1911, p. 354.)

[8] It should hardly be necessary to point out that adaptation is purely relative.

CHAPTER VII

FUNDAMENTAL EQUATIONS OF KINETICS (CONTINUED)—SPECIAL CASE: SINGLE DEPENDENT VARIABLE

If arithmetic, mensuration and weighing be taken away from any art, that which remains will not be much—Plato.

Law of Population Growth. It will add concreteness to the present exposition to consider at this point a numerical illustration.

The simplest possible example of numerical application of the equations set forth in the preceding pages will be one in which there is only a single variable X. The fundamental system of equations then reduces to a single equation

$$\frac{dX}{dt} = F(X) \tag{1}$$

A case in point arises when for any reason one particular biological species or group grows actively, while conditions otherwise remain substantially constant.

This seems to be essentially what has occurred in certain human populations. It is true that, in their growth, they have carried along with them a complicated industrial system or group, comprising both living and non-living elements. We may, however, look upon the number of the human population itself as a sort of single index or measure of the growth of the group as a whole.[1]

---

[1] This is an example in which certain of the variables X are connected by equations of constraint. So, for example, the number of head of cattle N_c has for many years past, in the United States, been about six tenths of that of the human population, N_h so that we have an equation of constraint

$$N_c = 0.6 N_h$$

or, putting the average mass of cattle at 1000 pounds per head, that of a human being at 100 pounds (an average to include all ages)

$$X_c = 6 X_h$$

Similar equations of constraint apply to the other species of domesticated animals and plants, so that the mass of each can be (approximately) expressed in terms of the single variable X_h.

Applying to this case the equation (1) and the general method set forth in the preceding pages, we are led to consider first of all the equilibrium equation

$$\frac{dX}{dt} = F(X) = 0 \tag{2}$$

This equation, obviously, has a root at $X = 0$, for at least one female is required to start the growth of a population. Expanding by Taylor's theorem we shall therefore have for F a series lacking the absolute term,[2] thus

$$\frac{dX}{dt} = F(X) = aX + bX^2 + cX^3 + \ldots \tag{3}$$

Furthermore, the equation (2) will have at least one other root, since there must be some upper limit to the growth of the population. The simplest case satisfying this condition is that in which the right hand member of (3) terminates at the second degree term, i.e.,

$$\frac{dX}{dt} = aX + bX^2 \tag{4}$$

The characteristic equation[3] for λ is in this case simply

$$\lambda - a = 0 \tag{5}$$

and the solution of (4) therefore is

$$X = G_1 e^{at} + G_{11} e^{2at} + G_{111} e^{3at} \ldots . \tag{6}[4]$$

Substituting this in (4) and equating coefficients of homologous terms we find

$$G_{11} = \frac{b}{a} G^2_1 \tag{7}$$

$$G_{111} = \frac{b^2}{a^2} G^3_1 \tag{8}$$

so that (6) is a simple geometric series. Its sum is

$$X = \frac{G_1 e^{at}}{1 - \frac{b}{aG_1} e^{at}} = \frac{\frac{a}{b}}{\frac{a}{bG_1} e^{-at} - 1} \tag{9}$$

_____

[2] Otherwise $\dfrac{dX}{dt}$ would not vanish with X

[3] Corresponding to equation (9), Chapter VI.

[4] The series (6) is divergent for large values of t if a is positive. But the expression (9) for the sum of (6) remains a solution of (4).

In formula (9) either G_1 or the origin of time is arbitrary. A simplification can be effected by so adjusting the origin of time that

$$\frac{a}{bG_1} = -1 \tag{10}$$

This fixes the value of the constant G_1

$$G_1 = -\frac{a}{a} \tag{11}$$

and the formula (9) becomes

$$X = -\frac{\dfrac{a}{b}}{1 + e^{-at'}} \tag{12}$$

the symbol t' denoting time reckoned from the origin indicated.[5]

The equation (9) can also be written in another form. If we denote by X_o the value of X when $t = o$, and write $x_o = X_o + \dfrac{a}{b}$, then (9) becomes

$$X = \frac{\dfrac{a}{b}}{\dfrac{x_0}{X_0} e^{-at} - 1} \tag{13}$$

Population of United States. Formula (12) has been applied by Pearl and Reed[6] to the population growth of the United States.[7] The calculated curve for the number N of the population fits the observed data over a long period of years (1790 to 1910) with remark-

---

[5] This result can also be obtained by direct integration of (4) in finite form. The process given above has here been followed to illustrate the general method of the solution (8), (9), of Chapter VI.

[6] P. F. Verhulst, Mem. Acad. Roy. Bruxelles, 1844, vol. 18, p. 1; 1846, vol. 20, p. 1; R. Pearl and L. J. Reed, Proc. Natl. Acad. Sci., vol. 6, 1920, p. 275; Scientific Monthly, 1921, p. 194; R. Pearl, The Biology of Death, 1922, p. 250. The last-mentioned work, especially, should be consulted for a detailed discussion. For a general treatment of the population problem see also particularly E. M. East, Mankind at the Crossroads, 1923 (Scribners).

[7] Measured, in this case, by the increase in the number N of persons. This is evidently, in first approximation at any rate, proportional to the total mass X of the population.

able faithfulness, as will be seen from table 2 and the graph shown in figure 4. Numerically the formula (12) here takes the form

$$N = \frac{197,273,000}{1 + e^{-0.03134t'}},$$ (14)

and the time t' (in years) is dated from April 1, 1914 (t', being negative for dates anterior to this). This epoch is one of peculiar interest. It represents the turning point when the population passed from a progressively increasing to a progressively diminishing rate of growth. Incidentally it is interesting to note that if the population of the

TABLE 2

Results of fitting United States population data 1790 to 1910 by equation (14)

YEAR	OBSERVED POPULATION	CALCULATED POPU-LATION BY EQUATION (14)	ERROR
1790	3,929,000	3,929,000	0
1800	5,308,000	5,336,000	+28,000
1810	7,240,000	7,228,000	−12,000
1820	9,638,000	9,757,000	+119,000
1830	12,866,000	13,109,000	+243,000
1840	17,069,000	17,506,000	+437,000
1850	23,192,000	23,192,000	0
1860	31,443,000	30,412,000	−1,031,000
1870	38,558,000	39,372,000	+814,000
1880	50,156,000	50,177,000	+21,000
1890	62,948,000	62,769,000	−179,000
1900	75,995,000	76,870,000	+875,000
1910	91,972,000	91,972,000	0

United States continues to follow this growth curve in future years, it will reach a maximum of some 197 million souls, about double its present population, by the year 2060 or so. Such a forecast as this, based on a rather heroic extrapolation, and made in ignorance of the physical factors that impose the limit, must, of course, be accepted with reserve.

Stability of Equilibrium. The equilibrium at $X = O$, i.e., with total absence of human population, is evidently unstable, since $\lambda = a$ and a is an essentially positive quantity, its numerical value being, for the population of the United States, 0.0313395. The second equilibrium, corresponding to the *saturation* point, is evidently at

$X = -\dfrac{a}{b}$, and here it is easily found by the substitution $x = X + \dfrac{a}{b}$, that $\lambda = -a$, the equilibrium is stable.

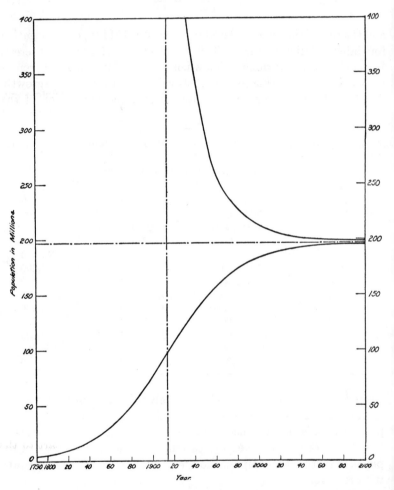

FIG. 4. THE LAW OF POPULATION GROWTH FOR THE UNITED STATES ACCORDING TO PEARL AND REED

The lower S-shaped limb corresponds to the actual approach to equilibrium from below. The upper limb represents the presumptive course of events for a diminishing population approaching equilibrium from above.

Experimental Populations. Pearl has also fitted the same formula to the population of a number of countries, but the range covered by the available observation in these other cases is less extended, so that there is less opportunity for comparison with observed figures. Of particular interest is an application of the same formula, also by Pearl, to an experimental population of fruit flies (Drosophila). In this case practically the entire range of the S-shaped curve defined by equation (12) is realized, and a glance at the plot in figure 5 shows that the agreement of the observed figures (represented by small circles) and the calculated curve is exceedingly satisfactory. Still closer is the agreement in the case of bacterial cultures studied

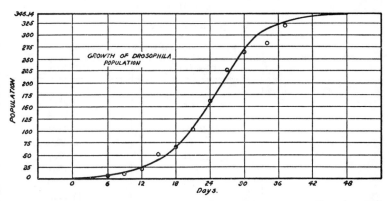

FIG. 5. GROWTH OF A POPULATION OF DROSOPHILA (FRUIT FLIES) UNDER CONTROLLED EXPERIMENTAL CONDITIONS, ACCORDING TO PEARL AND PARKER

by H. G. Thornton[8] (Annals of Appl. Biology, 1922, p. 265), whose observations are set forth in table 3 and are shown by the small circles in figure 6; the theoretical curve to fit these points, as computed here in the laboratory, is shown in the fully drawn line. As will be seen the agreement is excellent. This is due in part to the fact that the figures plotted represent the means of a number of individual cultures.

A very particular interest attaches to this example, inasmuch as it forms, as it were, a connecting link between the law of growth of a

[8] Similar results have been obtained by A. G. McKendrick and M. Kesava Pai, Proc. Roy. Soc. Edin., vol. 31, 1911; for a study of the growth of yeast, see A. Slator, Trans. Chem. Soc., 1921, vol. 119, p. 126.

population, and the law of growth of the individual. A colony of unicellular organisms, regarded as a whole, is analogous to the body of a multicellular organism. Or, to put the matter the other way about, a man, for example, may be regarded as a *population of cells*. We need not, therefore, be greatly surprised, if the growth of the multicellular organism should be found to follow a law similar to that exhibited by populations. And in point of fact, as will be shown a little further on, this expectation is in not a few instances fulfilled.

TABLE 3

Growth of bacterial colony, according to H. G. Thornton (Ann. Appl. Biol., 1922, p. 265)

For graph see figure 6

| AGE OF COLONY | AREA IN SQUARE CENTIMETERS | |
	Observed	Calculated*
days		
0.0	0.24	0.2511
0.5		0.7208
1.0	2.78	2.0324
1.5		5.4620
2.0	13.53	13.0761
2.5		25.1961
3.0	36.30	37.0479
3.5		44.2213
4.0	47.50	47.3930
4.5		48.5974
5.0	49.40	49.0231

*According to the equation $y = \dfrac{0.2524}{e^{-2.128x} + 0.005125}$

Diminishing Population. It may be noted here that in one respect the formula (12), while particularly simple in form, is of more restricted scope than (13). The former defines the characteristic S-shaped curve that appears in the graphs of actual populations shown in figure 4. But formula (13) gives a more complete definition of a curve composed of two limbs; one of these is the S-shaped curve already considered. The other is a steeply descending arc, shown in the upper portion of figure 4. This portion of the curve has not been realized in any recorded population. It represents the computed course of events if the population initially exceeds its equilibrium strength, i.e., if $\dfrac{x_o}{X_o}$ is positive.

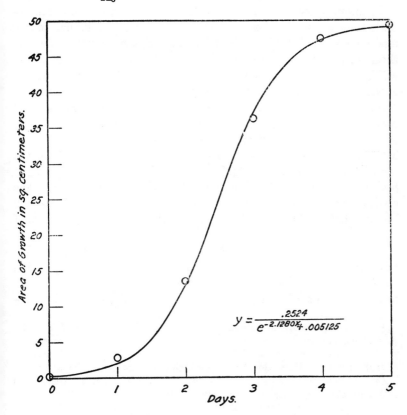

FIG. 6. GROWTH OF A BACTERIAL COLONY (B. DENDROIDES)

Observations by H. G. Thornton

Growth of Individual Organism. Although, strictly speaking, the growth of the individual organism is a subject properly belonging to the field that has here been termed "micromechanics" (Chapter V), yet, in view of the very close analogy which has been found to exist, in certain cases, between the law of growth of a population, and that of the individual, it may be noted here that the formula (9) has also been applied by T. B. Robertson[9] and by Wo. Ostwald[10] and others, to the growth of the individual organism. An example of such application is shown in figure 7, which exhibits the growth day by day, of male white rats according to observations by H. H. Donaldson[11] and computations by T. B. Robertson. The fully drawn curve represents the calculated values of the mass of the rats (in grams) at different ages. The circles indicate selected observed values, namely, those which diverge most widely from the computed values. It will be seen that up to about the one hundredth day the agreement is good. Above this there is no agreement worthy of the name.

Another example, and one in which the computed curve fits the observed values with remarkable agreement, is the growth (in *height*) of sunflower plants as studied by H. S. Reed and R. H. Holland.[12] The curve to fit these observations has been recomputed by the method of least squares by Dr. L. J. Reed, who has very kindly placed his results at the author's disposal. They are shown in figure 8. The observations on which they are based are shown in table 4. It will be seen that the fit is practically perfect through the whole range of observations.

In practice we are not usually given the differential equation (4), but data corresponding to points on the integral curve (12). We then have the problem of determining from these points the characteristic constants of the curve. The detailed working out of the prob-

[9] Archiv für die Entwickelungsmechanik der Organismen, 1907, vol. 25, p. 4; 1908, vol. 26, p. 108; The Chemical Basis of Growth and Senescence, publ. Lippincott, 1923. T. B. Robertson also quotes A. Monnier, Publications of Inst. of Botany, Univ. Geneva, 1905, which in turn refers to Chodat as having recognized the analogy of organic to autocatalytic growth. The idea is rather an obvious one, which probably has occurred to many. The earliest reference noted by the writer is L. Errera, Revue de l'Univeristé de Bruxelles, 1899–1900, May issue. Something very similar is found in Ostwald, Vorlesungen über Naturphilosophie, 1902, p. 342. These last-mentioned lectures were published in 1902, but were actually delivered somewhat prior to that date. The writer recalls that Ostwald referred to the matter in his lectures on General Chemistry in 1902, and probably others will recall similar references on earlier occasions.

[10] Die Zeitlichen Eigenschaften der Entwickelungsvorgänge, Leipzig, 1908.

[11] Boas Memorial Volume, 1906, p. 5; see also the same author's book The Rat, 1915.

[12] H. S. Reed and R. H. Holland, Proc. Natl. Acad. Sci., vol. 5, 1919, pp. 135–144.

lem may well be left to the reader, after pointing out the following interesting property of the curve (12). Taking reciprocals and writing A for a/b, we have

$$\frac{A}{X} = A\xi = 1 + e^{-a\,(t-t_0)} \tag{15}$$

$$\log\,(A\xi - 1) = -\,a\,(t - t_0) \tag{16}$$

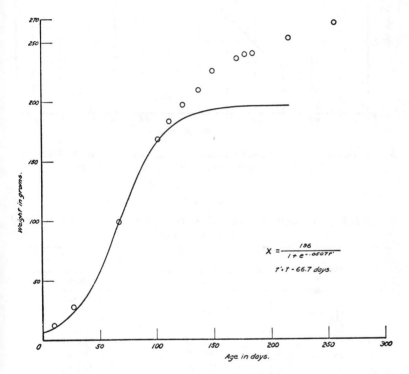

FIG. 7. GROWTH OF RAT ACCORDING TO H. H. DONALDSON AND T. B. ROBERTSON

Circles indicate only those observations that diverge most widely from the calculated curve.

where t_0 is the time corresponding to the point of inflection of the S-curve. Thus if we plot $A\xi - 1$ against t on logarithmic curve paper, we shall obtain a straight line diagram. This is shown in figure 9 for the same data (growth of sunflower) which have already been

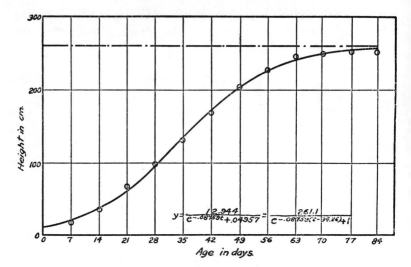

$$y = \frac{12.944}{e^{-.08759t} + .04957} = \frac{261.1}{e^{-.08759(t-34.26)} + 1}$$

FIG. 8. GROWTH OF SUNFLOWER SEEDLINGS ACCORDING TO H. S. REED AND
R. H. HOLLAND; COMPUTED CURVE BY L. J. REED

TABLE 4

Growth in height of sunflower plants (H. S. Reed and R. H. Holland; computed
values by L. J. Reed)

| DAYS | MEAN HEIGHT | |
	Observed	Computed
	cm.	*cm.*
7	17.93	21.89
14	36.36	37.74
21	67.76	62.08
28	98.10	95.42
35	131.00	134.56
42	169.50	172.99
49	205.50	204.64
56	228.30	227.16
63	247.10	241.56
70	250.50	250.14
77	253.80	255.05
84	254.50	257.79

*Proc. Natl. Acad. Sci., vol. 5, 1919, p. 140.

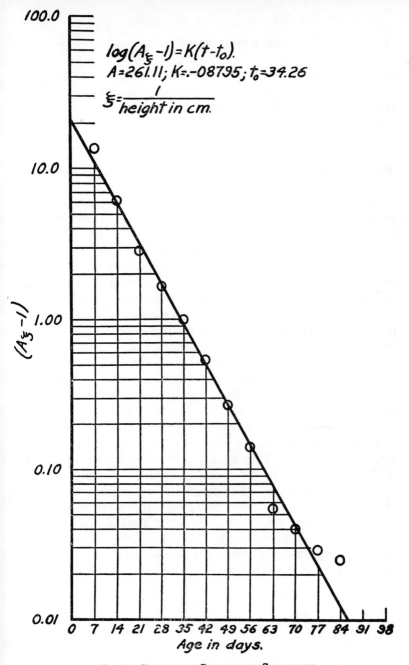

FIG. 9. GROWTH OF SUNFLOWER SEEDLINGS

The same data as in figure 8, but plotted in logarithmic diagram, with ordinates as indicated in the legend.

exhibited by another method in figure 8.   Taking now three equidistant points of time t_1 t_2 t_3 and the corresponding ordinates ξ_1, ξ_2, ξ_3, it is readily shown that

$$\frac{1}{A} = \frac{\xi_1\xi_3 - \xi^2_2}{(\xi_1 + \xi_3) - 2\xi_2} = \frac{1}{2} \frac{M^2 - \xi^2_2}{m - \xi_2} \tag{17}$$

where M denotes the geometric mean of ξ_1 and ξ_3 and while m denotes their arithmetic mean.

Thus the constant A can be determined from three suitably chosen points on the curve (after smoothing graphically if need be).   The other constants then follow easily.

Autocatakinesis.   Both Robertson and Wo. Ostwald draw attention to the similarity between the law of growth (12) and the law of formation of a chemical substance by autocatalysis under certain conditions.   The analogy is interesting, but must not be taken too seriously, inasmuch as in the one case the rate of growth is determined by ordinary chemical influence, in the other (organic growth) by a complicated combination of factors both of chemical and of physical character.   Rather more to the point seems to be the suggestion made above in connection with the law of growth of bacterial colonies, that, the body of a multicellular organism being a "population" of cells, it is not altogether surprising that it should be found to follow the law of growth of a population.

A suggestion of terminology by Wo. Ostwald is worth noting.   He proposes that growth of any kind, in which the substance or structure itself acts as nucleus for the formation about it of further quantities of the same substance or structure, be broadly termed autocatakinetic growth, the narrower terms autocatalysis of autocatalytic growth being reserved for that particular kind of autocatakinesis which is chemical in character.   This is a useful suggestion, as it leaves the term autocatakinesis quite neutral and free from any implication or restrictions as to the mechanism by which the growth takes place.

CHAPTER VIII

FUNDAMENTAL EQUATIONS OF KINETICS (CONTINUED)—SPECIAL
CASES: TWO AND THREE DEPENDENT VARIABLES

Life is a system of relations rather than a positive and independent existence—*G. A. Sala.*

Interdependence of Species. The case of two dependent variables, X_1, X_2, which we now approach, is of interest as the simplest example exhibiting the relation between interdependent species. This relation can take on a variety of forms. Most fundamental, perhaps, is that form of interdependence (1) in which one species S_1 serves as food to another species S_2, so that, in this sense, S_1 becomes transformed into S_2, thus

$$S_1 \longrightarrow S_2$$

All animal species, and many plants also, thus derive their substance from other species on which they feed. And several different types of this form of interdependence are observed. In the first type, (*a*) the organism S_2 kills S_1 outright in the process of feeding upon it. We might term S_2 in such a case an *episite* of S_1, in contradistinction from the second type, (*b*) in which S_2 lives on S_1 without killing it outright, being *parasitic* upon S_1. The host is in most cases more or less injured by the parasite, and all pathogenic organisms fall into this class. For this reason *quantitative epidemiology* appears as one of the special branches of the general subject under consideration here.

A third type (*c*) of interdependence, is that in which S_2 is *saprophagous* or *saprophytic*, feeding upon the cadavers of S_1 after death from other causes; or, S_2 may live on waste products discharged by S_1. In contrast to episites and parasites, saprophagous species are presumably beneficial rather than injurious to the host species, since they function as scavengers. Still another type, (*d*), of interdependence is that of symbiosis, in which S_1 and S_2 live in partnership which, as a rule, is in some degree mutually beneficial. Man and his domesticated animals and plants are obvious examples of this type.

In addition to these types (*1a*) to (*1d*), another large group of cases (2) are those in which two or more species compete for a common food supply.

In their general form the fundamental equations of kinetics for the case of two dependent variables are

$$\left.\begin{aligned} \frac{dX_1}{dt} &= A_{10} + A_{11}X_1 + A_{12}X_2 + \ldots \\[2mm] \frac{dX_2}{dt} &= A_{20} + A_{21}X_1 + A_{22}X_2 + \ldots \end{aligned}\right\} \tag{1}$$

or, after the transformation (5), of Chapter VI

$$\left.\begin{aligned} \frac{dx_1}{dt} &= a_{11}x_1 + a_{12}x_2 + \ldots \\[2mm] \frac{dx_2}{dt} &= a_{21}x_1 + a_{22}x_2 + \ldots \end{aligned}\right\} \tag{2}$$

We may note, first of all, as a general rule, the following observations regarding the coefficients a in the several types of interdependence enumerated above:

1a. S_2 lives on S_1 by killing S_1 outright (episistic type). In this case, evidently S_2 unfavorably influences the growth of S_1, while, on the contrary, S_1 is advantageous to the growth of S_2, so that

$$\frac{\partial}{\partial X_2} \frac{dX_1}{dt} < 0, \text{ i.e., } a_{12} < 0 \tag{3}$$

$$\frac{\partial}{\partial X_1} \frac{dX_2}{dt} > 0, \text{ i.e., } a_{21} > 0 \tag{4}$$

1b. S_2 parasitic upon S_1. Here $a_{12} < 0$, $a_{21} > 0$, as in case *1a*.

1c. S_2 saprophytic upon S_1, or living upon waste products of S_1. Here we may expect that $a_{12} \geqq 0$, $a_{21} > 0$.

1d. S_2 feeds on S_1, but at the same time cultivates it in symbiosis. Here $a_{12} > 0$, $a_{21} > 0$.

The characteristic equation for two variables is

$$\begin{vmatrix} a_{11} - \lambda & a_{12} \\ a_{21} & a_{22} - \lambda \end{vmatrix} = 0 \tag{5}$$

or, in expanded form,

$$\lambda^2 - (a_{11} + a_{22})\lambda + (a_{11}a_{22} - a_{21}a_{12}) = 0 \qquad (6)$$

$$\lambda = \tfrac{1}{2}\{(a_{11} + a_{22}) \pm \sqrt{(a_{11} - a_{22})^2 + 4a_{21}a_{12}}\} \qquad (7)$$

Certain general conclusions follow immediately. So, for example, if a_{21}, a_{12} are both of the same sign, as in the case of saprophytes and of symbiosis, the quantity under the radical is necessarily positive, and hence both roots for λ are real. The oscillatory type of approach to equilibrium is here excluded. In the case of two species of the type (1a) or (1b), the episitic or parasitic type, on the contrary, the possibility of oscillations is indicated, under conditions where the equations (1) are applicable.

CONCRETE EXAMPLES

Martini's Equations for Immunizing Diseases. Numerical applications of the case of two dependent variables are not easily obtained. Of concrete examples in general terms (with unknown or very imperfectly known values of the constants involved) several are to be found in the literature. The simplest of these is a case for which the equations are given, without solution, by Martini in his *Berechnungen und Beobachtungen zur Epidemiologie der Malaria* (Gente, Hamburg, 1921, p. 70), namely, the case of the growth of an endemic disease of the type that confers acquired immunity upon persons who recover from it (e.g., measles, scarlet fever, etc.) Martini writes

u = fraction of the population affected and infective

i = fraction of the population not available for new infection (i.e., immune or already affected)

$(1 - i)$ = fraction of the population *available* for new infection

p = fraction of the population newly affected per unit of time

q = fraction of the population of affected population that ceases to be so, per unit of time, by recovery or by death

m = fraction of "unavailable" population that loses immunity or dies per unit of time

α = infectivity (a proportionality factor)

Martini puts the newly affected population, per unit of time, jointly proportional to the infective population u and to the population available for new infection, $(1 - i)$, so that

$$p = \alpha u(1 - i)$$

Then, obviously,

$$\left.\begin{array}{l} \dfrac{du}{dt} = \alpha\, u(1 - i) - qu = (\alpha - q)u - \alpha\, ui \\[2mm] \dfrac{di}{dt} = \alpha\, u(1 - i) - mi = \alpha\, u - mi - \alpha\, ui \end{array}\right\} \quad (9)$$

The characteristic equation for λ here reduces, near the origin, simply to [1]

$$\{(\alpha - q) - \lambda\}\,(m - \lambda) = 0 \quad (10)$$

and the solution, near the origin, is

$$\left.\begin{array}{l} u = G_{1,1}e^{(\alpha-q)t} + G_{1,2}e^{-mt} + . \quad . \\[1mm] i = G_{2,1}e^{(\alpha-q)t} + G_{2,2}e^{-mt} + . . . \end{array}\right\} \quad (11)$$

from which it is seen that the equilibrium near the origin is stable if and only if $\alpha < q$

There is a second equilibrium at

$$\left.\begin{array}{l} u = \dfrac{m(\alpha - q)}{q} = U \\[3mm] i = \dfrac{\alpha - q}{q} = I \end{array}\right\} \quad (12)$$

Since, however, i can in reality assume only positive values, this equilibrium has a meaning only if $\alpha > q$, i.e., just in the case in which the equilibrium at the origin is unstable. Hence we conclude that if $\alpha < q$ the equilibrium at the origin is the only possible one, and is stable, so that the disease will die out.

In the other alternative, $\alpha > q$, the second equilibrium has a real meaning, and we can develop a solution in series

$$\left.\begin{array}{l} u - U = G'_{1,1}e^{\lambda_1 t} + G'_{1,2}e^{\lambda_2 t} + . . . \\[1mm] i - I = G'_{2,1}e^{\lambda_1 t} + G'_{2,2}e^{\lambda_2 t} + . . . \end{array}\right\} \quad (13)$$

where λ_1, λ_2 are given by

$$\lambda = -\tfrac{1}{2}\left\{\dfrac{\alpha m}{q} \pm \sqrt{\dfrac{\alpha^2 m^2}{q^2} - 4(\alpha - q)m}\right\} \quad (14)$$

---

[1] A. J. Lotka, Nature, vol. 111, 1923, p. 633.

We need not here consider the case $(\alpha - q) < O$, for, as pointed out above, in this case the second equilibrium is meaningless. But when $\alpha > q$, it is seen from (14) that the real parts of the two roots will then in any case be negative, so that the equilibrium, if it exists at all, is stable. Furthermore, there will be two real and distinct, two real and coincident, or two complex roots, according as

$$\frac{q^2}{\alpha^2} - \frac{q}{\alpha} + \frac{1}{4}\frac{m}{q} \gtreqless O \qquad (15)$$

In the last-mentioned case equilibrium will be approached by a series of oscillations above and below the final state of equilibrium, so that a series of "epidemic" waves will appear, a feature which has an obvious interest in connection with the type of disease here discussed.[2] The oscillations thus occasioned by the factors duly taken into account in this elementary analysis may in practise be enhanced by factors here neglected, such as varying virulence of the disease, exhaustion of susceptible population, seasonal influences, etc. The last-mentioned, however, will in general tend to produce a separate series of waves whose period will have no relation to that of the oscillations derived above.

For the special case $\frac{m}{q} = 1$, Prof. G. N. Watson has given a complete solution, which may be consulted in the original.[3] It is to be noted that this case cannot, according to the analysis here presented, lead to oscillations, since the condition for oscillations according to (15) reduces to

$$\left(\frac{q}{\alpha} - \frac{1}{2}\right)^2 < O \qquad (16)$$

and cannot be satisfied, as the square of a real quantity is necessarily positive.

The Ross Malaria Equations. A system of equations has been established by Sir Ronald Ross[4] to represent, under certain

[2] Compare J. Brownlee, Investigation into the Periodicity of Infectious Diseases, Public Health, vol. 25, 1915, p. 125.

[3] G. N. Watson, Nature, vol. 111, 1923, p. 808.

[4] Sir Ronald Ross, The Prevention of Malaria, second edition, 1911, p. 679. This volume also contains a bibliography. For a detaile ddiscussion of the Ross malaria equations see A. J. Lotka, Am. Jour. Hygiene, January Supplement, 1923.

conditions, the course of events in the spread of malaria in a human population by the bites of certain breeds of mosquitoes infected with the malaria parasite.   These equations are of the same form as Martini's equations discussed above, and inasmuch as Ross's malaria equations have been very fully treated by the writer in a separate monograph,[5] their detailed study may here be omitted. It will suffice to reproduce from this monograph one of the curves representing the course of events, the presumptive growth of malaria in a human population, as defined by the differential equations of Sir Ronald Ross.

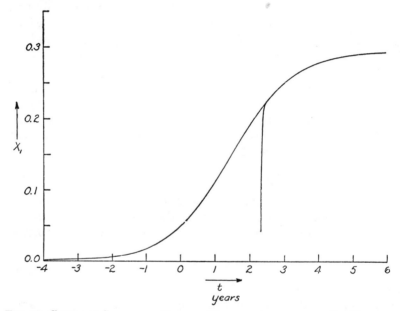

Fig. 10. Curve of Growth of Endemic Malaria According to Sir Ronald Ross's Equations

The upper (S-shaped) curve relates to the particular case in which the initial malaria rates in the human and the mosquito population stand in the ratio which they have at equilibrium or are both small.   The lower curve represents the course of events when the initial malaria rate is 4.2 per cent in the human population, and 1.4 per cent in the mosquito population. (The zero of the time scale is arbitrary.)   Ordinates are malaria rates (human) expressed as fraction of unity.   (Reproduced from A. J. Lotka, Am. Jour. of Hygiene, January Supplement, 1923.)

[5] A. J. Lotka, loc. cit.

It will be observed (fig. 10) that the curve shown consists of two parts, the one an S-shaped limb which, in point of fact, is very nearly identical in type with the Verhulst-Pearl population curve. The second limb ascends very steeply, almost vertically, and finally bends to join the S-shaped limb.

The meaning of these curves is as follows: If a small nucleus of malarial infection is introduced into a (constant) population of human beings and mosquitoes, *both* being previously free from such infection, then the growth of malaria in the human population will follow the course represented by the S-shaped limb. It will be seen that the process is a rather leisurely one, its essential completion occupying about ten years, according to Ross's figures. (Strictly speaking it is never quite complete in a finite time.) Seasonal effects are here disregarded.

On the other hand, if at the start there is already present a certain malarial rate in the human population, and also in the mosquito population, then, in the case here depicted, there is for a time a very rapid increase of malaria in the human population, until, in the brief space of about two months, the S-shaped curve is reached. After that the course of events is the same as in the first case.

In practise, in temperate climes, we can expect only short sections of the S-shaped curve to be realized, owing to the interruptions of the seasons. No data are available for a numerical comparison of these results with observed conditions. Close agreement is not to be expected, as the Ross equations refer to a rather highly idealised case, a constant population both of men and mosquitoes. The latter could be even distantly approached only in the tropics. There is room here for further analysis along more realistic lines. It must be admitted that this may lead to considerable mathematical difficulties. The case of periodic seasonal influences is perhaps the one that promises to yield most readily to mathematical treatment.

The Ross malaria equations are a typical example of equations affected with a lag, owing to the period of incubation. For a detailed discussion of this feature the reader must be referred to the author's monograph published by the American Journal of Hygiene.

An Example in Parasitology. An interesting and practically significant case of inter-group evolution, of conflict between two species, has been made the subject of an analytical study by W. R.

Thompson.[6]   He considers a host species, numbering initially n individuals, and a parasite species, initially p individuals.   On a number of simple assumptions, for which the reader must be referred to the original papers, he develops the following formula for the fraction α of the host population attacked, in the tth generation, by parasites

$$\alpha = \frac{pa^t}{n - p\,\dfrac{(a^t - a)}{a - 1}}$$

where a is the ratio of the "reproductive power" of the parasite to that of the host, the reproductive power being measured by the number of eggs deposited per female.   It is assumed that only one egg is deposited in each host.

Putting

$$a^t = e^{rt} \tag{18}$$

and

$$\frac{n(a - 1)}{p} + a = 1 + (a - 1)\frac{(n + p)}{p} = K \tag{19}$$

Thompson's formula becomes, after a simple transformation,

$$\alpha = \frac{a - 1}{Ke^{-rt} - 1} \tag{20}$$

which will be recognized, once more, as the equation of the law of simple autocatakinetic growth.   According to the value of a and K several different cases may arise, whose graphs are shown in figure 11.   It should be observed that

$$K \gtreqless 1 \text{ according as } a \gtreqless 1 \tag{21}$$

$$r \gtreqless O \text{ according as } a \lesseqgtr 1 \tag{22}$$

In the special case that $a = 1$ the formula (20) becomes indeterminate and α is then given by

$$\alpha = \frac{p}{n - p\,(t - 1)} \tag{23}$$

a hyperbolic relation (see fig. 11, the last diagram).

---

[6] W. R. Thompson, Comptes Rendus Acad. Sci., vol. 174, 1922, pp. 201, 1443, vol. 175, p. 65.   See also R. A. Wardle and P. Buckle, The Principles of Insect Control, Longmans, Green & Co., 1924.

Thompson gives a number of numerical examples exhibited in table 5. From these examples and from this formulae he concludes that the invasion of the host species by the parasite may at first

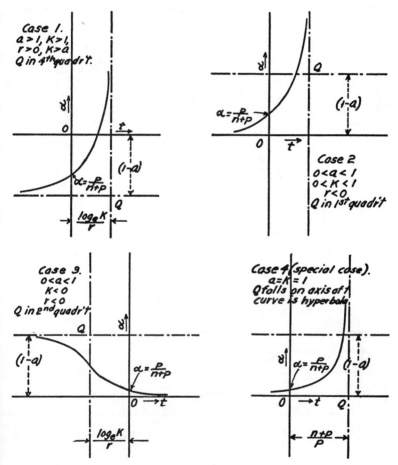

FIG. 11. COURSE OF PARASITIC INVASION OF INSECT SPECIES ACCORDING TO
W. R. THOMPSON

proceed only very slowly, and that nevertheless, after a certain time, the increase may become very rapid. From a practical standpoint this is important to observe, since it implies that the first effect of "sowing" the parasite among a species of insect hosts,

with a view to destroying them, may be quite discouraging, and
that this must not be taken as indicative of ultimate failure.   This

TABLE 5

*Percentage (100α) of host species attacked by parasite in t^{th} generation, according
to W. R. Thompson*

p	n	a	1	2	3	4	5	6	7	8	9	10
10	1,000	1.5	1.5	2.28	3.50	5.40	8.64	14.2	24.6	50.0	100.0	
10	10,000	1.5	0.15	0.23	0.33	0.51	0.77	1.16	1.76	2.7	4.15	6.5
10	100	1.0	10.0	11.1	12.5	14.35	16.6	20.0	25.0	33.3	50.0	100.0
10	200	1.0	5.0	5.25	5.55	5.88	6.25	6.66	7.14	7.7	8.3	9.1

p	n	a	11	12	13	14	15	16	17	18	19	20
10	10,000	1.5	9.6	18.6	34.2	78.0						
10	200	1.0	10.0	11.1	12.5	14.3	16.6	20	25	33	50	100

p = initial number of parasite species.
n = initial number of host species.

a = ratio of reproductive powers $\dfrac{\text{parasite}}{\text{host}}$.

The figures in the columns headed 1, 2, 3, etc., denote the values of
$100\,\alpha$ in the 1st, 2d, 3d, etc., generation.

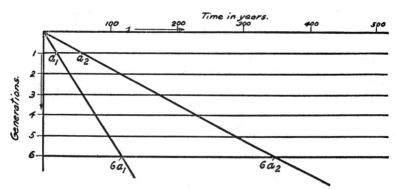

FIG. 12. INCREASING DIFFUSION-IN-TIME OF SUCCESSIVE GENERATIONS IN
THE PROGENY OF A POPULATION ELEMENT

observation is especially significant since in practise one must
often be satisfied with the introduction of a relatively very small
number of parasites.   So, for example, in using the parasite species

Liparis dispar, commonly about one thousand individuals have been sown. Supposing that there were one thousand million hosts, and that the parasite reproduced twice as fast as the host, it would require, according to Thompson's calculations, about 19 generations to exterminate the host; and then, even to the sixteenth generation, only 10 per cent or less of the host species would be attacked.

Thompson's formula is open to certain objections. Its derivation seems to involve the assumption that each generation of the parasite is coextensive in time with the corresponding generation of the host. Furthermore, the use of a generation as a sort of time unit is unsatisfactory, because a generation is a very diffuse thing, spread out over varying lengths of time. This is easily seen by considering the progeny of a batch of individuals all born at the same time $t = 0$. If we call this the 0th generation, and if a_1, a_2 are respectively the lower and the upper limit of the reproductive period, then it is clear that the next generation, the first, will extend over the interval of time from a_1 to a_2, the second from $2a_1$ to $2a_2$, the nth from na_1 to na_2, an interval which will ultimately become very large as n increases, as shown by successive intercepts between the two sloping lines in figure 12.

Less objectionable, perhaps, is the fact that Thompson's formula is expressed in terms of the "rate of multiplication per generation" of the two species. This term is not as clear as it might be. From the context it appears that it refers to the number of eggs deposited per female. This number is closely and simply related to the ratio R of the total births in two successive generations. If an individual of age a reproduces, on an average $\beta(a)$ individuals per unit of time, the ratio R is evidently given by

$$R = \int_0^\infty \beta(a)\, p(a)\, da \tag{24}$$

The relation of this R to the rate of increase r per head of the population is not altogether obvious and cannot be expressed in simple form. For a population with fixed age distribution, it will be shown in Chapter IX that r is given by

$$\left. \begin{aligned} 1 &= \int_0^\infty e^{-ra}\, \beta(a) p(a)\, da \\ &= \int_0^\infty \beta(a) p(a)\, da - r \int_0^\infty a\beta(a) p(a)\, da + \ldots \end{aligned} \right\} \tag{25}$$

Hence

$$R = 1 + r \int_0^\infty a\beta(a)p(a)da + \ldots \qquad (26)$$

In view of the doubtful features in Thompson's formula which have been indicated above, it appears desirable to attack his problem in quantitative parasitology from another angle. We may do this by following the general method which has here been set forth and exemplified.

Treatment of the Problem by the Method of Kinetics. Let N_1 be the number of the host population, b_1 its birthrate per head, (the deposition of an egg being counted a birth), and d_1 its death rate per head from causes other than invasion by the parasite. Let kN_1N_2 be the death rate per head due to invasion by the parasite, in the host population, the coefficient k being, in general, a function of both N_1 and N_2, the latter symbol designating the number of the parasite population.

The birth of a parasite is contingent upon the laying of an egg in a host, and the ultimate killing of the host thereby. To simplify matters we will consider the case in which only one egg is hatched from any invaded host. If an egg is hatched from every host killed by the invasion, then the total birthrate in the parasite population is evidently kN_1N_2. If only a fraction k' of the eggs hatch, then the total birthrate in the parasite population is evidently $kk'\ N_1N_2$, which we will denote briefly by KN_1N_2. Lastly, let the deathrate per head among the parasites be d_2. Then we have, evidently

$$\left. \begin{aligned} \frac{dN_1}{dt} &= r_1N_1 - kN_1N_2 \\[2mm] \frac{dN_2}{dt} &= KN_1N_2 - d_2N_2 \end{aligned} \right\} \qquad (27)$$

where r_1 has been written for $(b_1 - d_1)$.

Regarding the function k, we shall now make the very broad assumption that it can be expanded as power series in N_1 and N_2, thus

$$k = \alpha + \beta N_1 + \gamma N_2 + \ldots \qquad (28)$$

It will be convenient first of all to consider an approximation.[7] If the coefficients β, γ, etc., are sufficiently small, we shall have, for values of N_1, N_2 not too large, essentially

$$\left.\begin{array}{l} \dfrac{dN_1}{dt} = N_1(r_1 - \alpha N_2) \\[2mm] \dfrac{dN_2}{dt} = N_2(k'\alpha N_1 - d_2) \end{array}\right\} \qquad (29)$$

$$\frac{dN_1}{dN_2} = \frac{N_1(r_1 - \alpha N_2)}{N_2(k'\alpha N_1 - d_2)} \qquad (30)$$

Integrating, and putting

$$N_1 = x + \frac{d_2}{k'\alpha} = x + p \qquad (31)$$

$$N_2 = y + \frac{r_1}{\alpha} = y + q \qquad (32)$$

we obtain

$$d_2 \log(x + p) + r_1 \log(y + q) - k'\alpha x - \alpha y = M \qquad (33)$$

where M is an arbitrary constant of integration. Expanding by Taylor's theorem we find

$$d_2\left(\log p - \frac{x^2}{2p^2} + \frac{x^3}{3p^3} - \dots\right) + r_1\left(\log q - \frac{y^2}{2q^2} + \frac{y^3}{3q^3} - \dots\right) = M' \qquad (34)$$

By giving successively different values to the arbitrary constant M' a family of closed curves is obtained for the plot of (34) in rectangular coördinates, as indicated in figure 13. In the neighborhood of the origin, where terms of higher than second degree are negligible, (34) reduces simply to

$$\frac{d_2 x^2}{p^2} + \frac{r_1 y^2}{q^2} = \text{constant} \qquad (35)$$

and the integral curves are small ellipses.

[7] It will be observed that the "diagonal" terms in the linear part of (27), (29) are lacking, i.e., there is no linear term containing N_2 in the first equation of (27) and none containing N_1 in the second. This gives rise to an exceptional case to which the general solution given in Chapter VI is not applicable.

The course of events represented by these curves is evidently a cyclic or periodic process, corresponding to a circulation around the closed curves. The period of oscillation, near the origin,[8] is given by

$$T = 2\pi/\sqrt{r_1 d_2} \qquad (36)$$

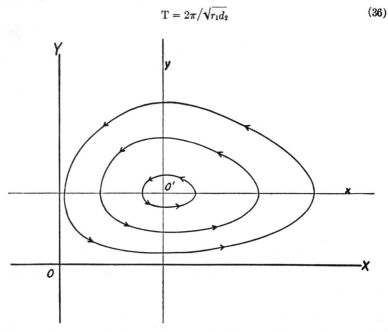

FIG. 13. COURSE OF PARASITIC INVASION OF INSECT SPECIES, ACCORDING TO LOTKA; ELEMENTARY TREATMENT

This finding accords well with the observation made by L. O. Howard:

With all very injurious lepidopterous larvae . . . . we constantly see a great fluctuation in numbers, the parasite rapidly increasing immediately after the increase of the host species, overtaking it numerically, and reducing it to the bottom of another ascending period of development.

---

[8] The purely periodic solutions have been discussed by the author in Proc. Natl. Acad. Sci., 1920, vol. 7, p. 410. The writer, however, at that time overlooked the existence also of the other types of solution, and also stated that the period of oscillation is independent of initial conditions. This is an error which he takes the present opportunity to correct. The expression given by him loc. cit. for the period of oscillation holds only in the neighborhood of $x = y = 0$. See also note 10 below.

The remarks of W. R. Thompson relative to this may also be quoted:

Recent studies on the utilization of entomophagous parasites seem to show that the rôle of these auxiliaries of man finds its maximum effectiveness when the noxious insect has increased in numbers to the point of a plague, one or more of the factors of natural equilibrium having somehow failed to act as a check. The expansion of the noxious species then automatically produces an increase in the number of parasites; generation

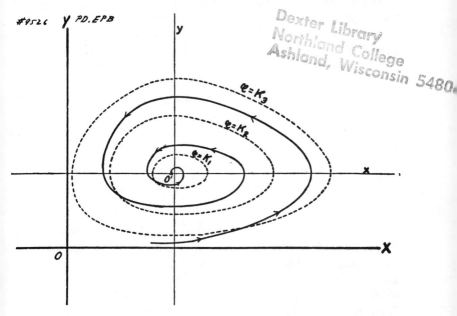

FIG. 14. COURSE OF PARASITIC INVASION OF INSECT SPECIES, ACCORDING TO LOTKA; MORE EXACT TREATMENT

after generation this number increases at the expense of the host, until it first equals, and presently surpasses the number of the host species, and finally almost annihilates the host; but then comes a moment when the parasite population, having grown to excess, largely disappears for the lack of food supply.[9]

---

[9] L. O. Howard, Bureau of Entomology, Technical Series No. 5, 1897, p. 48. It will be noted that the analysis given by W. R. Thompson fails to give any indication of this oscillatory process.

In this elementary discussion the terms of second and higher degree in N_1 and N_2 in equations (27) have been neglected, as in (29). When they are taken into account it is found that, *in general*, the system of closed curves in figure 13 is replaced by a spiral winding about the second equilibrium point (see fig. 14). The process is still oscillatory, but, in general, it is the nature of a damped oscillation. For detail of this more exact treatment the reader must be referred to the original literature.[10]

Annihilation of One Species by Another. The preceding example was suggested by W. R. Thompson's paper in the Comptes Rendus. Another case, leading to equations of the same form, had been previously treated by the writer, namely the following:

A species S_2 feeds on a species S_1, which, in turn feeds on some source presented in such large excess that the mass of this source may be considered constant during the period of time under consideration. Then we have the obvious relation

$$\begin{Bmatrix} \text{Rate of in-} \\ \text{crease of } X_1 \\ \text{per unit of} \\ \text{time} \end{Bmatrix} = \begin{Bmatrix} \text{Mass of newly} \\ \text{formed } S_1 \text{ per} \\ \text{unit of time} \end{Bmatrix} - \begin{Bmatrix} \text{Mass of } S_1 \\ \text{destroyed by} \\ S_2 \text{ per unit of} \\ \text{time} \end{Bmatrix} - \begin{Bmatrix} \text{Other dead} \\ \text{or excretory} \\ \text{matter elimi-} \\ \text{nated from } S_1 \\ \text{per unit of} \\ \text{time} \end{Bmatrix} \quad (37)$$

The first term in the right hand member, Mass of newly formed S_1 per unit of time, evidently must vanish with X_1, and we shall therefore write this term b_1X_1, where b_1 will, in general, be a function of both X_1 and X_2. Similarly, and for the same reasons we shall write for the third term, excretory matter, etc., eliminated from S_1 per unit of time, d_1X_1. Contracting these two terms into one we shall write for $b_1X_1 - d_1X_1$ the single term r_1X_1. The middle term, mass or S_1 destroyed per unit of time by S_2, must evidently vanish with either X_1 or X_2 separately. We shall accordingly write this term kX_1X_2, so that the equation now appears

$$\frac{dX_1}{dt} = r_1X_1 - kX_1X_2 \quad (38)$$

---

[10] H. Poincaré, Journal de Mathem., 4th ser., vol. 1, p. 172. (See also E. Picard, Traité d' Analyse, vol. III, Chapter IX, p. 214); A. J. Lotka, Jour. Washington Acad. Sci., 1923, vol. 13, p. 152.

For the species S_2 which feeds on S_1 we have a corresponding relation

$$\begin{Bmatrix} \text{Rate of in-} \\ \text{crease of } X_2 \\ \text{per unit of} \\ \text{time} \end{Bmatrix} = \begin{Bmatrix} \text{Mass of newly} \\ \text{formed } S_2 \text{ per} \\ \text{unit of time} \\ \text{(derived from} \\ S_1 \text{ as food in-} \\ \text{gested)} \end{Bmatrix} - \begin{Bmatrix} \text{Mass of } S_2 \\ \text{destroyed or} \\ \text{eliminated per} \\ \text{unit of time} \end{Bmatrix} \qquad (39)$$

which, for reasons precisely analogous to those set forth above with reference to equation (38), we shall write

$$\frac{dX_2}{dt} = KX_1X_2 - d_2X_2 \qquad (40)$$

It will be seen that these two equations are identical in form with those discussed in the preceding example, and it is therefore unnecessary to repeat the analysis there given. But one point invites attention, and will naturally lead us on presently to the consideration of a case in three dependent variables, which offers certain features of special interest.

Let us leave aside all other considerations, and restrict our enquiry here to the following question: Is it possible, under the circumstances represented by our equations, for the hostile species S_2 to exterminate completely the species S_1 upon which it feeds? This would, of course bring in its train also the extermination of S_2.

To answer this question we note that

$$\frac{dX_1}{dX_2} = \frac{X_1}{X_2} \frac{(r_1 - kX_2)}{(KX_1 - d_2)} \qquad (41)$$

is satisfied by the particular solution

$$X_1 = O \text{ for all values of } X_2 \qquad (42)$$

Hence if we plot the integral curves of (41) in rectangular coördinates, the axis of X_2 is itself one of the integral curves. Now if r_1, k, K, and d_2 are single-valued functions of X_1, and X_2, as it is reasonable to suppose that they are, then any point in the X_1X_2 plane is traversed by only one integral curve, since the derivative $\frac{dX_1}{dX_2}$ is uniquely determined by (41). It follows that no integral curve can cross the axis of X_2 and therefore X_1 can never fall to the value zero, it can be zero only if it had that value from the beginning. The food species cannot, therefore be exterminated by the predatory species, under the conditions to which our equations refer.

This argument fails, however, at the origin, where the derivative dX_1/dX_2 assumes the indeterminate form O/O. But in the neighborhood of the origin, where second degree terms are negligible, we have, essentially,

$$\frac{dX_1}{dX_2} = -\frac{X_1\,r_1}{X_2\,d_2} \tag{43}$$

from which it is seen that in the positive quadrant the integral curves always slope *downward* from left to right near the origin. They cannot, therefore, in the positive quadrant, cross the axis of X_2 at the origin, any more than at any other point, and the conclusion is now fully established, that the species S_2 cannot exterminate S_1 under the conditions here considered.

A word of caution, however, is perhaps in order. Although S_2 cannot exterminate S_1, it may so reduce the latter in numbers as to render it very vulnerable, and liable to extinction from those other influences which have deliberately been ignored in the development of the equations.

Case of Three Dependent Variables. A singularly interesting conclusion is reached when we enquire what may be the effect of introducing, into the system discussed in the preceding section, a third species, which also serves as food for S_2, so that this now has two sources to draw upon, after the pattern

One would perhaps naturally suppose that this alternative and additional source would in some measure protect S_1 from the attacks of S_2. But we shall see presently that this is not necessarily the case, that, in fact, in certain circumstances, the introduction of the third species S_3 may bring about the extermination of S_1, from which, as we have seen, S_1 is naturally protected by the diminution of growth forced upon S_2 when this species too greedily consumes its sole source of food.

The equations for this case are similar to those for the preceding, except that we must add a third equation for the species S_3

$$\frac{dX_3}{dt} = r_3 X_3 - h X_2 X_3 \tag{44}$$

and add a term to the equation for S_2 to represent the consumption of the species S_3 as food by S_2, so that this equation becomes

$$\frac{dX_2}{dt} = K X_1 X_2 + H X_2 X_3 - d_2 X_2$$

$$= X_2 (K X_1 + H X_3 - d_2) \tag{45}$$

We now have, near the axis of X_3,

$$\frac{dX_1}{dX_2} = \frac{X_1}{X_2} \frac{r_1}{H X_3 - d_2} \tag{46}$$

and, if X_3 is sufficiently large, the projection of the integral curves upon the $X_1 X_2$ plane will slope *upward* from left to right in the positive quadrant. Such an integral curve may therefore cut through the $X_2 X_3$ plane, that is to say, the species S_1 may be reduced to zero.

Similarly, near the axis of X_1

$$\frac{dX_3}{dX_2} = \frac{X_3}{X_2} \frac{r_3}{K X_1 - d_2} \tag{47}$$

and hence an integral curve may cut through the $X_2 X_1$, plane, thus reducing X_3 to zero.

This observation is of practical interest. It has been pointed out that in sea fisheries the accompanying presence of a common fish may cause the extermination of a rarer species which, were it present alone, would be protected by its very scarcity, since this would make fishing unprofitable. But the more abundant fish continues to render a balance of profit from the trawling operations, and thus the rarer species, so long as any of it remains, is gathered in with the same net that is cast primarily for common species.

Replaceable and Irreplaceable or Indispensable Components. The last two examples present an illustration of a point which calls for brief comment. So long as the species S_2 has only one source of food, S_1, it is to be observed that $\frac{dX_2}{dt}$ becomes negative as soon as X_1 is zero (see equation 40). In this sense S_1 is an essential component of the system, *relatively* to S_2, i.e., it is indispensable for the growth and even the mere continued existence of S_2. On the other hand, when two or more sources, such as S_1 and S_3 are provided, the vanishing of either X_1 or X_3 singly does not bring with it a negative value of $\dfrac{dX_2}{dt}$. The components S_1 and S_3 can more or less effectively replace, act as substitutes for, each other.

When the feeding species (S_2 in the example) is the human species, the facts indicated above find their expression in economic terms. It is an elementary fact of common knowledge that among the varied materials which the human race requires for its growth and sustenance are many that are more or less readily interchangeable. So, for example, a deficiency in the wheat crop may be in some degree met by increased supply of potatoes or other starchy food; or a deficiency in beef may be compensated by increased production in pork. On the other hand, there are certain requisites that are irreplaceable, and therefore absolutely essential. The most obvious example of such is our supply of oxygen.

In terms of our general analysis these facts would be expressed somewhat as follows. If we survey the various components whose masses $X_1, X_2 \ldots X_n$ appear in the function F_i

$$\frac{dX_i}{dt} = F_i (X_1, X_2, \ldots X_n)$$

we may effect a classification by first of all dividing them into two classes, namely those that adversely affect the rate of growth of X_i, that is to say, those for which

$$\frac{\partial}{\partial X_j} \frac{dX_i}{dt} < 0$$

and those that promote the rate of growth of X_i, those for which

$$\frac{\partial}{\partial X_k} \frac{dX_i}{dt} > 0$$

Among the latter components, those favorable to the growth of X_i, there is a special class distinguished by the following property:

If X_k is the mass of a component of this special class, then $\dfrac{dX_i}{dt}$ is invariably negative as soon as X_k is zero, no matter what may be the masses X_1, X_2 . . . of the other components. X_k is indispensable for the growth and the sustenance of X_i; X_k is an essential of irreplaceable component, relatively to X_i.

The ground upon which we are here treading is evidently close to the biological basis of economics. A detailed analysis of the relations involved belongs to the domain of the dynamics of life-bearing systems, and will in due course be considered in its natural place.

Limiting Factors. In general the several components that promote the growth of the component of S_i will be presented in varied abundance. If one essential component (or a group of components which jointly are essential) is presented in limited amount, any moderate increase or decrease in the ample supply of the other components will have little or no observable influence upon the rate of growth F_i of S_i. An essential component presented in limited supply thus acts as a check or brake, as a *limiting factor*, upon the growth of S_i. The significance of such limiting factors seems to have been first pointed out by J. Liebig:[11] "Der Ertrag (des Bodens) ist von dem *im minimo* in ihm enthaltenen Nährstoff abhängig." And again:

Für die Wiederherstellung der Erträge der durch die Cultur erschöpften Felder durch Stallmistdünguug ist die Zufuhr von allen den Nährstoffen welche das Feld im Überschuss enthält, vollkommen gleichgültig, und es wirken nur diejenigen Bestandteile desselben günstig, durch welche ein im Boden enstandener Mangel an einem oder zwei Nährstoffen beseitigt wird.

Limiting factors not only set certain bounds to the growth of the components to which they are thus related, but are competent also to give rise to the phenomenon of "moving equilibrium" the discussion of which is reserved for a later section dealing with equilibria generally, under the heading of *Statics*.

This chapter may fittingly be concluded with table 6, which exhibits the principal modes of interdependence of biological species, and summarizes the analytical characters of these, as discussed above.

[11] J. Liebig, Die Chemie in ihrer Anwendung auf Agricultur, 1876, p. 334. See also ibid., pp. 332, 333, 381, 382.

TABLE 6

Interdependence of biological species

Coördinate

- **Indirect** — Simple competition for common food supply, etc.
- **Mixed** — Competition combined with mutual destruction
- **Direct** — Simple mutual destruction without benefit on either side

Subordinate

- Bodies of one species consumed by other species
  - Food species killed by feeding species in the act of feeding
    - Random killing — Without cultivation (e.g., game under protective game laws)
    - Selective killing — With cultivation (farm animals)
  - Food species continues to live while feeding species consumes it
    - Without cultivation (e.g., wild honey)
    - With cultivation (e.g., milch cow)
- Body products of one species consumed by other species
  - Piracy of useful products
  - Utilization of waste products
    - Scavengers
    - Saprophagus and saprophytic species

Feeding species lives in or on body of food species
— *Parasitism*

Feeding species leads separate existence (animals feeding on wild fruit, etc.)
— *Physiological symbiosis*

Food species cultivated by feeding species (e.g., orchard crops)
— *Virtual symbiosis*

98

TABLE 6a

Summary of analytical characters

	TYPE OF INTERDEPENDENCE				
	Coördinate			Subordinate	
	Indirect	Mixed	Direct		
	Simple competition	Competition with mutual destruction	Simple mutual destruction	One-sided attack	Mutual promotion
$a_{21} = \dfrac{\partial}{\partial X_1} \dfrac{dX_2}{dt}$	−	−	−	+	+
$a_{12} = \dfrac{\partial}{\partial X_2} \dfrac{dX_1}{dt}$	−	−	−	−	+

CHAPTER IX

ANALYSIS OF THE GROWTH FUNCTION

Elegant intellects which despise the theory of quantity are but half developed.—*A. N. Whitehead.*

The Form of the Growth Function F. The fundamental equations (1) of Chapter VI express in a very general, and for that reason somewhat colorless way, the interdependence of the several components of evolving systems of the kind here under discussion.

In the special cases with one, two and three dependent variables that have been presented as examples, the particular form and the concrete meaning of the functions F appearing in these equations has been illustrated for these specific instances, without any attempt at systematization from a general standpoint. It is desirable now to make a somewhat detailed analysis of the functions F in their more general aspect.

A natural step to take is, first of all, to split up the function F into a positive and a negative term; that is to say, to express the rate of increase of the mass X_i of the component S_i as the balance, the surplus, of the mass U_i added to that component per unit of time, over the mass V_i eliminated therefrom per unit of time. Thus

$$\frac{dX_i}{dt} = F_i = U_i - V_i \tag{1}$$

Growth of Aggregates. Among the components of systems of the kind in which we are here mainly interested, a particularly important type are those built up of a large number of essentially similar units or individuals. Such are the aggregates of molecules that constitute the components (chemical elements and compounds) of the systems with which physical chemistry is concerned; such, also, are the aggregates of individual organisms that constitute the biological species, the component population groups, of which are built up the systems in which organic evolution takes its course.

In the case of an aggregate of this kind, if N is the number of individuals, and m their average mass per head, we have

$$X_i = m_i N_i \tag{2}$$

$$\frac{dX_i}{dt} = m_i \frac{dN_i}{dt} + N_i \frac{dm_i}{dt} \tag{3}$$

If the average mass per individual, m_i, is constant, the second term of the right hand member in (3) drops out, and we have simply,

$$\frac{dX_i}{dt} = m_i \frac{dN_i}{dt} \tag{4}$$

This holds strictly for aggregates of similar molecules, for example, whose masses are all equal and constant. It will often hold with close approximation (as will be set forth in greater detail shortly) for populations of living organisms of one species.

Now $\dfrac{dN_i}{dt}$, the rate of increase in numbers of the aggregate S_i, naturally appears, after the manner indicated above, as the balance of the number of newly formed individuals B_i per unit of time, and the number D_i eliminated per unit of time. When these symbols refer to a population of living organism, B_i is the (total) birth rate and D_i the (total) death rate per unit of time. We have, then,

$$\frac{dN_i}{dt} = B_i - D_i \tag{5}$$

which it is often convenient to write

$$\frac{dN_i}{dt} = (b_i - d_i)N_i \tag{6}$$

the lower case letters b, d denoting birth rate and death rate *per head* per unit of time.

Combining (4) and (5) we have

$$\frac{dX_i}{dt} = (B_i - D_i)m_i \tag{7}$$

Demographic Functions. The quantities B, D, or b, d lend themselves to further analysis in terms of more fundamental characteristics of the aggregate. In a qualitative way everyone is familiar with the manner of the elimination of individuals from a population by death: some are carried off in infancy, some in childhood, adolescence, and maturity, until the remnant is finally called in old age. Quantitatively this fact finds expression in an actuarian's life table, or the corresponding life curve, of which some examples are shown in figures 15 to 17. Starting with some large number, say a million, of newly born individuals, counted at birth, if we follow this sample batch of population through life, we find them thinning out, at first rather rapidly in infancy and childhood (steep part of curve on left): then more slowly (more gentle slope) in mid-life; and faster again as the natural term is approached. At any particular age a there are thus left, out of the original batch, a fraction $p(a)$ of survivors. The fraction $p(a)$, which we may speak of as the *survival factor*,[1] is a measure of the probability, at birth, that a random individual of the batch shall reach age a, under the conditions under which the data assembled in the life table were collected. The value of $p(a)$ for every age of life depends, of course, on the general conditions of life in the population. It therefore varies in different localities and at different epochs, as illustrated in figures 15, 16, 17. When it is desired to bring out the fact that $p(a)$ depends on the time, it may be written $p(a, t)$. But as a rule the change with time is not very rapid and we may often consider $p(a)$ as a function of the age a alone. We shall do this in the present analysis, which relates to a population in a selected locality under essentially constant conditions of life.

If we denote by N_a the survivors to age a, out of an original batch N_o counted at birth, we have

$$N_a = N_o p(a) \tag{8}$$

We will write

$$\frac{dN_a}{da} = - \mu_a N_a \tag{9}$$

or

$$- \mu_a = \frac{dN_a}{N_a da} = \frac{d \log_e N_a}{da} \tag{10}$$

The coefficient μ_a thus defined is termed the *force of mortality* at age a. From its definition it is clear that it measures the death rate per head in a population composed entirely of individuals of age a.

[1] The function $p(a)$ is that commonly denoted by 1_x in actuarial notation, and tabulated in the principal column of a "Life Table."

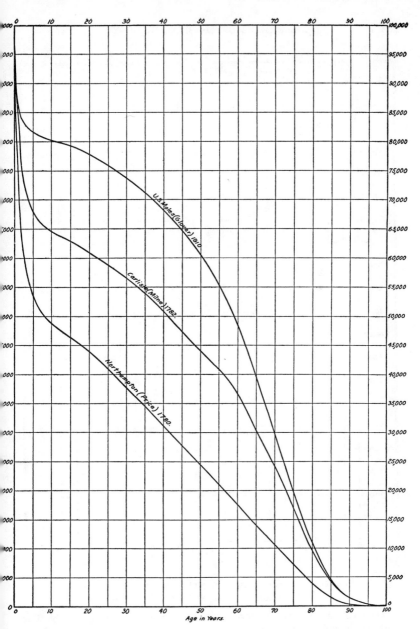

FIG. 15. SOME HISTORICAL HUMAN SURVIVAL CURVES, EXHIBITING AN EVOLU-
TIONARY TREND TOWARD LONGER AVERAGE DURATION OF LIFE

The improvement is probably rather one of general hygiene than of man's
physiological constitution. The earlier figures are of very doubtful accuracy.

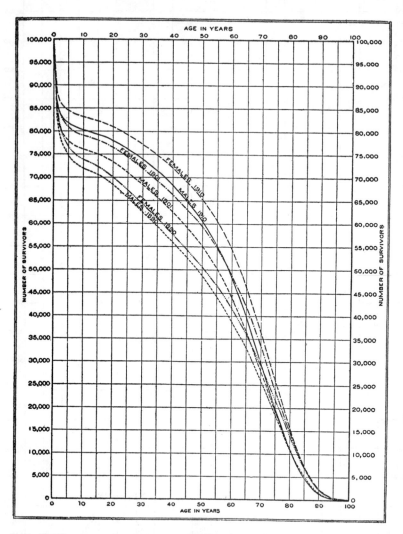

Fig. 16. Survival Curves for the State of Massachusetts, for the Three Decades 1890–1900–1910. After Glover

The data on which these curves are based are naturally more reliable than those of the older life tables shown in figure 14, and exhibit very clearly the upward trend of the average length of human life in recent decades.

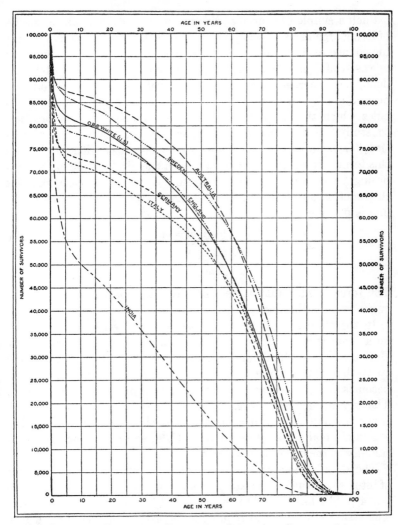

FIG. 17. SURVIVAL CURVES FOR DIFFERENT COUNTRIES, SHOWING INFLUENCE OF LOCAL CONDITIONS UPON LENGTH OF HUMAN LIFE. AFTER GLOVER

A particularly simple case is that in which μ_a is independent of a, the force of mortality is independent of the age, or is the same at all ages. We then have by integration of (10)

$$N_a = N_0 e^{-\mu_v} \tag{11}$$

and

$$p(a) = e^{-\mu_v} \tag{12}$$

Such a simple life curve as this is not to be expected in a species of living organisms. It implies that the individual does not *age*, that his chance of living another year is just as good at ninety years of age as at fifty or at ten or at five; he can die, as it were, only by accident; he is perpetually young. Survival curves of this form do occur and play a significant rôle in the aggregates of atoms and molecules which the chemist and the physicist make it their province to study. The atoms of an element in radioactive transformation, for example, are picked off, one by one, according to a law of this form, and so are the molecules of a chemical compound decomposing by a monomolecular reaction. If, in such a case, the plot the function $p(a)$ is drawn on logarithmic paper, evidently a straight line is obtained, since

$$\log_e p(a) = \mu a \tag{13}$$

$$\frac{d \log_e p(a)}{da} = \mu \tag{14}$$

The force of mortality is here seen as the (constant) slope of the curve representing $\log_e p(a)$.

In the more general case it is also often convenient to plot $p(a)$ on a logarithmic scale. This has been done in figure 18 for the United States survival curve shown in figure 17. It is seen that the curve thus obtained is at first convex toward the axis of a, but soon becomes concave toward that axis and then remains so to the end. The significance of this is, of course, that the force of mortality is very high in infancy, decreases in early childhood, until it reaches a minimum about the twelfth year of life; and finally increases continually to the end of the life span.

The detailed analysis of the human survival curve is a matter of interest not only to the student of evolution, but also to the guardian of public health and to the insurer of human life, the actuarian. The essentially practical requirements of these has led to a highly developed technique, amounting virtually to a separate branch of science, in the preparation and analysis of life tables. Of this phase of the subject no more needs to be said here, since there is a voluminous special literature available. Only the more strictly biological aspect of the matter is for us here of immediate interest, and of this more will be said later, in discussing the physical basis underlying the survival curve.

Survival Curve Data. Without having recourse to any refinements of mathematical analysis it is clear that a close relation exists between the survival curve of a given species and its rate of increase, its fate in the struggle for existence and for dominance. It might

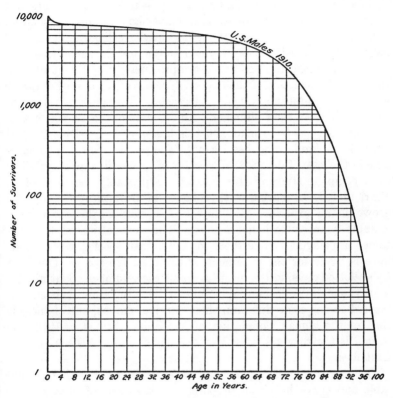

Fig. 18. Survival Curve Plotted on Logarithmic Scale.
United States 1910

The slope of the curve thus plotted measures the *Force of Mortality*. This slope is at first very steep, decreases to about the twelfth year of life, when it reaches a minimum (point of inflection), and then increases again continuously to the end of life.

be expected, therefore, that the study of such survival curves for different species of organisms should have formed an essential part of quantitative studies in evolution. As a matter of fact, however, data for survival curves of organisms in their natural environment are, for obvious reasons not easily obtained. It is difficult enough to make an accurate census of ages in a supposedly intelligent and responsible human community, where the coöperation of the individual can at least in a measure be engaged. A census of ages in the population of field, forest and stream must indeed be a severe test of the ingenuity of any investigator that should approach such an enterprise. Not that it is utterly hopeless. Isolated data can and have been gathered. Every layman knows that the age of trees, for example, can be estimated at least approximately by the number of rings in a cross section of the trunk. The age of certain fishes can be gaged from tell-tale marking on their scales. The age of certain birds can be told from their plumage. An estimate of the average age of herring gulls has been made, on this basis, by J. T. Nichols.[2] But data of this kind are at best scant. The problem is more manageable in the case of domestic species, or of species in captivity. The most complete study of this character is probably the work of R. Pearl and S. L. Parker with colonies of fruit flies (Drosophila) grown in an experimental "universe," a glass bottle containing a suitable quantity of banana juice.[3] The survival curves thus obtained are singularly like those for the human species, when allowance is made for the difference in the total life span. The fruit fly's allotted days, in the most favorable case, number about ninety, or, say, one day for each year of human life. In figure 19 are shown, plotted on the same diagram, three survival curves; one of these is that of the human population of the United States in 1910; the second is the survival curve for one of the numerous varieties of fruit flies.

For only one other organism, *Proales decipiens* (a rotifer), a life table and curve has been prepared, on the basis of observations by B. Noyes.[4] The life curve has been computed by Pearl and Doering[5] and compared with that of man, on the basis of the life span

[2] J. T. Nichols, in *The Condor*, vol. 17, 1915, p. 181; for other data on the longevity of animals see C. S. Minot, The Problem of Age, Growth and Death, 1908, pp. 226, 266; A. Weismann, Über die Dauer des Lebens, Jena, 1882. See also A. T. Masterman, Report on the scales of freshwater fish in relation to age determination. H. M. Stationery, Office 1924.

[3] R. Pearl and S. L. Parker, American Naturalist, vol. 55, 1921, p. 503; vol. 56, 1922, p. 403.

[4] B. Noyes, Jour. Exp. Zool., vol. 35, 1922, p. 225.

[5] R. Pearl and C. R. Doering, Science, vol. 57, 1923, p. 211.

measured from the point at which the force of mortality is a mimi-
mum to the extreme end of life.   It is the curves thus obtained that
are shown in figure 19.   As will be seen, they exhibit a close analogy.

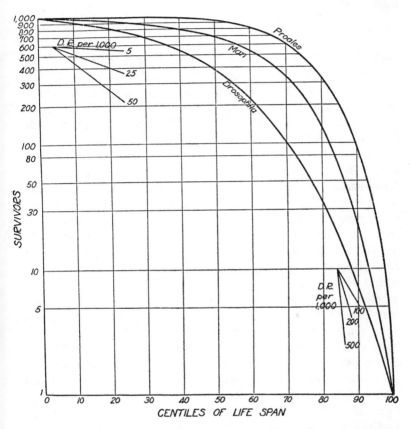

FIG. 19. LOGARITHMIC SURVIVAL CURVES FOR MAN, DROSOPHILA, AND
PROALES DECIPIENS

Plotted according to centiles of life-span; the human life curve is plotted
with the twelfth year of life (point of inflection, see figure 18) as zero of the
time scale. After R. Pearl.

Influence of Age Distribution Upon Rate of Growth of Population.
For our present purposes it is not sufficient to fix our attention on a
group of individuals at the moment of their birth, and to observe
the gradual diminution of this group by deaths; we must take in

view an actual population, comprising individuals of all ages, and we must enquire into the effect of deaths upon such a group as this.

If the survival curve for such a population were of the simple form

$$p(a) = e^{-\mu a} \tag{12}$$

with μ, the force of mortality, independent of a, it is evident that the age distribution in the population would have no influence upon the total death rate. For if individuals of all ages are equally susceptible to death, it is evidently immaterial how the population is constituted as regards age. The death rate per head, in such a population would, in fact, be simply equal to the force of mortality.

The Stable or "Normal" Age Distribution. But in the populations with which the biologist and the vital statistitian deals, the force of mortality varies very decidedly with the age, and it might therefore be supposed that any discussion of the rate of increase of a population of organisms must fully take into account the age distribution. This supposition, however, involves an assumption, namely, the assumption that the age distribution itself is variable. Now, in point of fact, the age distribution is indeed variable, but only within somewhat restricted limits. Certain age distributions will practically never occur, and if by arbitrary interference, or by a castastrophe of nature, some altogether unusual form were impressed upon the age distribution of an isolated population, the "irregularities" would tend shortly to become smoothed over. There is, in fact a certain stable type of age distribution about which the actual age distribution varies, and toward which it returns if through any agency disturbed therefrom.[6] The form of this distribution, in an isolated population (i.e., with immigration and emigration negligible) is easily deduced, as follows:

If we denote by $N(t)$ the total number of the population at time t, and by $N(t) c(a) da$ that fraction of the total whose age is comprised, at time t, within the limits a and $a + da$, it is evident that the individuals of this element of the population are the survivors of the $B(t-a)da$ persons born at times $(t-a)$. Hence if $p(a)$ is the survival factor, we have

---

[6] For a formal proof of this see F. R. Sharpe and A. J. Lotka, Phil. Mag., April, 1911, p. 435; A. J. Lotka, Proc. Natl. Acad., vol. 8, 1922, p. 339.

$$B(t-a)\ p(a)\ da = N(t)\ c(a)\ da \tag{15}$$

$$c(a) = \frac{B(t-a)}{N(t)}\ p(a) \tag{16}$$

If we denote by $D(t)$ the total death rate at time t, we have, evidently

$$D(t) = N(t) \int_0^\infty c(a)\ \frac{dp(a)}{p(a)\ da}\ da \tag{17}$$

We are supposing that we are dealing with a population in which the survival factor is constant, i.e., independent of t. If $c(a)$ also is independent of t, the integral in (17) is evidently a constant and we have

$$\frac{D(t)}{N(t)} = \text{const.} = d \tag{18}$$

where d is the death rate per head.

On the other hand, since $c(a)$ is independent of the time, we have

$$c(0) = \text{const.} = b \tag{19}$$

Brief reflection shows that the value of $c(a)$ for zero age is the birth rate per head. Thus we have

$$b - d = r = \text{const.} \tag{20}$$

where r is the "natural rate of increase" of the population.

We have further

$$B(t-a) = bN(t-a) \tag{21}$$

$$= bN(t)e^{-ra} \tag{22}$$

since the natural rate of increase r is constant. Thus by (16)

$$c(a) = be^{-ra}p(a) \tag{23}$$

The *normal* age distribution (23) is of *fixed* form in the sense that, once established, it perpetuates itself. More than this, it is also *stable*, in the sense that, if disturbed by a temporary change in the conditions of life (e.g., war), it will spontaneously return upon restoration of normal conditions.

A rigorous proof of this stability of the age distribution (23) cannot be briefly given, and for details of such proof the reader must be referred to the author's publications in the journal literature.[6] The general character of the proof may, however, be indicated. If the original population has any arbitrary age distribution, such as that represented by the more heavily drawn curve in figure 20, by judicious trimming we could reduce the population to the *normal* distribution represented by the lower curve tangent to the heavy curve; or, we could, by filling in gaps, supplement the population to fit the upper tangent normal distribution curve. The trimmed down population, having the normal age distribution, would always retain it. The same is true of the supplemented population. The actual population will therefore always lie between the trimmed and the supplemented. Moreover, it can be shown that at intervals of about one hundred years (the span of life) new tangent curves can be drawn to the actual distribution curve, the new tangents lying between the old. Thus the two tangent curves ultimately approach until they coincide, and then, necessarily, the actual distribution curve lying between them coincides with them also. That is to say, the actual conforms with the normal age distribution.[7]

It must be understood that the *normal* or *stable* form of age distribution represents merely a broad type, toward which actual age distributions will tend. However, the approach seems to be at times very close, as is shown by the figures in table 7 giving the observed and the calculated age distribution for England and Wales in decennium 1871–1880. A graphic representation appears in figure 21, which shows the observational data, plotted (in dotted lines) as a stepped curve. The corresponding figures calculated by the formula (13) are plotted in two ways, namely, first as a stepped curve (drawn in full), for comparison with the observational data; and also as a continuous curve. The latter brings out a feature that may be noted in passing, namely the fact that the curve of age distribution is very flat, roughly linear, over a wide range, from the

---

[7] An exceedingly interesting effort of early date to demonstrate the ultimate approach to geometric increase of the birthrate, independently of initial conditions (e.g. starting with a single pair of parents) is to be found in L. Euler, Recherches générales sur la mortalité. See also E. T. Gumbel, Jahresber. Deutsch Math. verein., vol. 25, p. 251.

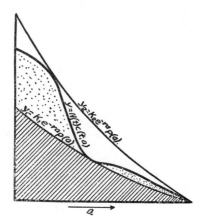

FIG. 20. DIAGRAMS TO ILLUSTRATE PROOF OF STABILITY OF NORMAL AGE DISTRIBUTION

Reproduced from A. J. Lotka, Proc. Natl. Acad. Sci., vol. 8, 1922, p. 339

TABLE 7

Population of England and Wales 1871–1880, as an example of "normal" age distribution

$a_1, \quad a_2$	MALES		FEMALES		PERSONS	
	Calculated	Observed	Calculated	Observed	Calculated	Observed
0 – 5	142	139	135	132	138	136
5 –10	118	123	114	117	116	120
10–15	107	110	104	104	106	107
15–20	98	99	95	95	96	97
20–25	88	87	86	91	87	89
25–35	150	144	148	149	149	147
35–45	117	112	117	115	117	113
45–55	84	84	87	87	86	86
55–65	57	59	63	61	60	59
65–75	29	31	36	35	32	33
75– ∞	11	12	13	15	12	13
	1,001	1,000	998	1,001	999	1,001

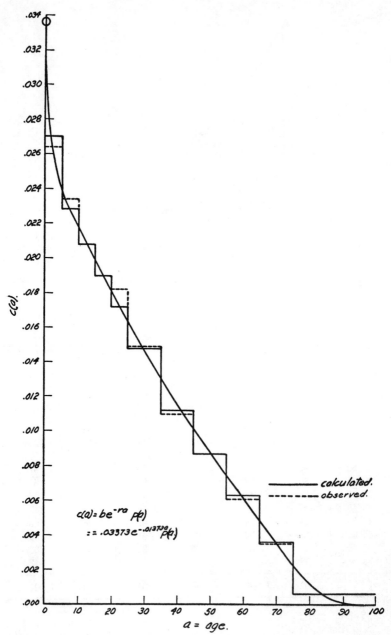

FIG. 21. "STABLE" AGE DISTRIBUTION, AS EXEMPLIFIED BY THE POPULATION
OF ENGLAND AND WALES IN THE DECADE 1871–1880

fifth to the eightieth year of life.[8]   This, of course, is a special feature of a human population when the natural rate of increase r lies in the neighborhood of a certain value.

Minor fluctuations of the age distribution will not greatly affect the birth rate and the death rate.   Since actual populations approximate the *normal* age distribution, i.e., that defined by equation (23), it seems permissible and it is certainly expedient to assume, in further discussion, that the normal age distribution is actually established; we may then virtually disregard the influence of the age distribution upon $\dfrac{dX}{dt}$ the rate of increase of the component.   This element is, as it were, automatically ruled out of further discussion, by the natural establishment of the normal age distribution;[9] a circumstance which is in so far fortunate, as we are here interested in the relation of the rate of growth to the more fundamental biological characteristics; the age-distribution appearing merely as an adventitious element complicating the relation, without being essential to the fundamental characterization of the species.

Demographic Relations in "Normal" Population.   It is worth while to note briefly in passing that in the case of a population in *normal* age distribution, many demographic relations assume a simple form.   So, for example, the relation between birth rate per head b and death rate per head d is here given by the formula[10]

$$1/b = \int_0^\infty e^{-ra}p(a)\,da \qquad (25)$$

which, to second order approximation, is reducible to the simple form

$$\frac{1-U}{b} + \frac{U}{d} = L \qquad (26)$$

where L is the mean length of life, defined as

[8] Compare J. Brownlee, The Use of Death Rates as a Measure of Hygienic Conditions, Report to Medical Research Council, London, 1922, pp. 36–37.

[9] Cf. C. Eijkman, On the Reaction Velocity of Organisms, Proc. Amsterdam Academy Sci., 1912, p. 269; Reichenbach, Zeitschr. f. Hygiene und Inf. Krankh, 1911, vol. 69, p. 161.

[10] A. J. Lotka, Quart. Publ. Am. Statist. Assoc., 1918, p. 121; 1921, p. 998.

$$L = \int_0^\infty p(a)\, da \tag{27}$$

while U is defined[11] by

$$L' = \int_0^\infty ap(a)\, da \tag{28}$$

$$U = \frac{L'}{L^2} \tag{29}$$

As an illustration it may be mentioned that in the same population (England and Wales, 1871–1880) which has already been referred to, the relation (26) is found by actual computation to be, numerically,

$$\frac{0.767}{d} + \frac{0.233}{b} = 41.35 \text{ (males)} \tag{30}$$

$$\frac{0.7369}{d} + \frac{0.2631}{b} = 44.62 \text{ (females)} \tag{31}$$

The observed values of b and d, together with those computed by the formulae (22), (23), are shown in table 8. It will be seen that the agreement is good.

The relation (26) between b and d lends itself readily to graphic representation by means of a diagram involving only straight lines. This is shown in figure 22. The method is as follows.

Along OX mark off a length OP $= \dfrac{1-U}{L}$

Along OY mark off a length OQ $= \dfrac{U}{L}$

Complete the rectangle QOPM.
Suppose we are now given
$$b = 0.0337$$
It is required to find d
   Along OX mark off OV $= 0.0337$
   Join VM and produce it to meet OY in W
   Read off at W on the scale of OY
$$d = 0.0200$$

---

[11] U is proper fraction. It then follows from (26) that L is intermediate between $\dfrac{1}{b}$ and $\dfrac{1}{d}$; this circumstance has been noted by Bortkewitch, Mittlere-Lebensdauer.

A single equation, such as (25), connecting the two quantities b and d, is of course insufficient to determine their value. To do this requires a second independent relation. Such a relation is furnished by the following considerations:

The law of the fixed age distribution holds separately for each sex. Thus, if we denote N_f the total number of the female popula-

TABLE 8

	b (OBSERVED)	d (OBSERVED)	d (COMPUTED)
Males	0.036921	0.022612	0.02221
Females	0.033727	0.020001	0.02000

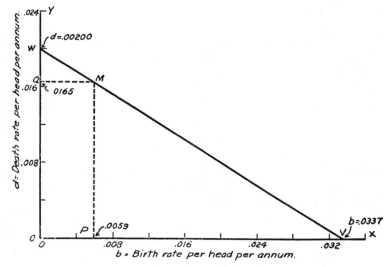

FIG. 22. DIAGRAM OF RELATION BETWEEN BIRTH RATE PER HEAD b AND DEATH RATE PER HEAD d IN POPULATION WITH STABLE AGE DISTRIBUTION

tion, by b_f the number of female births per unit of time and per head of female population, and finally by $p_f(a)$ the survival factor in the female population, then the number of females of an age between a and $a + da$ is given by $N_f b_f e^{-ra} p_f(a)\, da$. If these reproduce, on an average, $\beta_f(a)$ females per unit of time, then the total number of female births per unit of time is evidently given by

$$B_f = N_f b_f \int_{a_1}^{a_2} e^{-ra} p_f(a) \ \beta_f(a) \ da \qquad (32)$$

where a_1, a_2 are the lower and upper age limits of the female reproduction period.   But $N_f b_f = B_f$; hence

$$1 = \int_{a_1}^{a_2} e^{-ra} p_f(a) \ \beta_f(a) \ da \qquad (33)$$

$$= \int_{a_1}^{a_2} e^{-(b-d)a} p_f(a) \beta_f(a) \ da \qquad (34)$$

This is the required second relation[12] between b and d.   The birth rate and death rate in a population of fixed age distribution are thus completely determined as soon as the functions $p_f(a)$ and $\beta_f(a)$ are given.

Aside from its direct interest as the second relation required to complete the determination of b and d in a population with fixed age distribution, equation (34) is also of value in enabling us to deduce certain secondary results, of which two will here be noted.

Rate of Increase per Generation.   To derive our first conclusion from (33), we expand e^{-ra} under the integral sign.   We find

$$1 = \int_{a_1}^{a_2} \beta(a) \ p(a) \ da - r \int_{a_1}^{a_2} a\beta(a) \ p(a) \ da + \ldots \qquad (35)$$

A little reflection shows that the first integral measures the ratio between the total number of births in two successive generations. Denoting this by R, and the second integral by S, we have

$$R = 1 + rS - \ldots \qquad (36)$$

a formula which connects the rate of increase per head per annum r and the rate of increase R in the total number of births in one generation, per generation.   It will be seen that this relation is not one that could very well be foretold by any simple elementary or common sense principle.   It is this relation that is implicitly involved in W. R. Thompson's treatment of a problem in parasitology cited in Chapter VIII (page 87); at least, we must know this relation if we are to interpret his results in terms of the usual time unit, such as the year, whereas Thompson reckons in generations.

[12] A. J. Lotka, Jour. Washington Acad. Sci., 1913, p. 293.

Effect of Selective Slaughtering. A second deduction from equation (34) follows from the fact that the integral extends only between the age limits of the reproductive period. In consequence of this the rate of increase, per head, of the population is independent of the form of the life curve (the survival factor) outside this period; thus the slaughtering of the "superannuated" members of a herd has no effect upon its rate of increase, though both death rate and birth rate are augmented (by equal amounts).[12] The economic significance of this, as a means for raising the productive capacity of the herd, considered as a food factory, is self-evident.

It is true, as previously noted, that *generally* the influence of age distribution upon the rate of growth of a species is eliminated from discussion by the spontaneous establishment of the fixed or normal distribution. But the subject referred to in the preceding paragraph clearly shows that there are exceptions to this general rule. We have here an instructive example in which the influence of the age distribution upon the course of events is so fundamental that a discussion of the case which should fail to cover this feature would be lacking in an essential particular. Indiscriminate killing of one species by another, as practised by the untutored savage or the dumb animals, has the effect of reducing the ordinates of the life curve of the food species more or less along its whole extent. This is illustrated in figure 23. We may suppose that the life curve of some species, wild cattle, for example, is that shown in a full line, curve I, and that curve II represents the life curve for the same species after the habitat of the species has been invaded by a tribe of primitive hunters, too thoughtless or too unintelligent to regulate their depredations in accordance with anything of the nature of game laws. Curve III is the type of curve that would be produced by *selective* killing guided by intelligent control, as distinguished from *random* killing. The verticals erected at a_1 and a_2 represent the limits of the period of reproduction for the cattle. The slaughtering, in the case of curve III, takes place exclusively after the end of the period of reproduction. This is an extreme case, which, in practice, for obvious reasons, would be only distantly approached. For both in game preservation and in animal husbandry on the farm many factors have to be considered; not only the quality of the meat of animals at different ages, but the cost of raising and maintenance. It is out of the question to restrict the slaughtering to the post-

reproductive period.   The unnecessary male may, in fact, be slaughtered as soon as the cost of his upkeep exceeds the corresponding gain
in marketable value of his carcass.   Just what is the most advantageous time for his slaughter is a question in agricultural economics which
has been discussed, among others by A. Gouin and P. Andouard.[13]
These authors compute that to bring up three calves, from weaning
to the age of three and one-half years, requires about 33,000 kgm.
of hay (or their equivalent); this quantity would suffice to bring

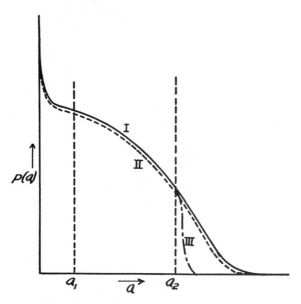

Fig. 23. Diagrammatic Illustration of Influence of Random and of
Selective Slaughtering upon Survival Curve of Biological Species

seven head of cattle to the end of their second year, which would
give a gain, in meat, of 40 per cent, as compared with three head
brought to the age of three and one-half years.

Intelligence as a Discriminating Agency.   It is particularly worth
while to note how in this connection human intelligence exerts
its influence upon the course of physical events by substituting
systematic selection in the place of the more haphazard, more random actions characteristic of the mentally less developed species.

[13] Bull. Soc. Natl. d'Agriculture, Paris, 1910, p. 695.

These latter must, in many ways, remain dependent upon certain average manifestation, whereas man, in a corresponding situation, is able to discriminate and address himself directly to individual elements of which these averages are the expression in the gross.

In the manifold interactions on a macroscopic scale that constitute the perennial struggle for existence on nature's battlefield, the lower organisms are in many respects situated in a position analogous to man's relation toward the ultra-microscopic elements of his environment, the molecules and atoms. These he can handle only in bulk, unable to avail himself of the distinctive features of this or that particular atom or molecule.

Just as our senses and our bodily members are inadequate for the task of handling individual atoms, so the mental or other discriminating powers of the lower organism are often inadequate to lead it toward any other than a rather random selection, and by no means an optimum selection, among the somewhat varied opportunities of self-service presented to it.

However, though man does far excel the other creatures in this respect, the difference is, after all, one in degree and not in kind. Many, if not all organisms, possess in some degree the power of selection, are in some measure independent of pure haphazard. This introduces an altogether peculiar complication into the dynamics of systems comprising living organisms, a complication of which the statistical dynamics of molecular physics are free. Not only is the living organism capable of performing, on a macroscopic scale, exploits analogous to those which in the world of molecules are permitted only to such figments of the imagination as Maxwell's demon; but this power of "cheating chance," as it were, is possessed in different degree by the several living organisms, and a dynamics of systems comprising living matter must necessarily take account not only of this faculty, but of the gradations in this faculty which have a large part in assigning to the several biological species their place in the scale of evolution. This will require the development of special methods. It is essential that we bear in mind constantly the ultimate aim of our reflections. The transformations of matter, the change in its distribution among the components of the physical system in the course of evolution, are the first to strike the eye, and are properly the first to receive our systematic consideration, just because they are of more obvious and elementary character.

But our fundamental aim must ultimately be to gain an enlarged understanding of the dynamic relation involved, of the play of forces, the transformations of energy.

Kinetics of Intra-Group Evolution. It is not intended to attempt here a systematic discussion in any sense exhaustive of the course of events in intra-group evolution, that is to say, in the redistribution of matter among the several sub-types of which a biological species is composed. We shall however briefly note an enterprise, led more particularly by J. B. S. Haldane,[14] to investigate the trend of evolution in a population in which selection is operating upon a character subject to Mendelian inheritance.

Case 1. Haldane considers first of all the simple case of a species of constant total population, consisting of two types (phenotypes) A and B that do not interbreed, but react upon each other merely through competition in the same environment.

Haldane treats the case as follows:

Let the nth generation, *counted immediately after fertilization,*[15] consist of types A and B in the ratio u_n: 1, and let the coefficient of selection be k, i.e., let $(1-k)$ of B survive (*to breeding age*)[16] for every one of A. Then the survivors (to breeding age) of the nth generation, and hence the *first numbers*[17] of the $(n+1)$th, will be in the ratio

---

[14] J. B. S. Haldane, Trans. Cambridge Phil. Soc., January, 1924, vol. xxiii, pp. 19–41. Part II, read July 14, 1924, has not yet reached the author.

[15] The words in italics are here added to Haldane's text, in accordance with the first paragraph of his paper, page 20.

[16] The words in italics are here added to Haldane's text, in accordance with his paper, page 23, line 6.

[17] The meaning of this term is not altogether clear. It seems to refer to the total births in the $(n + 1)$th generation, or, in other words, to the $(n+1)$th generation, counted at birth. This does not seem altogether consistent with the rest of the argument, notably the wording referred to in footnote 15. On the other hand the terms referred to in footnote 16 are vague unless reproduction takes place once and once only in the life of the individual, since in general there is not only one single age of reproduction, so that the fraction surviving to breed cannot be represented by any single number. It seems that it would be better to base the argument on the total number born in each generation, i.e., on the generation, counted at birth; and to regard the ratio R between the births in two successive generations as a function of β (a) and p (a), as set forth in Chapter VIII equation (24) and Chapter IX equations (35), (36). We would then start with equation (38) of page 123 as a fundamental assumption; beyond this the argument would remain essentially unchanged.

$$u_n : 1 - k = u_{n+1} : 1 \tag{37}$$

$$u_{n+1} = \frac{u_n}{1 - k} \tag{38}$$

If u_0 be the original ratio of $A : B$ in the 0th generation, then

$$u_n = (1 - k)^{-n} u_0 \tag{39}$$

If we write y_n for the proportion of B's to the total population of A and B in the nth generation, then

$$y_n = \frac{1}{1 + u_n} = \frac{1}{1 + (1 - k)^{-n} u_0} \tag{40}$$

$$1 - y_0 = y_0 u_0 \tag{41}$$

$$y_n = \frac{y_0}{y_0 + (1 - k)^{-n} (1 - y_0)} \tag{42}$$

If we start with an equal number of births of A and B

$$y_0 = \tfrac{1}{2} \tag{43}$$

$$y_n = \frac{1}{1 + (1 - k)^{-n}} \tag{44}$$

If k is very small, i.e., if selection is very slow, then approximately

$$y_n = \frac{1}{1 + e^{kn}} \tag{45}$$

or

$$k_n = \log \frac{1 - y_n}{y_n} \tag{46}$$

In equation (45) we recognize once more the Verhulst-Pearl relation. It is seen that in the circumstances to which the discussion relates, the better adapted of the two types grows, along the typical S-shaped curve, at the expense of the less well adapted, ultimately displacing it entirely. This is quite in accord with what we should expect, since the total population $A + B$ is constant, that is to say, it just holding its own. Any constituent of the population that falls below the average in adaptation, must therefore be unable to hold its own, and diminishes continually.

The curve representing graphically the change of the population—increase of type A at the expense of B, which is ultimately displaced entirely—is shown in figure 24 for the case $k = 0.001$, i.e., that 999 B's survive to reproduce, for every 1000 A's. In these circumstances 9184 generations are needed for the proportion of A's to increase from 1 per cent to 99 per cent.

Case 2. Selection of a Simple Mendelian Character, with intermingling of dominant and recessive type. Haldane next takes the following case:

Consider the case of a population containing two, one, or no "doses" of a completely dominant Mendelian factor A. Mating is at random and selection acts in equal degree in both sexes upon the character produced by the factor. Pearson[18] and Hardy[19] have shown that in a population mating at random, the square of the number of heterozygotes is four times the product of the numbers of the two homozygous classes. Let $u_n A. : 1a$ be the proportion of the types of gametes produced in the $(n-1)^{th}$ generation. Then in the nth generation the *initial* proportion of the two classes of zygotes will be

$$u_n^2 \, AA : 2u_n \, Aa : 1a \qquad (47)$$

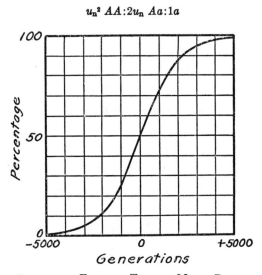

FIG. 24. GROWTH OF FAVORED TYPE IN MIXED POPULATION OF
TWO PHENOTYPES

Constant total population. Abscissae = number of generations; ordinates = percentage of favored type in total population. After J. B. S. Haldane.

The proportion of recessives to the whole population is

$$y_n = (1 + u_n)^{-2} \qquad (48)$$

Now only $(1 - k)$ of the recessives *survive to breed*, so that the survivors are in the proportion

$$u_n^2 \, AA : 2u_n \, Aa : (1 - k) \, aa \qquad (49)$$

---

[18] K. Pearson, Phil. Trans. Roy. Soc., 1904, A 203, p. 53.
[19] G. H. Hardy. Science, 1908, vol. 28, p. 49.

The numbers of the next generation can most easily be calculated from the new gametic ratio u_{n+1}. This is immediately obvious in the case of aquatic organisms who shed their gametes into the water. If each zygote produces N gametes which conjugate, the numbers of gametes of type A and a respectively, are, clearly,

$$(Nu_n{}^2 + Nu) \ A \text{ and } (Nu_n + N\{1 - k\})a \tag{50}$$

so that

$$u_{n+1} = \frac{u_n(1 + u_n)}{1 + u_n - k} \tag{51}$$

Now if we know the original proportion of recessives y_0, we start with a population

$$u_0{}^2 AA : 2u_0 Aa : 1Aa \tag{52}$$

where

$$u_0 = y_0{}^{-\frac{1}{2}} - 1 \tag{53}$$

and we can at once calculate

$$u_1 = \frac{u_0(1 + u_0)}{1 + u_0 - k} \tag{54}$$

and thence u_2 and so on.

For complete selection we have $k = 1$ (recessives all die). Then

$$u_{n+1} = \frac{u_n(1 + u_n)}{1 + u_n - 1} = 1 + u_n \tag{55}$$

$$u_n = n + u_0 \tag{56}$$

$$y_n = y_0(1 + ny_0{}^{\frac{1}{2}})^{-2} \tag{57}$$

If we start with a population containing $\frac{1}{4}$ recessives, the second generation will contain $\frac{1}{9}$ the third $\frac{1}{16}$, the nth $\dfrac{1}{(n + 1)^2}$. Thus 999 generations will be required to reduce the proportion to $1 : 1,000,000$, and we need not wonder that recessive sports still occur in most of our domestic breed of animals.

When selection is not very intense, we can proceed as follows:

$$u_{n+1} = \frac{u_n(1 + u_n)}{1 + u_n - k} \tag{58}$$

$$\Delta u_n = u_{n+1} - u_n = \frac{ku_n}{1 + u_n - k} \tag{59}$$

When k is small

$$\Delta u_n = \frac{k u_n}{1 + u_n} \tag{60}$$

or

$$\frac{du}{dn} = \frac{ku}{1 + u} \tag{61}$$

$$kn = \int_{u_0}^{u_n} \frac{1 + u}{u} \, du \tag{62}$$

$$= u_n - u_0 + \log \frac{u_n}{u_0} \tag{63}$$

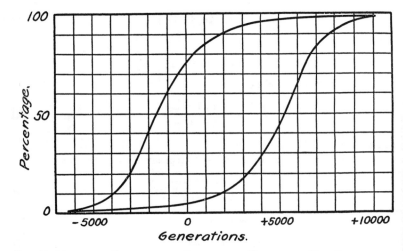

FIG. 25. EFFECT OF SELECTION ON POPULATION COMPRISING TWO PHENOTYPES
WITH MENDELIAN INHERITANCE

Upper curve, dominants favored; lower curve, recessives favored. Abscissae
= generations; ordinates = percentage of population with the favored character. After J. B. S. Haldane.

If we start from a population containing 25 per cent recessives $u_0 = 1$,

$$kn = u_n + \log_e u_n - 1 \tag{64}$$

In figure 25 is shown the growth curve for the dominants when $k = +0.001$ (upper curve) and for the recessives when $k = -0.001$ (lower curve), i.e., the favored type has an advantage of 1 in 1000, as in figure 24. In each case 16,582 generations are required to increase the proportion of the favored type from 1 per cent to 99 per cent, but dominants increase more rapidly than recessives when they are few, and more slowly when they are numerous. The change occurs most rapidly when y_n, the proportion of recessives to the total population, is 56.25 per cent.

Haldane deals also with several other cases, for the details of which the reader must be referred to the original. A continuation of Haldane's article is anticipated at the time of this writing.

CHAPTER X

FURTHER ANALYSIS OF THE GROWTH FUNCTION F

We fat all creatures else to fat us, and we fat ourselves for maggots.—Shakespeare.

Adjustment of Birth Rate to Optimum. In the preceding discussion of the equations (25) and (34) of chapter IX it has been supposed that the form not only of $p(a)$, but also of $\beta(a)$, the rate of procreation at different ages, is fixed. It is only on this supposition that the two equations (25) and (34) of Chapter IX together determine both b and d. In point of fact the function $\beta(a)$ is undoubtedly, for most species of organsms, very elastic (much more so than $p(a)$, the survival factor), and capable of adapting itself to varying circumstances. This is especially so in the case of man, who exhibits in particularly high degree the rather astonishing phenomenon of a portion of matter whose growth is at least partially under the control of a *will* in some manner associated with it. But, in the organic world at large also, there is presumably at least some tendency for the adjustment of the procreation factor so to take place as to make the rate of increase r a maximum under the existing conditions. Too high a procreation factor would lead to excessive sacrifices in progeny that could not be raised to maturity, and would increase the death rate more than the birth rate. On the other hand too small a procreation factor would obviously fail to give the maximum attainable rate of increase. Somewhere between the two extremes a certain optimum procreation factor will make r a maximum. From this point of view the two relations that effectively determine the actual values of the two variables b and d are

$$\frac{1}{b} = \int_0^\infty e^{-ra} p(a) \; da \tag{1}$$

and

$$\left. \begin{array}{l} r = \text{maximum compatible with} \\ 1 = \int_0^\infty e^{-ra} \beta(a) \; p(a) \; da \end{array} \right\} \tag{2}$$

128

The view that the rate of procreation thus expands or contracts in sympathy with the expanding or contracting food supply (or economic conditions generally) has been developed in detail (for the human species) by R. Lascaux in his work *La Production et la Population (1921)*. That some such adjustment occurs with many biological species is a very plausible, one might say an inevitable supposition; but the approach to the ideal optimum is probably often only very imperfect, if only because the nature of the case calls for a large "factor of safety."

In any event it is true that the birth rate does not play so unqualifiedly a dominant rôle in determining the rate of growth of a species as might appear on cursory reflection. The equation (5) of Chapter IX, expressing the rate of growth of the species in terms of the birth rate and death rate, while it renders correctly the quantitative relations to which it refers, is only a partial or one-sided representation of the facts, and is even open to misinterpretation. Incautiously construed it might be taken to imply that growth of an aggregate of living organisms takes place by births of new individuals into the aggregate. This, of course, is not the case. The new material enters the aggregate in another way, namely in the form of food consumed by the existing organisms. Births and the preliminaries of procreation do not in themselves add anything to the aggregate, but are merely of directing or catalyzing influences, initiating growth, and guiding material into so many avenues of entrance (mouths) of the aggregate, provided that the requisite food supplies are presented, provided that the system is, in a sense, "supersaturated" with regard to the species seeking to grow therein. The final result may not depend very greatly on the number of births, somewhat as the final state of a crystallizing solution is independent of the number of crystal germs initially sown therein.

It will be desirable to develop our analysis in such manner as to bring out the relations thus involved.

Aggregates of Constant Units. In aggregates of a simpler kind, as presented to our view in ordinary physico-chemical systems, each individual unit retains its identical substance unchanged throughout its period of existence as such unit. So, for example, a molecule of water consists of two particular atoms of hydrogen united to one specific atom of oxygen; and these same atoms continue to exist together as the building stones of the molecule as long as this continues in existence as a water molecule.

In these circumstances the mass of each unit is obviously constant throughout its period of existence as such; and furthermore, addition to the component, or elimination therefrom, can take place only by the actual entry or departure of a complete unit.   If, therefore, the mass of each unit is m_i, and if B_i new units are added to the aggregate per unit of time, while D_i are eliminated, we have, in this case, very simply,

$$\frac{dX_i}{dt} = (B_i - D_i)m_i \tag{3}$$

Aggregates of Variable Units.   For aggregates of living organisms we can also write an equation identical in form with (3), as has already been noted in Chapter IX; B_i is in this case the total birth rate, D_i the total death rate, and m_i the *average* mass per head of the living population.   But this is an inadequate representation of the significant facts.   The equation, thus written, glosses over certain important characteristics of living organisms.   Unlike molecules in a system in the course of chemical transformation, each unit in an aggregate of living organisms does *not* retain its substance unchanged in identity or in total mass.   In fact, each unit is itself an aggregate within the larger aggregate that constitutes the species or biological group, and for each individual unit (organism) separately we can write an equation analogous to equation (1) of Chapter IX

$$\frac{dm_i}{dt} = U'_i - V'_i \tag{4}$$

where U'_i is the total mass taken up (ingested) per unit of time by the unit organism, and V_i' is the total mass eliminated therefrom per unit of time.   So, for example, in the course of one year a boy ten years old and weighing 32.5 kgm. may consume about 600 kgm. of food (inclusive of water and oxygen), may eliminate about 599 kgm of wastes, and will grow in actual mass by about 1 kgm., so that we have

$$\frac{dm_i}{dt} = 600 - 599 = 1 = 0.03 m_i \tag{5}$$

The Stream of Substance Through the Form of the Organism. It will be observed that a portion of the intake, but a portion only, is expended in adding to the total mass of the unit.   The   remainder

$$R_i = U'_i - \frac{dm_i}{dt} \tag{6}$$

is expended without, apparently,[1] any resulting increase in the total mass of the unit. This constant expenditure of substance, and the equally constant intake required to balance it, is a fundamental characteristic of the units here under discussion. In the adult, whose mass is (on an average) approximately constant, we have simply

$$\frac{dm_i}{dt} = 0 = U'_i - V'_i \tag{7}$$

$$U'_i \quad = V'_i \tag{8}$$

and the entire intake goes to meet the requirements of maintaining the mass of the unit at constant level.[2]

Turning now from the consideration of the individual unit to that of the aggregate of N such units, evidently, if the average intake per unit of time per individual is $\overline{U}'_i$, and if the average elimination is $\overline{V}'_i$, then we shall have for the rate of increase of the total mass X_i of the aggregate.

$$\frac{dX_i}{dt} = N\overline{U}'_i - N\overline{V}'_i - Nm'_i d_i \tag{9}$$

where d_i is the death rate per head per unit of time and m'_i is the average mass of a unit (organism) at death.

Two Types of Organisms: Economical and Lavish Birth Rate. The relative importance of the second and the third term in the right hand member of the equation (9) differs greatly in different biological species. At the one extreme we have a type of which perhaps the most characteristic representative is man. With a mean length of life of about fifty years, his body must be replaced about twice in a century to maintain the population equilibrium. If we assume (as a rough but sufficient approximation) that the average weight of man at death is 50 kgm., this means that the third term, $Nm'_i d_i$

---

[1] Indirectly a part of the excess R_i of the mass intake over the mass increase may contribute to that increase, namely by furnishing some of the energy required for anabolism. But we are here discussing *mass* relations only. The *energy* relations are reserved for separate consideration later.

[2] Except during gestation, if the mass of the fetus is reckoned in with that of the mother.

in a stationary population, is about $\dfrac{N \times 50}{50}$ kgm. for the entire population, or just about 1 kgm., or say 2 pounds per head per annum. To put it crudely, of the food consumed by each human individual in a year, 2 pounds go, on an average, to replace the bodies of his fellows departed that year. This, it will be seen, is an insignificant, almost wholly negligible fraction of the 1000 pounds[3] or more than he consumes, in all, in a year. Of the total food consumed by the human race, then, about 0.2 per cent[3] goes to replace the bodies eliminated by death. The remainder is for current maintenance of the living. And the total food consumption[3] may be of the order of 7 to 10 times the mass of the population per annum.[4]

But, as already stated, man represents an extreme type, the extreme economy of life, with low death rate and correspondingly low birth rate. Of the opposite extreme, lavish, seemingly wasteful extravagance, examples are exceedingly common, though it may not be easy to give full quantitative detail. Among the most wasteful breeders are, no doubt many aquatic species, including fish, since their young are ill protected and become ready victims of other species. So a ling weighing 54 pounds was found to be carrying twenty-eight million eggs.[5] An oyster may have sixty million eggs. But some familiar land animals are prolific enough, even if they do fall far behind the standards just exemplified. The brown rat may have five or six litters averaging about eight or ten each, in a year.[6]

Domestic Animals Kept for Produce. Accurate figures can be obtained in case of domestic animals. While these do not represent so extreme an example, a special interest attaches to them owing to their direct relation to human food economics. The most prolific among domestic animals is the pig. In reasonably good farm conditions a sow should average three litters in two years, each of seven farrows, of which five are successfully raised and marketed.

Even with the high mortality artificially induced by man in his domestic stock the item of running expenditure in feed for mere maintenance is far in excess of the replacement cost, that is to say, the feed

---

[3] Exclusive of oxygen.

[4] For quantitative data on growth in man see C. S. Minot, The Problem of Age, Growth and Death.

[5] J. A. Thomson, The Wonders of Life, 1914, p. 130.

[6] H. H. Donaldson, The Rat, 1915, p. 190.

stored up and finally utilized in the carcass of the slaughtered animal.
From a detailed study of the vital economics of beef production made
at the University of Missouri[7] figure 26 is reproduced here to show
these relations. The convex curve shows the average growth per
head in a group of steers fed with a ration regulated to secure a maxi-

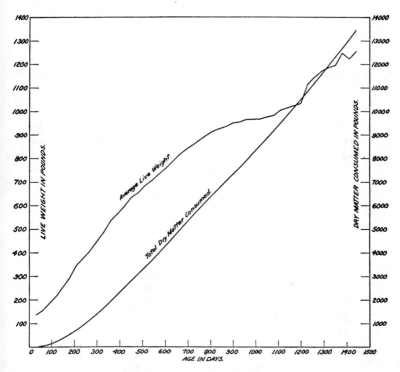

FIG. 26. FEED CONSUMED, AND INCREASE IN LIVE WEIGHT OF
STEERS AT SEVERAL AGES

Dry matter consumed is represented on one-tenth the scale of the live
weight. After Moulton, Trowbridge and Haigh.

mum of growth, without storage of surplus fat; the approximately
straight line mounting upward shows the steadily increasing integrated amount of feed consumed since birth. Only the dry weight
of the feed is plotted, and the scale employed is ten times more

[7] University of Missouri, College of Agriculture, Bulletins 43, 54, 55 (R. C.
Trowbridge and L. D. Haigh).

condensed than that used for the live weight—else the second curve would rise too steeply as to lie for the most part far beyond the limits of the page. Thus is shown the great disproportion between the feed

TABLE 9

Average Yearly Gains of Steers*

PERIOD		GROUP I	GROUP II	GROUP III
days		*pounds*	*pounds*	*pounds*
30 to 360	Weight gained..................	605.3	409.7	241.6
	Dry matter eaten..............	3,075.0	1,929.5	1,265.0
	Daily gain....................	1.83	1.24	0.73
	Dry matter per pound gain.....	5.08	4.71	5.24
360 to 720	Weight gained..................	560.7	320.8	235.6
	Dry matter eaten..............	6,314.1	3,619.3	2,420.1
	Daily gain....................	1.56	0.89	0.65
	Dry matter per pound gain.....	11.26	11.28	10.27
720 to 1,080	Weight gained..................	390.8	126.9	121.2
	Dry matter eaten..............	6,652.9	3,629.2	2,811.7
	Daily gain....................	1.09	0.35	0.34
	Dry matter per pound gain.....	17.02	28.60	23.20
1,080 to 1,440	Weight gained..................	268.9	270.6	311.2
	Dry matter eaten..............	6,304.6	4,259.9	3,562.3
	Daily gain....................	0.75	0.75	0.86
	Dry matter per pound gain.....	23.45	15.74	11.45
30 to 1,440	Weight gained..................	1,825.7	1,128.0	911.6
	Dry matter eaten..............	22,346.6	13,438.0	10,059.1
	Daily gain....................	1.30	0.80	0.65
	Dry matter per pound gain.....	12.24	11.91	11.03

Animals of group I were fed all they would eat.

Animals of group II were fed to secure maximum growth without storage of surplus fat.

Animals of group III were somewhat underfed, to represent animals not properly cared for.

* Moulton, Trowbridge and Haigh, University of Missouri, Agr. Exp. Sta. Research Bulletin 43, p. 14.

that is recovered in the body of the growing steer, and the far greater amount that is wasted, so far as the interest of the producer is concerned, in mere maintenance, for the private satisfaction and benefit

of the animal, so to speak.   The numerical data on which figure 26
is based are exhibited in table 9, together with the corresponding
figures observed when the animals are somewhat underfed and over-
fed respectively.

The instances that have been cited—man on the one hand, and the
highly prolific species, both feral and captive, on the other—are eloquent illustrations of the elasticity of adaptation.   Clearly, a species
may hold its own, in the struggle for existence, either by the aid of
well-developed protective devices resulting in a low death rate, and
requiring only a correspondingly low birth rate; or, a less well protected species may balance a high death rate by an equally high birth
rate.   Which of these two methods would be chosen in the natural
course of events is a question that it might be difficult to answer on
any general *a priori* principle, so long as attention remained fixed on
a single species.   Perhaps one would have expected evolution to turn
in a favor of the more economical method of meeting a low death rate
with a low birth rate.   In point of fact both types of organism—the
economical type (as judged by its own standard) with low death rate,
and the wasteful with high death rate—exist side by side in abundance.   This is a good example to illustrate the purely relative character of fitness, and to remind us once more that we cannot expect any
success in attempts to define the direction of evolution in terms of a
single species.   It is not the individual species, the individual components of the system, that evolve, but the system as a whole, comprising all the species and their environment.   The species of the
economical type, with low death rate, are largely dependent for their
subsistence on the presence of species of the opposite type; we must
think here of a competition, not between individual species, but between groups of species, groups consisting, in the simplest case, of
two species each, a food species or prey, and a feeding or predatory
species.   Of two such *groups*, that one will, other things equal, have
the advantage in the struggle, in which high productivity of the food
species is accompanied by economy of life on the part of the feeding
species.   From the point of view of the hog, so to speak, the high mortality in the pen is a disastrous inefficiency and maladaptation, a
misfortune to be borne, as best it may, with porcine philosophy.
From the point of view of the consumer on the other hand, this high
mortality is, quite on the contrary, a measure of the efficiency, the
eminent fitness of swine as producers of pork; and his only regret

is that so much of the feed placed in the trough goes merely to carry on "what may be called the personal activities of the animals themselves."[8] It is to be noted, however, that only a part of the material accountable as waste from the standpoint of the food species is gain for the feeding species. Deaths from disease are a pure loss to both species.

Similar reflections, of course, apply, *mutatis mutandis*, to those cases in which the feeding species derives its nourishment from some current product of the life activity of the food species or host, instead of from its carcass. The most notable example of this in the food economy of man is his exploitation of the milch cow, who is a far more efficient producer than the beef steer. The latter at best consumes over 6 pounds of nutriment for every pound of product.[9] According to the investigations of the National Research Council about 18 per cent of the energy of grain fed to cattle is recovered for human consumption in milk, but only about 3.5 per cent in beef. Similarly, crops on a given area will yield about four to five times as much protein and energy when fed to dairy cows as when used for beef production. In providing mineral substances and vitamines the milk of cows contrasts even more favorably with the beef animal. The vitamines and calcium salts contained in hay and grain are stored in the muscular tissue only to a slight extent, but are in relative abundance in milk.[10] From the standpoint of the dairyman a thoroughbred prize cow, such as Glista Ernestine (a Holstein), which gave in one year 833 pounds of butter fat, and in one hundred days 10,000 pounds of milk, is a very model of efficiency, producing more than her own weight in milk each month. But from the point of view of the bovine species such record performances are gross inefficiency, approaching in some cases perilously near to total biological unfitness, for some of the record Jersey cows are probably unable, under the conditions of the stable at any rate, to raise their own calves—the over-rich milk would probably kill the young animal.

Network of Chains of Interrelated Species. The relation between man and the domesticated species of animals and plants on which he

[8] I have here borrowed a felicitous phrase from an anonymous writer on the editorial page of the New York Times, February 10, 1921.

[9] University of Minnesota, Agr. Exp. Station Bulletin 193, pp. 68, 69 (T. L. Haecker).

[10] Jour. Franklin Inst., vol. 190, 1920, p. 155.

so largely depends for food, in the present state of civilization, is only a particularly tangible, a particularly accessible example of an intricate network of relationships that connect more or less closely all living species. In this network each species or component is interlaced, like a link in a meshed coat of mail, with other species, which in turn connect with still others, and so forth. In our effort to get some sort of mental grasp of the complicated interlocking of these elements we seize upon some one link, some one species or component, and we note, first of all, that whatever is eliminated from one component of a self-contained system must pass into one or more other components of the system. So, for example, the component S_i may be a herd of cattle. The matter eliminated from this component goes in part as food to build up or sustain a human population; in part it goes as fertilizer on the fields to furnish nutriment for crops; still other parts are worked up into various industrial products, such as leather, glue, etc. We thus have, in schematic representation,

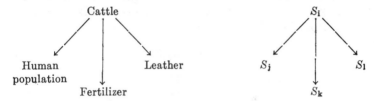

On the other hand, the substance of the herd itself is recruited from certain other components of the system, grass, clover, corn, etc., so that we may further develop the scheme

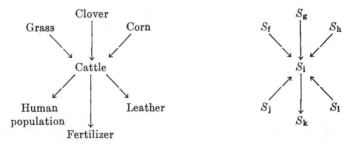

Transformation Factors and Their Economic Significance. In general any one component thus appears as a link in a complicated chain or rather network of chains; the component S_i, for example, receives a certain fraction $\alpha_{f,i}$ of the mass $V_f X_f$ eliminated per unit of time from the component S_f; it passes on to the component S_k a certain fraction β_{ik} of the mass $V_i X_i$ eliminated from X_i itself. The rate of growth $\dfrac{dX_i}{dt}$ of X_i is the balance of the sum U_i of all contributions it receives over and above the sum V_i of all the contributions which it makes to other components, thus

$$\frac{dX_i}{dt} = u_i X_i - v_i X_i = U_i - V_i \tag{10}$$

$$= \Sigma \alpha_{fi} v_f X_f - \Sigma \beta_{ik} v_i X_i \tag{11}$$

the first summation being extended over all those components S_f which contribute to X_i and the second over all those components S_k to which S_i contributes.

But we may also analyse the contributions to and from the component S_i in another way. We may say that, of the total contributions per unit of time $u_i X_i$ to the mass X_i, a certain fraction $\gamma_{if} u_i X_i$ is derived from S_f. Then

$$\gamma_{if} u_i X_i = \alpha_{fi} v_f X_f \tag{12}$$

$$u_i X_i = \frac{\alpha_{fi}}{\gamma_{if}} v_f X_f \tag{13}$$

and, substituting (13) in (10),

$$\frac{dX_i}{dt} = \frac{\alpha_{fi}}{\gamma_{if}} v_f X_f - v_i X_i \tag{14}$$

Lastly, if the system is not self-contained, we must add a term I_i for "imports" per unit of time, and a term $-E_i$ for "exports" per unit of time, that is to say,

$$\frac{dX_i}{dt} = \frac{\alpha_{fi}}{\gamma_{if}} v_f X_f - v_i X_i + I_i - E_i \tag{15}$$

When S_i is the human species, the coefficients α, β, γ have an obvious economic significance. The restriction of this remark to the human species must not be taken to imply that there is in this feature something wholly peculiar to man, but rather, that underlying our economic manifestations are biological phenomena which we share in common with other species; and that the laying bare and clearly formulating of the relations thus involved—in other words, the analysis of the bio-physical foundations of economics—is one of the problems coming within the program of physical biology. Hints as to the direction in which we may or must look for light on this phase of our problem have now been noted upon several occasions. So it was observed that the components of a life-bearing system can be divided into two classes, *relative* to the component S_i, namely, on the one hand those components S_j for which $\dfrac{\partial}{\partial X_j}\dfrac{dX_i}{dt}$ was positive, or, as we may say, those useful to the species S_i, those having for it a positive *value*, and, on the other hand, components S_k for which $\dfrac{\partial}{\partial X_k}\dfrac{dX_i}{dt} < 0$, components harmful to S_i, or having for it a negative value. Elsewhere we have noted the classification of components into replaceable and indispensable components, a classification that at once recalls elementary economic reflections.

These hints we note in passing. They may serve to put our minds in a state of preparedness for the more formal and decisive attack of the problem, to which we shall be led in the last division of our enquiry, dealing with the dynamics of life-bearing systems.

PART III
STATICS

CHAPTER XI

GENERAL PRINCIPLES OF EQUILIBRIUM

Repeatedly, in preceding chapters, occasion has arisen to refer to stationary states or equilibria. Inevitably, in the discussion of the kinetics of evolution, one is led to consider *incidentally* certain conditions and special cases in which the velocities of the changes in the evolving system are zero; when, that is to say, the system under discussion is in a steady or stationary state, in equilibrium. Viewed from this avenue of approach equilibrium presents itself as a special case of motion or change, namely motion or change with zero velocity. Indeed, something very like equilibrium occurs also with velocities that are merely small, not vanishingly small. In such case the phenomenon of moving equilibrium may present itself, as we shall have occasion to observe in greater detail in due course.

Stationary states—equilibria and near-equilibria—play an important rôle in nature, and it is desirable at this point to give them something more than incidental consideration; to sketch, at least in outline, their systematic study; to stake out, in the rough, that field which, in our survey of the Program of Physical Biology (Chapter V) was designated as the Statics of Evolution, and was systematized according to the schedule

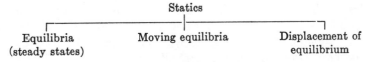

Statics

| Equilibria (steady states) | Moving equilibria | Displacement of equilibrium |

It will be convenient, in the development of the subject, to follow, in the main, the schedule thus set forth.

Kinetic, Dynamic, and Energetic Conceptions of Equilbrium. While we shall, in this section, conceive a stationary state from the standpoint of kinetics, defining it as a state in which certain *velocities vanish*, it must be noted that there are also other conceptions of equilibrium. Etymologically the word equilibrium is tied, in stricter usage, to a dynamic conception: *Aequa libra*, the poised balance, is symbolic of a state in which *forces* are balanced, in which the *resultant force vanishes*.

143

A third conception of equilibrium, differing from the second, the dynamic, only in point of view, not in scope, is derived from a consideration of *energy* relations. A system in dynamic equilibrium is found to be characterized by the attainment of a minimum (or sometimes a maximum) of certain functions having the dimensions of energy; a state in which the virtual *work done* in any very small displacement compatible with the constraints *vanishes*.[1] So, for example, a ball placed in a hemispherical cup, is in equilibrium when its potential energy is a minimum compatible with the geometry of the system. More generally, equilibrium is, according to this view, defined as a state in which certain potentials have a minimum (or a maximum).

Pedantic usage would demand that the term equilibrium be reserved for states satisfying the dynamic and energetic conditions of rest or invariability in time. It would deny the appellation equilibrium to certain states commonly so designated. Metabolic equilibrium, population equilibrium, and the like, are not true equilibria, in this narrower sense, but are steady states maintained with a constant expenditure, a constant dissipation, of energy. It is not necessary, however, at present, to lay any stress on this distinction. The occasional use of the word equilibrium in speaking of what is merely a steady state maintained with a continuous expenditure of free energy is not likely to cause any serious confusion; and we may as well take the usual liberties in the matter, whenever this course is dictated by convenience and does not offend against essential principles. Where express distinction becomes necessary, we may speak in specific terms of true equilibrium and quasi-equilibrium, respectively, to denote the two separate types included in the generic term "stationary state" or "steady state."

A complete treatment of the entire field of the statics of evolving systems should, to be entirely systematic, cover both types of stationary states. There are, however, two reasons for departing somewhat from such strictly systematic arrangement. The first is that the statics of true equilibria have been developed to a high degree in the discipline of thermodynamics, so that an exposition of the pertinent principles and conclusions would be little more than

---

[1] Stability of equilibrium demands, further, that the work done on the system in any small, but finite, displacement, be positive, that the potential energy be a minimum (maximum being, in this case, excluded).

a transcription into these pages of what can be found abundantly set forth elsewhere in the standard literature. However much one might be tempted, in the interest of a well rounded presentation, to sketch at this point at least an outline of the relevant chapters of thermodynamics, economy of space dictates the briefer expedient of referring the reader to the existing literature, so abundant that it seems superfluous to mention titles.

A second reason for passing lightly over true equilibria at this point, is that the steady states with which we are most frequently and most closely concerned in the field of organic evolution (our main topic here), are of the second class; not true equilibria in the dynamic sense, equilibria in which all forces are balanced; but what we have termed above quasi-equilibria, states maintained constant or approximately so with a continual expenditure, a continual dissipation or degradation of available energy. To such as these we shall give our chief attention, though in part our discussion will be framed broadly to cover indifferently either type of steady state. For the sake of example, too, reference will be made, on occasion, to systems evolving toward a true equilibrium; systems for which the law of evolution is capable of direct expression in comparatively simple thermodynamical terms; systems which, by that very fact, are peculiarly adapted to serve as paradigms exhibiting the characteristic form of a law of evolution.

General Equilibrium Condition. As has already been noted incidentally, the general condition for equilibrium, or, to be more precise, for a stationary state, is obtained by equating to zero the velocity of growth of each component of the system, thus

$$\frac{dX_i}{dt} = F_i(X_1, X_2, \ldots X_n) \tag{1}$$

$$F_1 = F_2 = \ldots = F_n = 0 \tag{2}$$

This condition, in general, furnishes n independent equations, which determine one or more sets of values of the variables X, thus

$$\left.\begin{array}{l} X_1 = C_1 \\ X_2 = C_2 \\ \cdots \cdots \\ X_n = C_n \end{array}\right\} \tag{3}$$

If the values C thus determined are real and positive[2] they evidently define an equilibrium or a steady state, the character (stability, mode of approach) of which depends upon the nature of the roots λ of a certain characteristic equation, as has been indicated on an earlier occasion.

Different Types of Equilibrium. Graphic Representation. A particularly graphic representation of the different types of equilibrium is obtained if, instead of seeking solutions of the fundamental equations (1) expressing $X_1, X_2 \ldots X_n$ in terms of t, we on the contrary eliminate t from this system of equations. This is very readily effected by division, which leads to the new system

$$\frac{dX_1}{F_1} = \frac{dX_2}{F_2} = \ldots = \frac{dX_n}{F_n} \tag{4}$$

This system of equations defines a family of curves passing through the equilibrium points, which here appear as singular points. The situation is particularly transparent in the case of two variables X_1, X_2, since this readily permits of plotting the integral curves in rectangular coördinates in the plane of the paper. We have already had occasion incidentally to employ this method of treatment in an example in Chapter VIII, in which the conflict between a host species and a parasite species was examined analytically. Without going into extensive technical details it is advisable now at least to enumerate and briefly describe the several types of equilibria and the topography, characteristic of each type, presented by the integral curves in and about a singular point. These types are somewhat numerous, even if we restrict ourselves to the case of two variables, and brevity is therefore imperative.

Type 1. Roots λ_1 and λ_2 real and negative. Equilibrium is stable; integral curves run directly into singular point as in figure 27, A.

Type 2. Roots λ_1 and λ_2 real and positive. The topography is similar to that of type 1, but integral curves are traversed outward from singular point. Unstable equilibrium, figure 27, B.

Type 3. Roots λ_1 and λ_2 real and of opposite sign. Integral curves in general do not pass through singular points, but curve away from it. Unstable equilibrium, figure 27, C.

---

[2] Masses cannot assume negative or imaginary values. Hence negative roots may fail to define equilibria; a similar statement holds regarding complex roots.

Type 4. Roots λ_1 and λ_2 complex, real parts negative. The integral curves are spirals winding into the origin, forever approaching it without ever reaching it. Stable equilibrium, figure 27, D.

Type 5. Roots λ_1 and λ_2 complex, real parts positive. The topography is similar to that of type 4, but integral curves are traversed outward from singular point. Unstable equilibrium. figure 27, E.

Type 6. Roots λ_1 and λ_2 pure imaginaries. This gives rise to several distinct subtypes.

Subtype F. Integral curves are closed loops enclosing the origin. Process is purely periodic. Figure 27, F.

Subtype G. Integral curves are spirals winding inward. Stable equilibrium. This is the case treated in Chapter VIII, where a representative diagram will be found. Figure 27, G. Another subtype is similar to G but spiral winds outward. Unstable equilibrium.

Subtype H. Integral curves are spirals winding about a closed loop.

Types I AND J occur when $\lambda_1 = \lambda_2$. Figure 27, I, J.

As an example illustrating the occurrence of two types of equilibrium, two types of singular points, the topographic chart of the integral curves defined by the Ross equations for the spread of malaria under certain conditions is shown in figure 28. It will be seen that there are two singular points, one at the origin O, unstable, of type C; the other at T, stable, of type A. This chart obviously suggests "stream lines" and a three dimensional model. Such a model (purely qualitative) is shown in figure 29. The feature of interest is that a singular point like O, of type C, is represented by a *col* ("notch") in the landscape; whereas the stable equilibrium of type A is represented by a pit, as at the point T.

While this model refers to a very particular case, it serves to bring out a noteworthy fact, namely, that there are necessarily certain regularities in the occurrence of the various types of equilibria. So, for example, it is clear that two pits of the character of the point T cannot occur without some other type of singular point between them, just as it is physically impossible for two mountains to rise from a landscape without some kind of a valley between. For a detailed study of this phase of the subject the reader must be referred to the mathematical literature.[3]

[3] For further discussion of the various types of singular points that may occur the reader is referred to the mathematical literature, of which the following may be mentioned: E. Picard, Traité d'Analyse, 1891, vol. 1, pp. 83, 123; 1893, vol. 2, pp. 183, 193, 196 (footnote); 1896, vol. 3, pp. 228, 238; v. Dyk, Sitzungsber Bayer. Akad. Wissensch. München, March 6, 1909, Abhandl. 15; Abhandlungen der Kgl. Bayer. Akad. Wissensch., March, 1913, vol. 26, Abhandl. 10; Sitzungsber, 1891, p. 23; 1892, p. 101; H. Liebmann, Lehrbuch der Differentialgleichungen, 1901, pp. 101, 102, 134.

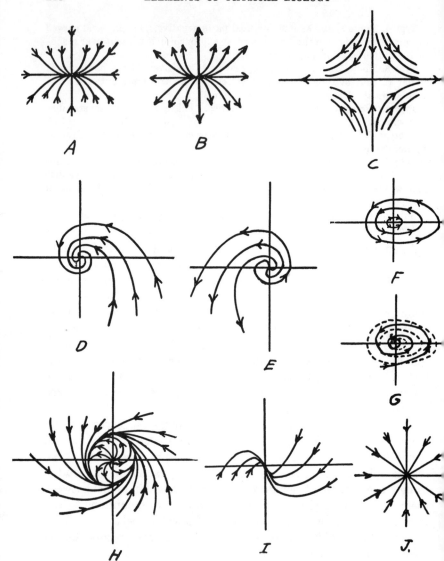

FIG. 27. SOME FUNDAMENTAL TYPES OF EQUILIBRIUM, IN A SYSTEM WITH TWO DEPENDENT VARIABLES

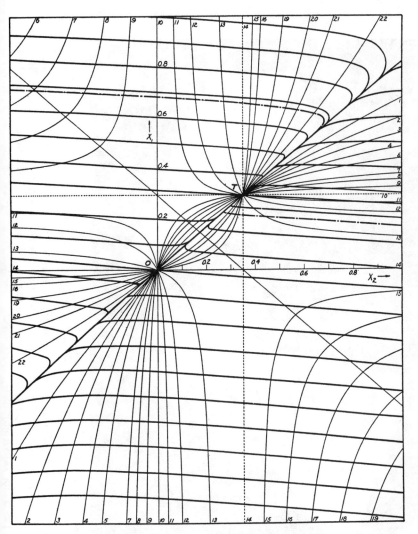

Fig. 28. Map of Integral Curves for the Ross Malaria Equations, as an Example Exhibiting Two Singular Points, of Type 1 and 3 (see Figure 27, A and C)

The heavy lines are integral curves; the lighter lines are auxiliaries (isoclines) employed in constructing the graphic solution of the differential equations. (Reproduced from A. J. Lotka, Am. Jour. Hygiene, January Supplement, 1923.)

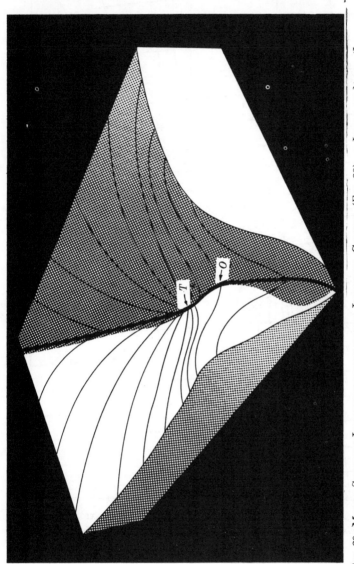

Fig. 29. Model Showing Interpretation of the Integral Curves (Fig. 28) as Lines of Flow (Lines of Steepest Descent on a Topographic Surface)

The pit at the center of the model corresponds to the point of stable equilibrium (T in fig. 28); the center of the notch (the point of intersection of the diagonal curve and the second integral curve counting from the front corner) corresponds to the point of unstable equilibrium (O in fig. 28). The correspondence between figures 28 and 29 is qualitative only.

Metastable Equilibrium. The graphic representations of the malaria equilibrium furnish the occasion for another remark of general character regarding certain equilibria. The circumstance that gives rise to the first malaria equilibrium, the one in which the malaria rate is zero, (point O in figs. 28 and 29) is the autocatakinetic character of the growth of a malaria endemic. This is a common characteristic of the growth of living systems; growth is initiated by a nucleus of the same species of matter that is added by the growth. Conversely, in the entire absence of any nucleus of a particular species of living matter, growth of that species cannot take place, even though all other conditions for such growth may be satisfied, even though the system may be, as it were, supersaturated with regard to that species of matter. In these circumstances an equilibrium may be presented which is unstable in the sense that, upon the introduction of a suitable nucleus, growth immediately sets in.[4] Equilibria of this type, which are stable in the absence of a suitable "nucleus" but in which change is immediately initiated upon introduction of such a nucleus, have been termed "metastable" equilibria.

Exceptional Cases. A brief reference must suffice regarding certain exceptional cases that may arise. So it may happen that one of the roots λ of the characteristic equation vanishes. An example of this was encountered in dealing with the Ross malaria equations. It was found that as the number of mosquitoes per head of the human population approaches a certain critical value, two singular points approach each other, and finally fuse, giving one "double" point.[5]

Another special case that may arise, and whose mention must here suffice, is that of multiple roots of the characteristic equation, the case in which two or more of the roots are equal.[6]

[4] In inorganic systems an analogous state of affairs is observed in supersaturated solutions or vapors which are brought to crystallization or to condensation by the introduction of a suitable nucleus. Dynamically the characteristic of a metastable equilibrium is that the thermodynamic potential of the system, though a minimum, is not an absolute minimum.

[5] See A. J. Lotka, Am. Jour. Hygiene, 1923, vol. 3, January supplement, p. 12.

[6] Compare H. Liebmann, loc. cit., pp. 102, 134; A. J. Lotka, Zeitschr. f. physikal. Chemie, 1912, vol. 80, p. 16.

CHAPTER XII

CHEMICAL EQUILIBRIUM AS AN EXAMPLE OF EVOLUTION UNDER A KNOWN LAW

I wanted to remind the biologists that in the early stages of life what they are accustomed to speak of as natural selection passes over into what might be described as a mere physical selection of stabler compounds.—K. Pearson.

One of the simplest examples of equilibria in systems of the type that interests us here—systems composed of several groups each consisting of numerous similar individuals as units—is the equilibrium resulting from a pair of balanced or opposing chemical reactions.

This case illustrates so well, in their simplest form, a number of typical traits of the phenomena here under discussion, that it will pay to give it brief consideration.

We shall select for this purpose the simplest possible type of balanced chemical reaction at constant volume and temperature, namely a reaction which is monomolecular in both directions. A substance S_1 undergoes a transformation into S_2, and S_2 in turn is converted back into S_1, one molecule alone taking part, in each case, in the transformation. If x_1 and x_2 are the respective concentrations of S_1 and S_2, we have, at a given temperature, by the law of mass action, the rate of decomposition of S_1 and S_2 respectively.

$$(Dx_1) = -k_1 x_1 \tag{1}$$

$$(Dx_2) = -k_2 x_2 \tag{2}$$

Or, since at constant volume concentrations x are proportional to numbers n of molecules

$$(Dn_1) = -k_1 n_1 \tag{3}$$

$$(Dn_2) = -k_2 n_2 \tag{4}$$

where k_1, k_2 are coefficients (functions of the temperature) characteristic of the reaction.

152

The rate of increase of the substance S is the excess of its rate of formation b over its rate of decomposition, in strict analogy to the birth rate and death rate in a human population

$$\frac{dn_1}{dt} = (b_1 - k_1)n_1 \tag{5}$$

$$\frac{dn_2}{dt} = (b_2 - k_2)n_2 \tag{6}$$

In a population of living organisms the material for the formation of new individuals must ultimately be derived from the bodies of those that have died. But the connection is a complicated one involving many steps. In the population of molecules here under consideration the relation between birth rate and death rate is of the simplest possible form. Each molecule of S_1 that "dies" becomes a molecule of S_2, and vice versa. Thus equations (5), (6) assume the form

$$\frac{dn_1}{dt} = k_2 n_2 - k_1 n_1 \tag{7}$$

$$\frac{dn_2}{dt} = k_1 n_1 - k_2 n_2 \tag{8}$$

and in equilibrium

$$\frac{n_1}{n_2} = \frac{k_2}{k_1} \tag{9}$$

If we fix our attention upon n_1 molecules of S_1 at the moment of their formation, we can apply to these particular molecules the equation (3), from which we have, by integration

$$n_1(t) = n_1(O)e^{-k_1 t} \tag{10}$$

similarly for S_2

$$n_2(t) = n_2(O)e^{-k_2 t} \tag{11}$$

But $\dfrac{n_1(a)}{n_1(O)}$ is the probability $p_1(a)$, at the moment of its formation, that a molecule of S_1 picked at random at such moment, will reach age a. The life curve for the molecules of S_1 is thus defined by

$$p_1(a) = e^{-k_1 a} \tag{12}$$

and for S_2

$$p_2(a) = e^{-k_2 a} \qquad (13)$$

while the mean lengths of life are

$$L_1 = \int_0^\infty e^{-k_1 a}\, da = \frac{1}{k_1} \qquad (14)$$

$$L_2 = \int_0^\infty e^{-k_2 a}\, da = \frac{1}{k_2} \qquad (15)$$

and in equilibrium

$$\frac{n_1}{n_2} = \frac{L_1}{L_2} \qquad (16)$$

the molecules are present in amounts proportional to their respective mean lengths of life, although, they are "born" in equal numbers, since $k_2 n_2 = k_1 n_1$. The significance of this is brought out in the diagram figure 30, in which the population of molecules is plotted "in age groups," for the substance S_1 and S_2 separately. Since the birth rate is the same for both populations, they begin at a common ordinate; but the curve for S_2, the substance with greater k, greater *force of mortality*, lies entirely below that for S_1; the areas of the two curves are, in fact, proportional to the mean lengths of life of the molecules of the corresponding substances. Thus, in the struggle for existence the stabler (fitter) molecules of S_1 have the advantage, being, on an average, longer-lived.

There is thus an obvious analogy between the course of events in such a population of different species of molecules, on the one hand, and a mixed population of different species of organism on the other, an analogy which extends into details for the exposition of which space is lacking here.[1] The analogy is not a meaningless accidental circumstance, but depends on identity of type in the two cases. It can be said quite generally (so as to apply to either case), that in a material system in which physical conditions vary from instant to instant and from point to point, certain individual constituents (molecules, organisms) may have a transitory existence *as such*, each lasting just so long as its conditions and those of its neighborhood continue within certain limits. Although the "life period" of each individual constituent may be thus limited, an aggregate of a number

---

[1] For such details see A. J. Lotka, Am. Jour. Sci., vol. 24, 1907, pp. 199, 375.

of such individuals may nevertheless have prolonged existence, provided that the fluctuations in the conditions of the system, from point to point and from instant to instant, do not exceed certain limits, and that by some process or other new individuals are formed as the old are eliminated. Of the character of the fluctuations, and their relation to the "length of life" in the case of living organisms, more will be said in a later chapter. As to the circumstances, the fluctuations, that lead to the translation of a molecule in chemical reaction from one state into another, we may with advantage adopt a view-

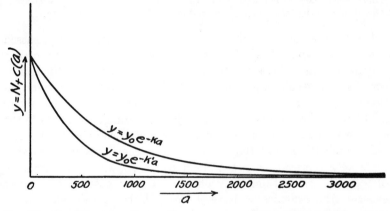

FIG. 30. AGE DISTRIBUTION IN POPULATION OF MOLECULES OF TWO SUBSTANCES IN MONOMOLECULAR CHEMICAL EQUILIBRIUM

The *birth rate* per head, of both species, is the same as indicated by their common zero ordinate; but the species having the lesser *force of mortality* (reaction constant) predominates, as shown by the greater area under the corresponding curve. (Reproduced from A. J. Lotka, Am. Jour. Science, 1907, p. 208.)

point set forth in some detail by the writer on an earlier occasion,[2] and expressed more recently by Professor Baly[3] in these terms:

Every complete reaction consists of three separate stages, with each of which is associated its characteristic energy change. In general, molecules in the free state exist in a phase which is non-reactive, and in order to carry out any reaction it is first of all necessary to bring them into a reactive phase. This, which is the first stage of the reaction, requires that a definite amount

[2] A. J. Lotka, Am. Jour. Sci., 1907, p. 213 et seq.
[3] E. C. Baly, Photosynthesis. Nature, 1922, p. 344.

of energy should be supplied to each molecule, the amount necessary being the difference in energy contents of the initial phase and the particular phase necessary for the reaction in question.

The second stage of the reaction is the atomic rearrangement whereby new molecules are produced, and it is this stage, and this stage alone, which is represented by the equation of the reaction.

The third and final stage is the change in phase of the newly synthesised molecules, whereby they pass into their normal and non-reactive phases. These last two stages are both accompanied by an escape of energy. If the sum of the amounts of energy evolved in the second and third stages is greater than that absorbed in the first stage, the reaction is exothermic; whilst an endothermic reaction is one in which the energy necessary for the first stage is greater than the total amount evolved in the second and third stages.

It should be remarked that the second stage is, apparently, passed through in an exceedingly brief space of time, so that at any instant only an imperceptibly small amount of substance exists in the transitional state. We are, in fact, almost wholly devoid of any information regarding matter in this state, and the words of Schönbein[4] hold true in almost their full force today: "Presumably, between the state in which two portions of matter exist after completion of chemical combination, and the state in which they previously existed separately, there is a series of transition states of which the chemistry of today knows nothing." Probably the only positive and direct experimental evidence we have of matter in this intermediate state between two compounds is furnished by the superlatively refined methods of Sir J. J. Thomson and Dr. F. W. Aston, which not only reveal but actually weigh such decapitated molecules as CH_3, whose length of life is measured in ten-millionths of a second.[5]

As to the agencies, the "fluctuations" that provide, every now and again, the requisite energy to carry a transforming molecule "over the crest of the hill," there is first the thermal agitation of the molecules, second the influence of incident light in photochemical reactions, and third the influence of catalysts, whose action probably depends on a flattening of the path over the hill crest, the point of

[4] Jour. Prakt. Chem., vol. 55, I, p. 152.

[5] Compare A. J. Lotka, loc. cit., p. 214. F. W. Aston, Science Progress, 1912; I. Langmuir, Jour. Am. Chem. Soc., 1920, vol. 42, p. 2190. Perhaps in this connection should be mentioned also recent studies on the duration of atoms in their several quantum states. See R. C. Tolman, Proc. Natl. Acad. Sci., 1924, vol. 10, p. 85; L. A. Turner, Phys. Rev., 1924, vol. 23, p. 464; F. M. Kannenstine, Astrophys. Jl., 1924, vol. 59, p. 13.

departure and the final state remaining unchanged. For discussions of these technical details the reader must be referred to the literature, a few of the more recent publications being noted in a footnote below.[6]

While the details of the manner of the "birth" and "death" of the molecules in chemical transformation are, as yet beyond the range of the observation of the physicist, the fundamental laws of energetics, which hold true generally, and *independently of* particular features of *mechanism*, are competent to give substantial information as to the end product, at any rate, of the evolution of such a system as considered in the simple example above. The final equilibrium must accord, as regards its dependence on temperature, pressure and other factors, with the second law of thermodynamics, which may thus be said to function as a *law of evolution* for a system of this kind. This is a point worth dwelling on a little at length, inasmuch as our knowledge of the form and character of the law of evolution for this special type of system may be expected to serve as a guide in the search for the laws of evolution in the more complicated systems, belonging to an essentially different type, which confront us in the study of organic evolution. The second law of thermodynamics can be expressed in various ways, but the form in which it serves our present purpose best is that which states that the system evolves toward a state in which certain functions (thermodynamic potentials) of the variables defining its condition are at a minimum, somewhat as a ball placed in a hemispherical bowl ultimately comes to rest in the position in which its (gravitational) potential is a minimum, namely, at the lowest point of the bowl. Many laws of nature are conveniently[7] expressed in this form, as minimum (or maximum)

[6] Regarding the rôle played by thermal agitation and by radiation see G. W. Todd and S. P. Owen, Phil. Mag., vol. 37, 1919, p. 224; I. Langmuir, Jour. Am. Chem. Soc., 1920, vol. 42, p. 2190; W. H. Rodebush, Jour. Am. Chem. Soc., vol. 45, 1923, p. 606; J. M. Lowry, Trans. Faraday Soc., vol. 17, 1922, p. 596; J. A. Christiansen, Zeitschr. phys. chem., vol. 103, 1922, p. 91. Regarding the influence of radiation see especially the publications of Professor Baly. See also J. Mellor, Chemical Statics and Dynamics, 1904, pp. 394, 414, 415; and Perrin and Hammick, Atoms, 1923, p. 168. The literature on catalysis is so extensive that no attempt is made here to give even a key to it.

[7] Fundamentally this is a matter of convenience, and does not predicate anything narrowly characteristic of natural laws. The fact that the course of events is *uniquely* determined implies that the laws which determine that course can be expressed in the manner referred to. For a discussion of this question see J. Petzoldt, Maxima and Minima und Ökonomie, Altenburg, 1891, pp. 17 et seq.

laws, and it is to be expected that the law of evolution in life-bearing systems also, (where, as we shall see later, mechanism cannot be lightly waved aside into the convenient catch-all of the laws of thermodynamics), will be found to receive its most convenient expression in this form. In another respect the case of chemical evolution may confidently be expected to be found a good model in the treatment of the broader problem of evolution. It is to be noted that the law of chemical evolution is expressed in terms of the system as a whole. It is the thermodynamic potential of the entire system that approaches a minimum. Biologists have rather been in the habit of reflecting upon the evolution of individual species. This point of view does not bear the promise of success, if our aim is to find expression for the fundamental law of evolution. We shall probably fare better if we constantly recall that the physical object before us is an undivided system, that the divisions we make therein are more or less arbitrary importations, psychological rather than physical, and as such, are likely to introduce complications into the expression of natural laws operating upon the system as a whole.

As regards the formulation of the laws of evolution in form of a maximum or minimum principle, it should be remarked that one such principle follows directly from the fundamental equations of kinetics as set forth in Chapter VI.

If we multiply the first of these equations by x_1, the second by x_2, and so on, we obtain

$$\left.\begin{aligned}
x_1 \frac{dx_1}{dt} &= a_{11}x_1{}^2 + a_{12}x_2x_1 + \ldots + a_{1n}x_nx_1 + \ldots \\
x_2 \frac{dx_2}{dt} &= a_{21}x_1x_2 + a_{22}x_2{}^2 + \ldots + a_{2n}x_nx_2 + \ldots \\
&\quad \cdot \quad \cdot \quad \cdot \quad \cdot \quad \cdot \quad \cdot \quad \cdot \quad \cdot \quad \cdot \quad \cdot \quad \cdot \quad \cdot \quad \cdot \\
x_n \frac{dx_n}{dt} &= a_{n1}x_1x_n + a_{n2}x_2x_n + \ldots + a_{nn}x_{n2} + \ldots
\end{aligned}\right\} \qquad (17)$$

Hence by addition

$$\frac{d}{dt}\Sigma\, x^2 = 2Q(x_1,\, x_2,\, \ldots\, x_n) + \ldots \qquad (18)$$

where Q represents a quadratic form. The relation thus obtained is not of general utility in this form. However, by a linear substitution

$$\xi_i = N_1 x_1 + N_2 x_2 + \ldots + N_n x_n \tag{19}$$

the equation (18) can be transformed into

$$\left.\begin{aligned}\frac{d}{dt}\Sigma\ \xi^2 &= \lambda_1\xi_1{}^2 + \lambda_2\xi_2{}^2 + \ldots + \lambda_n\xi_n{}^2 + \ldots \\ &= 2Q'(\xi_1,\ \xi_2,\ \ldots \xi_n) + \ldots\end{aligned}\right\} \tag{20}$$

where $\lambda_1, \lambda_2, \ldots \lambda_n$ are the n roots of the characteristic equation for λ, the same λ's that function as exponents in the series solution of the original system of equations.[8]   Now it will be recalled that the condition for stability at the origin is that all the real parts of the roots shall be negative.   But in that case the quadratic form Q' is definite and negative.   Hence the condition for stability at the origin can be expressed by saying that the quadratic form Q' must be definite and negative; or, by saying that Q' must have a minimum at the origin.   And the law of evolution, near the origin, evidently is, according to (20), that $\Sigma\xi^2$ continually decreases. (At points remote from the origin the terms of higher order, which have here been omitted, may cause increases in $\Sigma\xi$.)

The chief interest of the minimum principle here indicated lies in its analogy[9] to certain theorems in dynamics and thermodynamics, for which reference must be made to the literature, in particular to P. Duhem, Traité d'Énergétique, 1911, vol. 1, pp. 460 et seq.; F. Michaud, Ann. de Phys., 1921, vol. 16, pp. 148 et seq.

---

[8] For the sake of simplicity the argument has here been presented in the form in which it appears when all the roots λ are distinct and real.   For a detailed discussion of the conditions of stability when some of the roots λ are multiple or complex see E. Goursat, Cours d'Analyse, 1915, vol. 3, pp. 31–43.

[9] The analogy to the dynamical cases treated in the reference cited becomes particularly plain if we bear in mind that

$$\frac{\partial Q'}{\partial \xi_i} = 2\lambda_i\xi_i$$

$$\frac{\partial^2 Q'}{\partial \xi_i \partial \xi_j} = 0 \text{ when } i \neq j$$

$$= 2\lambda_i \text{ when } i = j$$

so that the quadratic form Q' can be written

$$\frac{1}{2}\left(\frac{\partial Q'}{\partial \xi_1}\ \xi_1 + \frac{\partial Q'}{\partial \xi_2}\ \xi_2 + \ldots + \frac{\partial Q'}{\partial \xi_n}\ \xi_n\right)^{(2)}$$

where the bracketed exponent (2) denotes the symbolic square, in which $\left(\dfrac{\partial Q'}{\partial \xi}\right)^2$ is replaced by $\dfrac{\partial^2 Q'}{\partial \xi^2}$, and the product $\dfrac{\partial Q'}{\partial \xi_i} \cdot \dfrac{\partial Q'}{\partial \xi_j}$, is replaced by $\dfrac{\partial^2 Q'}{\partial \xi_i \partial \xi_j}$.

The condition that the form so defined shall be negative, is that the determinant

$$
\begin{vmatrix}
\dfrac{\partial^2 Q'}{\partial \xi_1{}^2} & \dfrac{\partial^2 Q'}{\partial \xi_1 \partial \xi_2} & \cdots & \dfrac{\partial^2 Q'}{\partial \xi_1 \partial \xi_n} \\[2ex]
\dfrac{\partial^2 Q'}{\partial \xi_2 \partial \xi_1} & \dfrac{\partial^2 Q'}{\partial \xi_2{}^2} & \cdots & \dfrac{\partial^2 Q'}{\partial \xi_2 \partial \xi_n} \\[2ex]
\cdot & \cdot & \cdots & \cdot \\[1ex]
\dfrac{\partial^2 Q'}{\partial \xi_n \partial \xi_1} & \dfrac{\partial^2 Q'}{\partial \xi_n \partial \xi_2} & \cdots & \dfrac{\partial^2 Q'}{\partial^2 \xi_n}
\end{vmatrix}
$$

shall be negative, and also all determinants derived from it by striking out the last p lines and the last p columns.

In the present case the same condition, can be expressed in simpler form to the effect that $\lambda_1, \lambda_2, \ldots \lambda_n$ must all be negative. But it is worth while, in order to bring out the analogy, to note also the more complicated general form of the condition.

CHAPTER XIII

INTER-SPECIES EQUILIBRIUM

Since the struggle for existence is chiefly a struggle for subsistence, a careful comparative account of the food of various competing species and genera at different places and seasons and at all ages of the individual . . . . cannot fail to throw much light upon the details, causes and effects of the struggle.—*Forbes.*

Equilibrium Condition in More Particular Form. The fundamental relations of statics are derived immediately from the corresponding equations of kinetics by substituting in the latter the value zero for the several velocities. This has already been noted with regard to the equations of kinetics in their most general form. In somewhat more particular form, useful in common numerical applications, we have a condition for equilibrium derived from the system of equations (14) of Chapter X

$$\frac{dX_i}{dt} = 0 = \frac{\alpha_{fi} v_f}{\gamma_{if}} X_f - v_i X_i \tag{1}$$

$$= \frac{\alpha_{fi} v_f}{\gamma_{if}} X_f - u_i X_i \tag{2}$$

$$\frac{X_f}{X_i} = \frac{\gamma_{if} u_i}{\alpha_{if} v_f}, \text{ or } X_f = \frac{\gamma_{if} u_i}{\alpha_{if} v_f} X_i \tag{3}$$

It should be noted that these formulae hold equally well if the masses are measured in ordinary units (e.g., pounds) or if they are measured in "head of population," with the proviso, of course, that the coefficients u_i, v_i, are in each case expressed in corresponding units.

The equation (1) expresses the fact that, for each component, the total inflow is just balanced by the total outflow, so that nowhere in the system is any accumulation of mass going on. This clearly implies that, unless there is complete equilibrium, the matter in the system must be in circulation, it must be going through one or more cycles. Such cycles are, indeed, very characteristic features in the scheme of nature.

161

Numerical Illustration.   We may, by the way of illustration, apply the formula (3) to the equilibrium between the several biological species comprised in a life-bearing system.   For obvious reasons numerical data are most readily available for man and the species directly under his control.   So, for example, we may let X_i represent the mass (or number) of a human population, and X_f the mass (or number) of a population of sheep serving as food for that human population.   In the United States in 1918 the consumption of mutton (or lamb) per head of the population per annum was 5.417 pounds. This is not strictly an equilibrium ration, since our population is increasing.   However, the difference between this and the equilibrium ration is probably small.   In our example we will therefore put

$$\gamma_{if}u_i = 5.417 \text{ pounds} = 0.1096 \text{ sheep}[1] \tag{4}$$

Again in the United States in 1918 the number of sheep slaughtered per annum was 23.22 per cent of the standing herd.   Hence

$$\alpha_{fi}v_i = 0.2322 \tag{5}$$

so that

$$X_f = \frac{0.1096}{0.2322} X_i \tag{6}$$

$$= 0.4718 \, X_i \tag{7}$$

In 1918

$$X_i = 103,587,955 \text{ head} \tag{8}$$

Hence

$$X_f = \ 48,873,000 \text{ head} \tag{9}$$

---

[1] According to the Year Book of the Department of Agriculture, 1920, p. 759, the number of sheep slaughtered under Federal inspection in 1918 was 8,769,498.   According to R. Pearl, The Nation's Food, 1920, p. 61, this represented 77 per cent of all the sheep slaughtered in that year, so that the total number slaughtered was 11,370,000.   The total dressed weight of these, according to the Year Book, p. 826, was 562,214,000 pounds, which makes the average of one sheep carcass 49.45 pounds.

The standing herd of sheep in 1918, according to the Year Book, p. 701, was 48,603,000 on farms, or, adding a correction for animals not on farms, say 48,963,000.   The percentage of animals slaughtered in a year out of the standing herd, was therefore 23.2216 per cent.

For a review of various estimates of the output of herds of cattle, sheep, swine, etc., the reader is referred to a paper by R. H. Rew in the Journal of the Royal Statistical Society, 1902, vol. 65, p. 666.

The actual standing herd of sheep in 1918 was 48,963,000 head of which 90,000 head furnished mutton for export, the United States not being a self-contained system.

It is to be noted that in this example the products $\gamma_{if}\, u_i$ and $\alpha_{fi}\, v_i$ are more easily ascertained than the individual coefficients γ u, α, v. Inasmuch as these coefficients, in the formula (3), appear only in these products, it is not necessary, for the purposes of this example, to ascertain the values of the coefficients separately.

The example of the equilibrium between a human population and the national herd of sheep, cited primarily for the purpose of illustrating the equilibrium equation (3), incidentally brings out some other points that may be noted in passing. We meet here a pointed suggestion of economic factors entering into play in the processes which we are studying. For the coefficients $\alpha\, \gamma, u, v$, have obvious economic relationship. So, for example, v_f, the proportion of sheep slaughtered per annum (in a stationary state of the system), is of the nature of interest on the standing herd, which latter, in turn, is of the nature of capital. The gross interest rate of 23.2 per cent is, of course, greatly diminished, in effect, by the extensive accessories, representing a further investment of capital, and by the general running expenses required, in addition to the mere herd, to produce, transport, and market the ware. On the other hand, certain secondary products (e.g., wool) add their quota to the returns on the invested capital.

Again, the coefficient λ_{if}, which measures what fraction of the total consumption by the component S_i (human population) is derived from S_f (sheep), is clearly a factor of economic significance. Mutton is typically a commodity of the *replaceable* type—beef, pork, fish, etc., furnishing ready substitutes. In such case as this the factor γ_{if} will be elastic, capable of assuming, in ready response to slight changes in general conditions, a whole range of values from zero up. In the case of less readily replaceable commodities the coefficient γ will be of more rigid habit.

The full significance and the precise nature of the relation between the biological and the economic characteristics of a system must form the subject of special considerations to which we shall find ourselves led inevitably later, in our efforts to gain insight into the dynamics of life-bearing systems. At this juncture it may not be amiss to indicate in preparation of a viewpoint to be more fully developed later, that if economic factors force themselves upon our notice primarily in the consideration of systems comprising a human population, this is not because the operation of economic stresses is peculiar to human aggregations, but only because these stresses find their ready numerical expression and measure in such communities; owing to the development of a system of social coöperation and division of labor, coupled with a very special mechanism of adjustment by "economic exchange," which is peculiar to man. For though not a few other species, bees, ants, etc., display a social organization in some respects perhaps superior to ours, their organizations make use of other expedients than the transfer of *ownership* through a universal medium of exchange, in bringing about the allocation, to each individual, of his share in productive effort and in product.

For obvious reasons our information regarding the interdependence of the several biological species and other components of our life-bearing system is most complete and most exact in so far as it relates to species under human cultivation, species that contribute, as producers, to our political economy. However, this does not mean that we are wholly cut off from all information regarding the life balance of other species. Two sources, two methods of observation furnish us with data on this subject, namely, first, biological surveys, and second analyses of the stomachs of sample specimens. A third method would consist in establishing experimental systems comprising several species of organisms and making periodic censuses by direct count, after the manner of the work of Pearl and Parker with a single species (Drosophila). There is here an attractive field open for research. Perhaps the readiest, though not the most interesting approach to this problem would be the study of mixed bacterial growths, say along the lines followed, for a single species, by H. G. Thornton, Annals of Applied Biology, vol. 9, 1922, p. 241.

Biological Surveys. Biological surveys, supplemented by estimates depending more or less on personal judgment, are aimed to give us some degree of quantitative description of our world by investigating both the number and the variety of living organisms. A perfect biological survey would enumerate the several general and species found in the locality examined, and would furthermore give us a measure of the extent of each species, either in numbers or in some other suitable terms. It would give us a species of "General Demology" of our globe. Needless to say, in this matter we are very far from having attained perfection. The best that can be done is to give rather crude estimates, based, in the most favorable instances, on counts or observations made with some degree of care, but without pretense of great precision.

As to the number of species, some interesting figures are given by J. A. Thomson.[2] On the small island of Britain alone 462 different birds have been observed; the total number of living species of birds he estimates at not less than ten thousand. Of vertebrates he quotes an estimate by H. Gadow.[3] The total number of recent species this author puts at 24,241, as follows:

Mammals	2,702
Birds	9,818
Reptiles	3,441
Amphibians	925
Fishes	7,328
Primitive vertebrates	27
	24,241

The vertebrate élite, however, forms but a small minority in the scheme of nature. It has been intimated that, if the present order of things should come to a term, the supremacy would, as likely as not, pass from the crowned vertebrate *Homo sapiens* to the now despised, presently perhaps to be feared, creeping thing, the insect. Indeed, it has been pointed out that were it not for the relentless internecine warfare which its members carry on among themselves, we should very soon find ourselves driven out of house, home and granary by the insect pest. Even as it is, though the largest insects barely exceed, individually, the size of some of the smallest vertebrates, yet, as D. Sharp remarks, "the larger part of the animal matter existing on the lands of the globe is in all probability locked up in the form of insects." He estimates the number of insect species that have been definitely named, at 250,000, and suggests that this is only about a tenth of the total. The number of plant species has been estimated at 200,000. Darwin records the finding of 20 species in a patch of turf four feet by three.

As to the numerical strength of the several species, here again some telling figures are given by J. A. Thomson.[4]

[2] J. A. Thomson, The Wonder of Life, 1914, p. 11.
[3] See also H. Gadow, The Wandering of Animals, 1913, p. 74.
[4] J. A. Thomson, loc. cit., pp. 9–10.

At the spring maximum of the Rotifer *Synchoeta* there may be about three millions to a square yard of lake. At the summer maximum of the slimy Alga Clathrocystis ceruginosa there may be 500 millions to the square yard; at the autumn maximum of a well-known diatom *Melosira varians*, which has a summer maximum as well, there are about 7000 millions to the square yard, so that the waters of the lake form a veritable living soup. . . . . In an ordinary sample from a warm part of the Atlantic and from a depth of 500 metres (which is the most densely populated as far as plants go), there are likely to be about 5,000 plant-cells to a liter; but there may be as many as a quarter of a million. . . . .

Elsewhere Thomson tells us that in the midst of a swarm of fish at spawning time in the Norwegian fjords a boat may be so densely packed in among the mass of fish that an oar stuck upright into the swarm remains standing for an appreciable time after the hand relinquishes its hold.[5]

Examination of Stomach Contents. The second method by which information has been gathered regarding the interdependence of biological species consists, as already stated, in examining the contents of the stomachs of sample specimens. This method has been applied particularly to birds and fishes. The results of such an analysis of the feeding habits of the common crow and of the starling are strikingly brought to view in the accompanying charts figures 31 and 32, reproduced by courtesy of the Department of Agriculture from Bulletins 868 and 1102. Such a chart does not, of course, yield any direct information regarding the relative abundance of the several species upon which the crow feeds, but it does give us at least an indication of a resultant compounded of that relative abundance and a number of other factors, such as the preference or selective tastes of the crow, the greater or less degree of protective characters with which nature has endowed the various species exposed to attack, etc.

The converse problem, also, has been investigated, namely the extent to which different species of birds participate in the destruction of one selected noxious insect. So, for example, Bulletin 107 (1914) of the Department of Agriculture lists 45 different species of birds that were found to have fed upon the alfalfa weevil. A similar study by H. C. Bryant[6] was carried out during a grasshopper outbreak in

[5] For an account of bird censuses in the United States see M. T. Cooke, Bulletin No. 1165, Bureau of Biological Survey, U. S. Department of Agriculture.

[6] University of California Publications in Zoology, 1912, no. 1, vol. 11.

California, when "in the infected areas the grasshoppers were computed to number from 20 to 30 per square yard." Bryant's results are shown, in part, in tabular and diagrammatic form in figures 33 and 34, reproduced from his original publication.

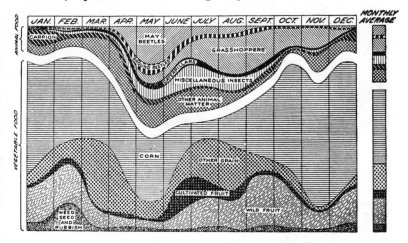

FIG. 31. SEASONAL ANALYSIS OF THE STOMACH CONTENTS OF CROW

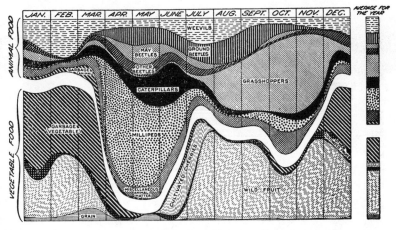

FIG. 32. SEASONAL ANALYSIS OF THE STOMACH CONTENTS OF STARLING

The same author has also given us a classic in his extended study "A Determination of the Economic Status of the Western Meadow Lark in California." This paper contains among other things a

detailed bibliography up to 1913, and a historical survey of the
methods employed and the investigators who have labored in the

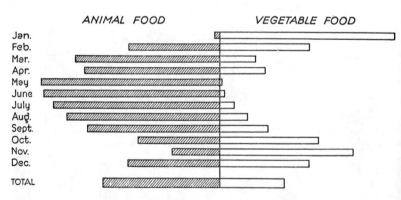

*Number of Grasshoppers
Consumed per Day*

Bicolored Red-wing·	78,590
Western Meadowlark·	24,720
Killdeer·	5,445
Bullock Oriole ·	4,050
Cliff Swallow·	2,265
Western Kingbird·	1,280
Burrowing Owl·	1,260
California Shrike·	1,200
Anthony Green Heron·	1,050
Sundry·	593

TOTAL DESTRUCTION OF GRASSHOPPERS PER SQUARE MILE DAILY, 120,453

FIG. 33. COMPARATIVE DAILY DESTRUCTION OF GRASSHOPPERS BY SEVERAL
SPECIES OF BIRDS

After H. C Bryant

ANIMAL FOOD   VEGETABLE FOOD

Jan.
Feb.
Mar.
Apr.
May
June
July
Aug.
Sept.
Oct.
Nov.
Dec.

TOTAL

FIG. 34. SEASONAL FOOD HABITS OF THE MEADOW LARK

After H. C. Bryant

field. The results obtained by Bryant exemplify the proverbial
voracity of birds. Young birds require about one-half their own
weight in food each day. In the course of a year the average meadow

lark, weighing say, 4 ounces, consumes about the following quantities of food.

	pounds
Grain	$1\frac{1}{3}$
Weed seed	$\frac{1}{2}$
Insects	$3\frac{3}{4}$
Total	6

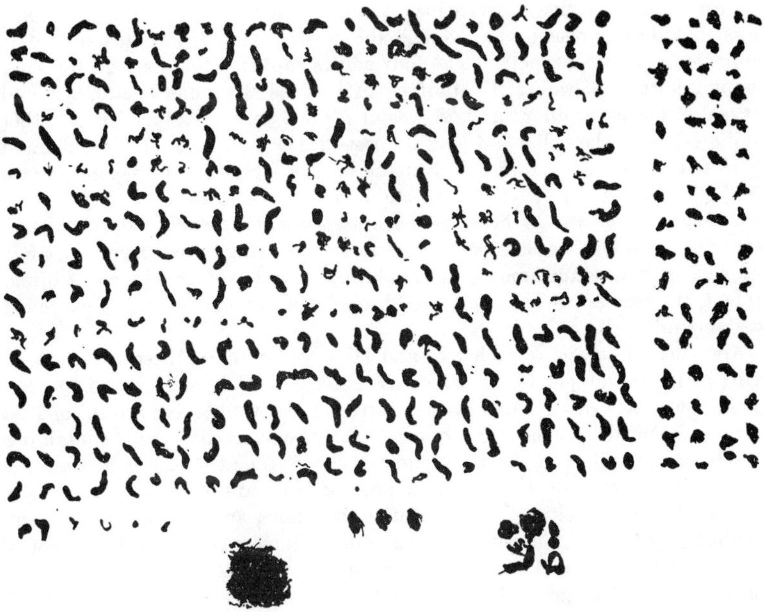

FIG. 35. STOMACH CONTENTS OF A BREWER'S BLACKBIRD

Since an adult bird weighs about 4 ounces, this means that it consumes on an average about 24 times its weight of food in a year. Dr. Bryant remarks: "If we consider that there is an average of one meadow lark to every two acres of land available for cultivation (11 million acres) in the Sacramento and San Joaquin Valleys, and that each pair of birds raises an average of four young, it takes over $343\frac{1}{2}$ tons of insects each day to feed the young birds in the valley alone." His findings regarding the seasonal changes in the food of the meadow lark are summarized in a number of charts of which one is reproduced in figure 38. An illustration of the voracity of birds, and their destructiveness to insects is also seen in figure 35 (from Bulletin 107 of the Department of Agriculture) showing the stomach contents of a Brewer's Blackbird, for this bird was found to have gorged upon 374 larvae, 65 pupae and 3 adults of the alfalfa weevil. Observations on the feeding habits of young English sparrows are recorded by E. R. Kalmbach in Bulletin 107 of the United States Department of Agriculture. This author remarks (p. 54):

From a series of five observations it appears that the parent English sparrows visited their nest on an average about once every 5⅓ minutes, or a little more than 11 trips an hour. The four adults captured had as food for their young 2 kernels of wheat; 17 alfalfa weevil larvae; 1 ground beetle, 9 weevil larvae and a caterpillar; and 28 weevil larvae, respectively. Three other adults taken in the fields had food for nestlings in their bills. This amounted to 18 weevil larvae and an aphid in the first, 5 larvae in the second, and 3 coccinellid larvae, 13 weevil larvae, and 2 pupae in the third.

Though this is rather heterogeneous assortment, it would appear that 15 larvae of the weevil or their equivalent in bulk of other insects would be a fair estimate of an average amount of food brought in at each trip by adult birds. In fact, it is certain that the material brought in frequently greatly exceeded this amount.

Allowing 15 larvae at each trip and 11 trips per hour, these birds would bring in 165 larvae per hour. Then, assuming that the young were being fed for 12 hours each day, a conservative estimate, we would have a total of 1980 larvae consumed by one brood in one day. Straw-thatched sheds containing upward of 100 nest holes, both old and new, are frequent, and it is not uncommon to find farmyards where this number of nests are occupied. There are also ample nesting sites about the other buildings and in the ever-present Lombardy poplar, cottonwood, or box elder. Such a colony of birds would devour a daily total of 198,000 larvae, or an equivalent bulk in other food. As the young birds remain in the nest for at least 10 days and are probably fed several days longer by the adults, they will have eaten food equivalent to the bulk of 1,980,000 larvae during their nestling life.

Intra-Species Equilibrium. As has been remarked on a previous occasion, it is not intended, in this volume, to take up the discussion of the evolutionary changes within the confines of a species. Passing notice may, however, be given to the fact that the equilibrium within a Mendelian population has been discussed by G. H. Hardy[7] and by R. C. Punnett[8] and latterly by J. B. S. Haldane.[9] (See p. 122.)

[7] G. H. Hardy, Science, 1908, vol. 28, p. 49.
[8] R. C. Punnett, Mimicry in Butterflies.
[9] J. B. S. Haldane, Cambridge Philosophical Society, 1923.

CHAPTER XIV

INTER-SPECIES EQUILIBRIUM—AQUATIC LIFE

Aquiculture is as susceptible to scientific treatment as agriculture; and the fisherman, who has been in the past too much the hunter, if not the devastating raider, must become in future the settled farmer of the sea, if his harvest is to be less precarious.—*W. A. Herdman.*

From what has already been set forth the direct economic importance of studies in *general demology* should be sufficiently clear, if this term be used to denote the quantitative study of the population of the several species of organisms living together in mutual interdependence through their food requirements, feeding habits, and in other ways.

In no other field, perhaps, has the study, from this angle, and under this economic impetus, been so systematically undertaken, as in the biology of aquatic species. On the one hand the three-dimensional extension of the systems here involved (as distinguished from the essentially two-dimensional spread of land species over the earth's *surface*), facilitates, in certain respects, the operation of sampling (by the use of the dragnet) and counting; on the other, the close relation of such investigations to the practical problems of our inland and our ocean fisheries has furnished alike the economic occasion and the financial support for work on an extended scale. The methods employed have by this time developed into a more or less standardized technique. The dragnet, already referred to, and the stomach and gills of fish, acting, as it were, as natural dragnets, themselves caught within the collector's man-made dragnet, are among the principal accessories in this field of investigation. L. H. Tiffany recommends particularly the gizzard shad as a convenient collector and sampler of Algae.[1]—Contrasting these natural samplers with man-made contrivances he remarks:

These *living tow nets* (i.e., gizzard shad) do not get caught on snags and roots, the string does not break, and the algal collection is very representative of the body of water from which the fish were taken. It is only neces-

---

[1] Science, 1922, vol. 56, p. 285.

sary to catch the young fish and examine their stomachic and intestinal content to secure a proportionate sample of the plankton.

Tiffany examined specimens from streams and ponds in Illinois, and also from Ohio. He points out that the gizzard shad fulfills an important rôle as an intermediary link in the *food chain:* algae, shad, game-fishes, man.

Thus, the gizzard shad is making useful for man the energy stored in plant forms which occupy no land areas, which do not interfere with the ordinary disposition or utilization of bodies of water (except the occasional contamination of water for drinking purposes by some algae), which involve no labor of cultivation on the part of man, and which are of no value for direct human consumption.

The world's population in the last hundred years has increased about 150 per cent. Along with this increase has had to come a corresponding increase in the world's food supply. One of the ways in which this necessity has been met is the securing of new acres of soil in which to grow crops. It is easily seen, however, that there is a limit to new acreage. In the future, therefore, we may have to turn more of our attention to the cultivation of the waters for food supplies. We may have to develop an industry of aquiculture as we have developed an industry of agriculture. The time is rapidly approaching when fish will be more highly prized as food and more extensively used than now. As that time comes, the cultivation of algae will be a first step toward greater fish production. A second step may be the introduction of fish like the gizzard shad into fish ponds and lakes to make more readily available the phytoplankton for fish food.

In a summary survey of the *Food Resources of the Sea,*[2] G. W. Martin makes similar observations. He remarks: "So far as the actual cultivation of the sea's resources, as distinguished from their mere exploitation, is concerned, we have made only the feeblest beginnings." Somewhat in the same vein is W. A. Herdman's comment: "Aquiculture is as susceptible to scientific treatment as agriculture; and the fisherman who has been in the past too much the hunter, if not the devastating raider, must become in the future the settled farmer of the sea, if the harvest is to be less precarious." Viewing the matter from a slightly different angle W. F. Wells of the New York Conservation Commission draws attention to the fact that in our modern great cities, with the widespread adoption of the water system of sewage disposal, valuable fertilizer material is lost from its natural place in the fields. By enriching

[2] Scientific Monthly, 1922, p. 456.

the vegetation in the water and furnishing abundant life thereto, it may again be restored to the people as fish and shell fish in the place of beef and mutton. And the exchange is not such a bad bargain. For it has been found that in carp ponds, for example, the production of market ware was 95 pounds per acre, as contrasted with 73 pounds of beef per acre of farmland.[3] Perhaps one of the most telling illustrations of the economic importance of pisciculture is presented to us in the Alaska purchase: Within fifty years after the acquisition of our Northern province, it had yielded, in its salmon fisheries alone, seven and a half times its purchase price.

The quantitative study of ocean life (on which must be based an intelligent system of marine aquiculture) may be said to date from 1880, when Henson introduced the use of the dragnet. To this has since been added the use of bottom samplers or grabs; also an ingenious, if less trustworthy method of making a census of the marine population, which consists in catching a number of live fish, marking them, throwing them back in the water, and then noting the percentage of marked fish in the fishermen's catch during the period that follows. In this way it has been estimated, for example, that the North Sea contains about fifteen hundred million plaice, a figure about equal to the earth's human population.

The field of utility of the dragnet and most of the other methods described is evidently limited to the larger denizens, such as are effectively held in the meshes of a net. Even a fine silk net will fail to hold a very numerous constituent of the population of the sea, a constituent that is highly important not only on account of its great extent, but also because of the rôle it plays in the food traffic of marine life. Lohmann showed (1911) how these fine organisms (*the nannoplankton*) can be collected by the use of a centrifuge.[4] Allen has developed a special dilution culture method of count for the nannoplankton organisms, which is modelled after the pattern of bacterial count technique. He showed sea water to contain 464,000 organisms per liter (exclusive of bacteria). Al-

[3] It is true that beef is much superior in food value, pound for pound, but it is also much more costly to produce. It should also be noted that the yield from carp ponds is very high as compared with that of marine fisheries. E. J. Allen (*Food from the Sea*, 1917, quoted by W. F. Thompson, *Scientific Monthly*, 1922, p. 546) estimates the yield in the North Sea at 15 pounds per acre.

[4] G. W. Martin, loc. cit., p. 461.

lowing for systematic errors Allen thinks a population of one million organisms per liter (one per cubic millimeter) to be a conservative estimate. This is not excessive crowding, in view of the size of these organisms, as illustrated by the diagram, figure 36, reproduced from G. W. Martin's article. Before the extent and significance of this nannoplankton was realized, the amount of food required by the animals of the sea seemed so much in excess of the amounts

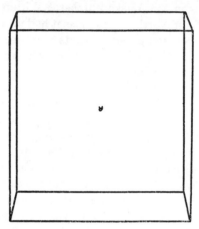

Fig. 36. Density of Microorganisms (Exclusive of Bacteria) in Sea Water

About one organism. measuring 6 microns in diameter, is found per cubic millimeter of water. The relative dimensions are here shown. After G. W. Martin.

revealed by the earlier methods of collection, as to give rise to the suggestion (Pütter 1907–1909)

that the nutrition of marine animals was on an entirely different plane from that of land animals, and that a large number of them, especially the smaller ones, absorbed dissolved organic matter directly from the water, without the mediation of plants. Pütter's arguments have not been generally accepted, and more recent studies have invalidated many of them. Nevertheless, it is possible that something of this sort is more general than we realize. Mitchell (1917) reported an experiment strongly indicating that an oyster can utilize dextrose dissolved in sea water.

The most elaborate attempts to calculate the production of the sea have been those of the Danish biologist Petersen and his associates. As a result of their studies, these workers have come to the conclusion that the plankton plays a very small part in the nutrition of the animals of the sea, and

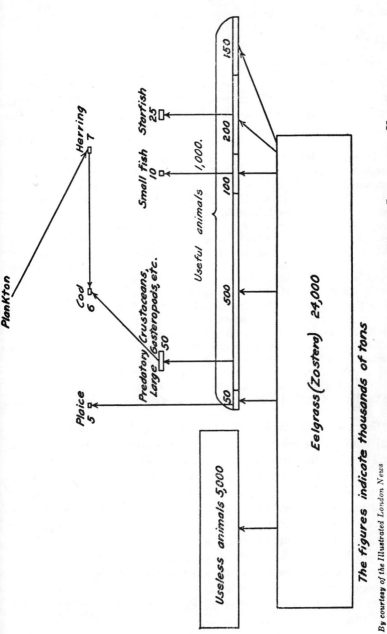

The figures indicate thousands of tons

FIG. 37. SOME OF THE MOST IMPORTANT FOOD-CHAINS OF ANIMAL LIFE IN THE KATTEGAT
After G. W. Martin

that the fundamental food of all marine forms in northern waters at any rate is the "dust fine detritus" of the sea bottom, derived primarily from the eel grass, *Zostera.*

These investigators have studied in particular the conditions in the Kattegat, a rather shallow arm of the sea between Denmark and Sweden, about 150 miles in extreme breadth and 90 miles in extreme width. Their principal conclusions are exhibited in the diagram figure 37, and are as follows:

It is assumed that about half of the total amount of Zostera annually produced in this area is washed elsewhere by the currents. The balance, estimated at 24,000,000 tons, serves as the basis for the animal life of the area. The useless animals, that is, those that are of no value to man and do not serve as food for fish, feeding directly on the Zostera, amount to about 5,000,000 tons. Useful animals, mainly those capable of serving as food for fish, are estimated at 1,000,000 tons. These are not all utilized by food fish, however. Starfish account for perhaps 200,000 tons; 500,000 tons are eaten by the larger gastropods and crustaceans, of which only a part are consumed by fish; while plaice and other flatfish consume about 50,000 tons producing 5000 tons of human food annually. Cod are much less economical, since they get their food at third hand, so to say, and each ton of the 6000 tons produced annually represents about one hundred times as much of the original synthesized organic food. On the other hand, the cod help to keep down the predatory gastropods and crustaceans (see figs. 38 and 39). The herring is the most important food fish feeding on the plankton, (mainly on copepods) and it in turn is eaten by the cod. Perhaps the most striking feature brought out by these figures is the comparatively trifling amount of human food finally produced from such a large amount of organic material.

Summary of Methods. A tabular summary of some of the principal methods by which data have been secured regarding relative and absolute frequency of organisms and species is given in table 10.

Food Chains. It has already been remarked, in dealing with the general kinetics of the type of systems here under consideration, that each component of the system appears as a link in a chain or a network of chains, receiving contributions from components (*sources*) above, and discharging material into other components (*sinks*) below. Food chains, such as spoken of by Tiffany in the passage quoted on page 172, are a particular example of such chains of components. The study of food chains is one of the important tasks of the economic biologist. For we cannot afford to restrict our attention to the immediate source from which we draw our

Fig. 38. The Varied Diet of the Codfish

TABLE 10
Summary of Methods of Biological Surveying

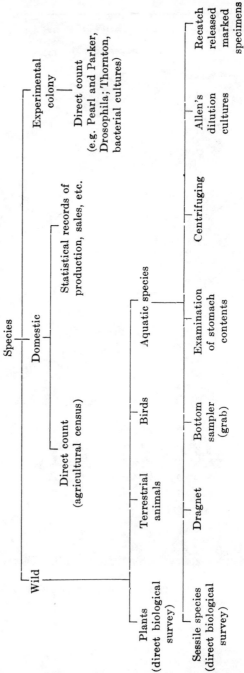
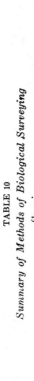

supplies of food for the human population. The sources of these sources also demand attention. The problem forces itself upon our notice primarily (in the present state of society) in connection with agriculture. The fields cannot continue indefinitely to yield undiminished annual crops if the materials drawn from them are not in some way replenished. One important constituent needs no human intervention: carbon dioxide, owing to its gaseous form, automatically seeps in by diffusion as fast as it is absorbed by the

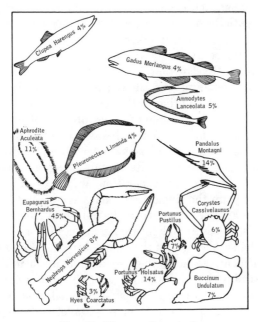

FIG. 39. KEY TO FIGURE 3

green plants. The same is true in some degree of free nitrogen, though the capacity of plants to assimilate this element is strictly limited.[5] Water, also, is, in most agricultural areas, provided by the automatic meteorological processes of evaporation and condensation in rainfall. But as to certain other essential materials, notably combined nitrogen, phosphorus, potash and sulphur, the *inherently immobile*[6] constituents of the fertile soil, for these auto-

[5] Science, November 24, 1922, p. 605.

[6] "Für sich nicht beweglich," Liebig, Die Chemie in ihrer Anwendung auf Agricultur, 1876, p. 382.

matic replacement does not occur in sufficient measure to satisfy the agricultural needs of the densely populated countries of this age. It becomes necessary for man to feed his food. Early man and primitive man, may reap where he has not sown. But long ago our tribe turned from the life of a nomad and hunter to tilling the soil and to animal husbandry. Thus was established a system of symbiosis with the links next above us in the food chain: the harvest ripening on the plain; and the cattle, grazing upon the pasture in summer, fed from the crib in winter. But early agriculture was essentially of the nature of a mining industry. It drew from the soil as from a bottomless well, without thought of a possible exhaustion of the source, or of any feasible replenishment to diminishing resources. Except that, by a semi-automatic, semi-empirical process, natural fertilizer was allowed to restore to the soil at least a part of its strength to bring forth a crop. One more step forward and man graduated from mining farmer into manufacturing farmer. The field became a factory fed with raw materials in the form of saltpeter, potash salts and phosphate fertilizer, imported, if need be, from afar; and producing its output of agricultural flora and fauna. Lastly, in our own generation, we have learned to divert into the life stream the sluggish element, so essential to life, so ill-named by the French—*azote*; to make ourselves independent of the saltpeter beds, to assure our future against a nitre famine by opening the inexhaustible mine of the atmosphere. It is a singular thing that this element, so accessible, so abundant, in which we are literally bathed within and without, every instant of our life, should so long have remained foreign to our industrial economy. Strange circumstances, yet not without close parallel. For even now we are powerless to avail ourselves effectively of the golden flood of energy that daily pours upon us without limit from above—while we turn earthward to dig laboriously for the plainly exhaustible supply of coal to supplement our limited bodily energies.

Food Chains in Aquatic Species. The principle that long food chains are essentially wasteful finds particular application also in the practical problem of the economic and rational utilization of marine organisms for human sustenance. As Professor Martin observes, the most economical course would be to utilize marine vegetation directly as food for man and his domestic animals. The use of algae as food for the table can hardly be expected to become an item of any consequence. Its use as cattle fodder presents better prospects. But our chief reliance will no doubt continue to be on the assimilation of marine plants by fish. To quote again Professor Martin:[7]

Since man prefers to harvest the plant life of the sea indirectly, those animals which feed directly on the plants are able to increase with less waste and at a more rapid rate, considered in total populations, than those which feed on other animals. Most of our food fish, for example, feed on smaller fish; these in turn feed upon small crustaceans and the latter eat the microscopic plants and detritus, so that in many instances the fish we eat are removed three or four steps, perhaps more, from the original food source. This is more significant than may seem apparent at first glance, since it involves an enormous waste. Before any organism can grow, the energy needed merely to live must be supplied, and by the time a crustacean is eaten by a minnow, or a minnow by a food fish, it will, on the average, have consumed a quantity of food several times its own weight. These facts are well brought out in the statistics of Petersen, and the diagram figure 37 based thereon. The edible shellfish, however—oysters, clams, mussels and the like—feed for the most part directly on the marine plants and this is one reason why the extension of the shell fisheries represents so much promise.

Another advantage of this branch of aquiculture is also to be noted, namely, that

most shellfish, like land crops, stay where they are planted. Even the scallop, which can swim about after a fashion, is restricted in its movement, and could readily be controlled. Oyster culture is already a great and important industry, but it has not nearly approached its possibilities. Clam culture is still in an embryonic state, and scallop culture has yet merely been suggested. When some of the problems confronting the establishment of these industries have been solved, we may hope to have acquired additional information concerning the ecology of the sea, which will help us in our approach to the more difficult problems of the future.

Primary, Secondary and Tertiary Foods. It is often convenient to classify the foods for human consumption according to their relative position in that portion of the food chain which is under human control. Commonly the meats of domestic animals are

[7] For some further bibliographic indications regarding the food consumed by fishes see A. S. Pearce, *Ecology*, vol. 1924, p. 258. See also W. A. Herdman, Founders of Oceanography, 1923; J. Johnstone, Introduction to Oceanography, 1923.

classed as secondary foods, since the production of these meats takes place in two steps, first the growing of the fodder (for the most part materials not comestible by man), and second the transformation of a part of this fodder, in the animal economy, into food adapted for human consumption. On the other hand the fisherman's haul is for us primary food, growing feral, without human intervention.

This classification must not be pressed. Where fields are supplied with fertilizer it might well be maintained that the crops of wheat, potatoes, etc., commonly classed as primary, are secondary foods, while butchers' meats are tertiary. Even the catch of fish, and huntsman's quarry may not be strictly primary, in so far as game laws and regulations regarding the pollution of lakes and rivers represent some degree of symbiotic intervention on the part of man. Fine points apart, the distinction between the primary foods (crops and fish) and the secondary foods (butchers' meats) is economically most significant, for the consumption of fodder by farm animals is an item not merely comparable with human food consumption, but exceeding this latter manyfold. The fact, of course is, that farm animals are far from being economical and efficient converters of raw materials into food for human consumption. They represent a luxury, a humoring of the tastes of men at the expense of their purses. With the present density of population we can afford the luxury. Presumably the future will see retrenchments, with pastures and cornfields converted to wheat. Still tastes are not accidental things. Allowing for vagaries and exceptions, the things we like are, on the whole, good for us and for the species. Whether man can maintain his present status with a materially abridged meat ration is perhaps an open question. Should the answer be in the negative, the conclusion would seem to be forced upon us that an overcrowding of the earth would react unfavorably upon the vigor of the race; quality would be sacrificed to quantity. How this might affect the ultimate fate of our species is a subject for speculation. The pessimist might take a cue from palaeontology, recalling that the extinction of a species seems to follow, not infrequently, close upon its period of greatest development. The optimist, on the other hand, might perhaps extend the suggestion that when overcrowding does come, the ones to survive most surely, if not most abundantly, will be those whose superior qualities will enable them, in spite of intensified competition, to draw to themselves a sufficiency of the more desirable, though perhaps not absolutely essential articles of consumption. Natural selection would thus operate by the preferential *survival of an aristocracy*, while a *submerged tenth* would furnish a drain for the discharge of the unfit. Certainly, in the interests of the species, it were better that the inferior constituents be purged from the system than that they should drag down the general level to mediocrity and perhaps below the line of viability. But these are speculative reflections.

Cycles. Food chains, were we able to trace them through their entire course, would undoubtedly be found to form closed cycles or a network of cycles. This is indeed a practical necessity for the continued performance of the processes or organic nature, processes that have gone on essentially unchanged in their general character, however modified in detail, for many millions of years.

A few of the simpler food chains we may be able to follow with something approaching completeness through their cycle. For the most part, however, the system of interlocking cycles in nature is complex beyond all reasonable hope of detailed analysis in its entirety.

If we are satisfied to omit innumerable details, we can trace, for each of the most important chemical elements[7] concerned, the broad outline of its cycle in nature. The elements and simple compounds principally concerned are

Carbon (dioxide) .... CO_2
Oxygen .... O_2
Nitrogen .... free N, NH_3, nitrites and nitrates
Water .... H_2O
Phosphorus .... (phosphates, etc.)

Brief consideration will presently be given to each of these cycles in turn. First, however, it will be well to review some of the essential facts regarding the occurrence of the chemical elements, generally, in nature. For the drama of life is like a puppet show in which stage, scenery, actors and all are made of the same stuff. The players, indeed, "have their exits and their entrances," but the exit is by way of translation into the substance of the stage; and each entrance is a transformation scene. So stage and players are bound together in the close partnership of an intimate comedy; and if we would catch the spirit of the piece, our attention must not all be absorbed in the characters alone, but must be extended also to the scene, of which they are born, on which they play their part, and with which, in a little while, they merge again.[8]

[8] Since the words above were written I have run across the following singularly apposite passage in John Morley's Introduction to Wordsworth Collected Poetic Works: "Wordsworth's claim, his special gift, his lasting contribution, lies in the extraordinary strenuousness, sincerity and insight with which he first idealizes and glorifies the vast universe around us, and then makes of it, not a theatre on which men play their parts, but an animate presence, intermingling with our works, pouring its companionable spirit about us, and 'breathing grandeur upon the very humblest face of human life.'"

CHAPTER XV

THE STAGE OF THE LIFE DRAMA

When the elements have been *mingled* in the fashion of a man, and come to the light of day, or in the fashion of the race of wild beasts or plants or birds, then men say that these *come into being*; and when they are *separated*, they call that in common parlance, *death* . . . . let not the error prevail over the mind that there is any other source of all the perishable creatures that appear in countless numbers.—*Empedocles*.

Our stage is a tripartite world: The heavens above, the waters of the sea, and the solid ground beneath our feet; the atmosphere,

TABLE 11

Principal components of earth's surface

	VOLUME MILLIONS	DENSITY	MASS MILLIONS	PER CENT
	cu. miles		*short tons*	
Atmosphere.....................			5.82×10^{16}	0.03
Ocean..........................	302	1.03	1.42×10^{18}	6.58
Solid crust.....................	1,633	2.7	2.01×10^{19}	93.39

the hydrosphere and the lithosphere. The total mass of the earth is about 6.5×10^{21} tons. But it is only the outer crust that interests us here, for the deeper layers have little or no part in terrestrial life. If we arbitrarily take a layer ten miles thick for the crust, the distribution of the material among the three main divisions is, according to F. W. Clarke, about as shown in table 11.

The Atmosphere. There are two ways of confining a gas. The one most familiar in the laboratory and in products of human workmanship generally, is to enclose the gas in a suitable envelope, such as a glass vessel, or the cylinder of an engine; to put something *around* the body of gas to be confined. The other way, nature's way on a large scale, is just the opposite, and consists in putting something *into* the gas, or putting the gas around something. It is so the earth holds her atmosphere by gravitational attraction. Her hold is not impartial. She draws closest to her the densest constituents, and gives longer leash to the lighter. The atmosphere, in consequence, is not a homogeneous body, but varies in composition with altitude. At the same time, owing to its elasticity, the air in its lower strata is compressed by the weight of the overlying atmosphere, so that 99 per cent of the whole is contained within a shell 30 km. (18½ miles) thick. The remaining 1 per cent extends out into space without any

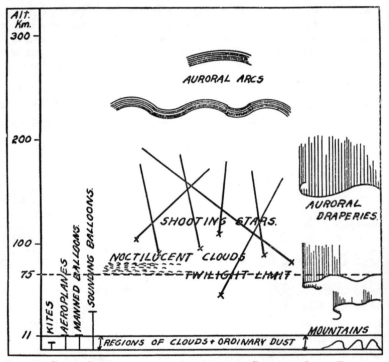

FIG. 40. CROSS SECTION OF THE ATMOSPHERE, SHOWING SOME FEATURES CHARACTERISTIC OF DIFFERENT ALTITUDES

After W. J. Humphreys

assignable limit, but at any rate to a height of some 300 km. (185 miles), as evidenced by the aurora. A graphic representation of the broad divisions of the atmosphere is shown in figure 40, adapted from Wegener and Humphreys.[1] A more detailed and exact statement of

[1] Physikalische Zeitschrift, 1911, vol. 12, p. 172. See also W. J. Humphreys' work, *The Physics of the Air* (Lippincott, 1920), pp. 68, 69. Also, the same author, Bulletin Mt. Wilson Weather Observatory, vol. 2, 1909, p. 67;

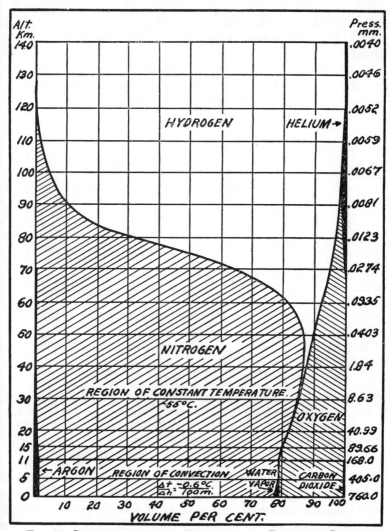

FIG. 41. COMPOSITION OF THE ATMOSPHERE AT DIFFERENT LEVELS
After W. J. Humphreys

Journ. Franklin Institute, vol. 175, 1913, p. 208, 212. A singular view has lately been put forward by L. Végard. He identified certain green lines in the auroral spectrum with lines observed when solid nitrogen is rendered phosphorescent by x-rays. He concludes that the upper atmosphere contains solid nitrogen. (See Nature 1924 vol. 113 p. 716.) Végard's view has been opposed by J. C. McLennan, Roy. Soc., June 19, 1924.

its composition at different altitudes, up to 140 km., is given in table 12 and illustrated graphically in figure 41, derived from Humphrey's work.

A complete discussion of the rôle played by the atmosphere in the round of terrestrial life would amount to nothing less than a treatise on meteorology, such as forms no part of the present project. What

TABLE 12

Percentage distribution of gases in the atmosphere

HEIGHT	GASES								PER CENT OF TOTAL ATMOSPHERE
	Argon	Nitrogen	Water vapor	Oxygen	Carbon dioxide	Hydrogen	Helium	Total pressure	
km.								mm.	
140		0.01				99.15	0.84	0.0040	
130		0.04				99.00	0.96	0.0046	
120		0.19				98.74	1.07	0.0052	
110		0.67	0.02	0.02		98.10	1.19	0.0059	
100		2.95	0.05	0.11		95.58	1.31	0.0067	
90		9.78	0.10	0.49		88.28	1.35	0.0081	
80		32.18	0.17	1.85		64.70	1.10	0.0123	
70	0.03	61.83	0.20	4.72		32.61	0.61	0.0274	
60	0.03	81.22	0.15	7.69		10.68	0.23	0.0935	
50	0.12	86.78	0.10	10.17		2.76	0.07	0.403	
40	0.22	86.42	0.06	12.61		0.67	0.02	1.84	
30	0.35	84.26	0.03	15.18	0.01	0.16	0.01	8.63	99.0
20	0.59	81.24	0.02	18.10	0.01	0.04		40.99	94.5
15	0.77	79.52	0.01	19.66	0.02	0.02		89.66	85.5
11	0.94	78.02	0.01	20.99	0.03	0.01		168.0	78.0
5	0.94	77.89	0.18	20.95	0.03	0.01		405.0	46.7
0	0.93	77.08	1.20	20.75	0.03	0.01		760.0	0

important factors weather and climate are in the business of providing the sustenance of life is a matter of common knowledge, and a very particular concern of the farmer. Yet we must here be satisfied with little more than a passing reference to meteorology, noting only a few elementary facts which bear directly upon the subject in hand, the circulation of the chemical elements in nature.

Losses from the Atmosphere. A first question that suggests itself in this discussion of the economy of nature is this: Since the atmosphere is "open at the top," so to speak, is there not a loss, a constant leakage of gas out into space? The answer to this question must be sought in terms of the molecular constitution of the gases of our atmosphere. A cubic centimeter of air contains (at 0°C.) about 3.15 × 10^{19} molecules. These are in continuous agitation, somewhat after the manner of a swarm of gnats, except that they flit about with speeds comparable with that of a rifle bullet (about 500 meters per second) rather than with the leisurely flight of an insect. At a temperature of 0°C. a molecule of nitrogen has, *on an average*, a velocity of 492 meters per second. A molecule of hydrogen, under the same conditions, would have an average velocity of 1839 meters per second. It must be understood that these figures represent, in each case, a mean about which the velocities of individual molecules cluster, so that a certain proportion of them will fall below and others will exceed the figures stated. At the earth's surface the average distance travelled between two successive collisions is about $\frac{1}{1,000,000}$ cm. But in the upper ranges of the atmosphere conditions are very different. If we follow the estimates and computations of J. H. Jeans, we find that at an altitude of 3200 km. the atmospheric pressure is reduced to about $1/10^{14}$ of its value at sea level; but even at this low pressure there are still about 300,000 hydrogen molecules per cubic centimetre. (At this altitude all other gases except hydrogen are practically absent). The mean free path between collisions is now 10,000 km. or about $1\frac{1}{2}$ times the earth's radius. In such circumstances collisions between molecules are rare, and for the most part the molecules move freely through space in parabolic or elliptical orbits, and become virtually diminutive satellites of the earth. Since the day of Jules Verne's story *From the Earth to the Moon* it has been a matter of popular knowledge that a body projected from the earth with a velocity exceeding 7 miles per second will go off in a hyperbolic orbit, never to return. This applies to the molecules of a gas. Any of them that may be travelling outward with such a speed in the region where collisions are so rare as to be negligible, will leave the earth for good and will thus be lost to our atmosphere. The rate of leakage from the atmosphere thus depends on the number of molecules per unit of time that acquire the limiting (outward) velocity of 7 miles per second. This number, in turn, depends on the temperature in the region under consideration, a point regarding which our information is very uncertain. But an exact knowledge of this temperature is not needed to compute a major limit, a maximum figure which the rate of escape certainly cannot exceed. It is thus found that under present conditions[2] the earth holds her atmosphere so effectively that there cannot be any appreciable leak even in many millions of years.

Cosmic losses from the atmosphere then, are, for all practical purposes, wholly negligible. Certain other subtractions from and accessions to the atmosphere we shall have occasion to note as we consider the circulation of the several elements. As a matter of fact the composition of the atmosphere in the region in which living organism have their habitation is very nearly uniform[3] and constant, *except*

TABLE 13

Constituents of the atmosphere

| | AT EARTH'S SURFACE | | IN ENTIRE ATMOSPHERE |
	Per cent by volume	Per cent by weight	Total amount
			metric tons
Nitrogen.............................	78.03	75.45	3.9×10^{15}
Oxygen...............................	20.99	23.21	1.2×10^{15}
Carbon dioxide......................	0.03	0.05	2.2×10^{12}
Argon................................	0.94	1.30	6.2×10^{13}
Hydrogen............................	0.01	0.0003	1.3×10^{11}
Water................................			1.3×10^{13}
Neon.................................	0.0012		4.7×10^{10}
Krypton..............................			6.4×10^{9}
Helium...............................	0.0004		6.3×10^{9}
Xenon................................			1.2×10^{9}

Earth's surface = 1.97×10^8 square miles = 5.5×10^{15} square feet.
One square mile = 2.79×10^7 square feet.
One metric ton = 2205 pounds.

[2] It may be noted in passing that in the earth's past history conditions may have been different. If at any time the temperature of the upper atmosphere was about 750°C., then there must have been a very distinct loss of hydrogen by leakage into space. The moon, and certain of the planets having a lesser gravitational pull or a higher temperature (Mercury), have probably lost in this way any atmosphere that they may have had. For a detailed discussion of this and other points in connection with the escape of gases from the atmosphere the reader may be referred to J. H. Jeans's *Dynamical Theory of Gases*, 1921, Chapter XV. See also E. A. Milne, Trans. Cambr. Phil. Soc., vol. 22, 1923, p. 483; J. E. Jones, ibid., p. 535.

[3] Except in the neighborhood of volcanoes, and in lesser degree, in or near large cities or manufacturing centers, where large amounts of waste gases may be discharged into the atmosphere.

TABLE 14

Average composition of the ocean

	CUBIC MILES	CUBIC KILOMETERS	SHORT TONS	METRIC TONS	PER CENT BY VOLUME	PER CENT BY WEIGHT	PER CENT OF TOTAL SOLIDS BY WEIGHT
Water..................	2.97×10^8	1.23×10^9	1.35×10^{18}	1.23×10^{18}	98.44	96.6	
Dissolved gases.				8.2×10^{13}			
Oxygen*.............				1.2×10^{13}			
Free nitrogen*......				1.0×10^{13}			
Carbon dioxide†......				5.4×10^{13}			
Solids‡..............	4.8×10^6	2.0×10^7	4.94×10^{16}	4.50×10^{16}	1.56	3.4	
Sodium chloride......							77.76 NaCl
Magnesium chloride....							10.88 $MgCl_2$
Magnesium sulphate....							4.74 $MgSO_4$
Calcium sulphate.....							3.60 C,SO_4
Potassium sulphate....							2.46 K_2SO_4
Magnesium bromide.....							0.22 $MgBr_2$
Calcium carbonate.....							0.34 $CaCO_3$

*G. Linck, Kreislaufvorgänge in der Erdgeschichte, Jena, 1911, p. 11, 12.

†F. W. Clarke, Data of Geochemistry, 1920, p. 142, CO_2 in sea water at 15°C. = 42.7 mgm. per liter.

‡F. W. Clarke, loc. cit., p. 23. Linck, loc. cit., p. 33.

as regards its moisture content, and we may accept for the composition of the atmosphere at the earth's surface, moisture excluded, the figures shown in the first two columns of table 13. The third column shows the total amounts of the several constituents of the entire atmosphere, according to W. J. Humphreys (Monthly Weather Review, vol. 49, June, 1921, p. 341).

Cosmic Accessions to the Atmosphere. Meteorites falling upon the earth from space bring with them certain quantities of entangled or occluded gases. While this contribution to the atmosphere is at the present time, presumably, of negligible dimensions (see also page 195, *Cosmic Accessions to the Lithosphere*), yet in the course of the

TABLE 15

Comparison of air and aquatic atmosphere

	AIR PER LITER*	SEA WATER 15°C. PER LITER*	AIR BY VOLUME	SEA WATER 15°C. BY VOLUME	AIR BY WEIGHT	SEA WATER 15°C. BY WEIGHT
	cc.	*cc.*	*per cent*	*per cent*	*per cent*	*per cent*
O............................	209.9	5.8	21.0	15.0	23.2	12.8
N............................	780.3	11.3	78.0	29.0	75.4	21.7
CO_2........................	0.3	21.7†	0.03	56.0	0.05	65.6

* Measured at 0°C. and 760 mm. Hg.

† 42.7 mgm.; according to F. W. Clarke, Data of Geochemistry, Geological Survey Bulletin 491, 1920, p. 142; G. Linck, Kreislaufvorgänge in der Erdgeschichte, Jena, 1912, p. 6.

long procession of ages past this source may not have been wholly insignificant. Data on this question are at best very uncertain, and a mere passing reference must suffice.[4]

The Hydrosphere. In comparison with the ocean all other aggregations of water upon the earth are insignificant in amount. The bald statement of the total volume of the ocean—302 million cubic miles—conveys but little to the mind. More impressive it is to recall that the average depth of the sea is 2½ miles, and that, even if these waters were spread over the whole earth, leaving no continents, the average depths would still be 1½ miles.

The average composition of the ocean is shown in table 14. Here again, the figure for the volume of total dissolved solids, 4.8 million cubic miles, is made more readily comprehensible by a graphic illustration. The salts of the ocean, made into one solid block, would

[4] F. W. Clarke, Data of Geochemistry, U. S. Geological Survey Bulletin 695, 1920, pp. 58, 269, 282.

cover the entire United States and Alaska to a depth of $1\frac{6}{10}$ miles; or according to J. Joly, they would encrust the whole earth to a depth of 112 feet.[5]

The Aquatic Atmosphere. Aquatic species perform their respiration in contact with an atmosphere of gases held in solution in the water that surrounds them. This atmosphere is very different both in concentration and also in composition from that in which we live, as is apparent from table 15.

A comparison of the several columns in table 15 is an object lesson on the adaptability of living organisms to varied conditions. The atmosphere in which fish and other marine animals live in comfort would not only drown us with its principal constituent, water, but, even if this were removed, the residual gases would suffocate us for lack of oxygen; and if the deficiency in this gas were made up by the addition of the amount required to bring the percentage up to that to which we are accustomed, we would still be choked by the excessively high percentage of carbon dioxide.[6]

The Lithosphere. Immense as the ocean appears to us, with its average depth of $2\frac{1}{2}$ miles, yet it constitutes less than $\frac{1}{4300}$ of the total mass of the earth, whose bulk is thus concentrated chiefly in lithosphere. Of the deeper layers of this lithosphere we have but scant and indirect knowledge. Earthquakes give evidence of some change in constitution about half way down to the center of the globe. Conditions and occurrences at such depth as this would seem, in the present state of our knowledge, to have little bearing upon the life at the surface. Other indirect evidence regarding the earth's interior is derived as follows: The volume of the globe being known from triangulation, and its weight from direct determination with a balance[7] or in other ways, the mean density of the earth is found to be

[5] F. W. Clarke, loc. cit., p. 24; Sci. Trans. Roy. Soc. Dublin, 1899, vol. 7, p. 30.

[6] It must be admitted, however, that much of this CO_2 in sea water is partially neutralized by alkali.

[7] A concise survey of the principal determinations of the mass of the earth will be found in J. H. Poynting's little book (in the Cambridge Manuals series) *The Earth* (1913) It may add interest to the bald figures to note here in passing that the density of the earth's crust (2.7) is not very widely different from that of the moon (3.46). This fact has a certain significance in connection with Sir Charles Darwin's theory of the origin of the moon, according to which our satellite originally formed part of the earth and was thrown off by a species of tidal disruption. The bulk of the moon, then, would be formed of material derived from the outer layers of the earth.

TABLE 16

*Average composition of terrestrial matter**

	LITHOSPHERE (93 PER CENT)	HYDROSPHERE (7 PER CENT)	AVERAGE INCLUDING ATMOSPHERE
Oxygen	49.19	85.79	46.68
Silicon	25.71		27.60
Aluminum	7.50		8.05
Iron	4.68		5.03
Calcium	3.37	0.05	3.63
Sodium	2.61	1.14	2.72
Potassium	2.38	0.4	2.56
Magnesium	1.94	0.14	2.07
Hydrogen	0.872	10.67	0.145
Titanium	0.648		0.696
Chlorine	0.228	2.07	0.095
Bromine		0.008	
Phosphorus	0.142		0.152
Carbon	0.139	0.002	0.149
Manganese	0.108		0.116
Sulphur	0.093	0.09	0.100
Barium	0.075		0.079
Chromium	0.062		0.066
Zirconium	0.048		0.052
Vanadium	0.038		0.041
Strontium	0.032		0.034
Fluorine	0.030		0.030
Nickel	0.030		0.031
Nitrogen	0.030		
Cerium, yttrium	0.019		0.020
Copper	0.010		0.010
Lithium	0.005		0.005
Zinc	0.004		0.004
Cobalt	0.003		0.003
Lead	0.002		0.002
Boron	0.001		0.001
Glucinum	0.001		0.001
	100.000	100.000	100.172

* Adapted from F. W. Clarke, Data of Geochemistry, 1921, p. 35; Clarke and Washington, Proc. Natl. Acad. Sci., 1922, vol. 8, p. 114.

5.5.   But the mean density of the rocks outcropping at the surface[8] is only 2.7.   Whatever may be the character of the earth's interior,

[8] Compare also E. D. Williamson and L. H. Adams, Jour. Washington Acad. Sci., 1923, vol. 13, p. 413; H. S. Washington, ibid., p. 453.

it is thus evident that it is composed of denser material than we find at the surface. In point of fact, comparison with meteorites, and other evidence, make it appear likely that the earth's interior is virtually a metallic regulus (chiefly iron), encrusted with a slag not unlike that which separates out and floats on the molten mass of metal in a blast furnace. Such, essentially, is the raw material of our landscape, such our habitation, such the ground on which we tread and from which we draw the substance of our body. For the fertile soil in the plain is but the weathered variant of the granite strength of the hills, and we ourselves but a strangely metamorphosed portion of the world-stuff, the slag coating of a metal core.

Cosmic Accessions to the Lithosphere. The earth receives a constant shower of meteorites from interstellar space, at an annual rate of some 20,000 tons.[9] This seems a large amount. As a matter of fact, spread over the surface of the globe (197 million square miles), the accumulated meteoric material of a thousand million years would make a layer only 1 inch thick, if its density were that of water, or a correspondingly thinner layer of denser material.

Composition of the Earth's Crust. Table 16 adapted from F. W. Clarke's Data of *Geochemistry* and a more recent publication by Clarke and Washington, shows the average composition of the known terrestrial matter. The first column, in particular, gives the figures for the solid crust. This table exhibits a number of facts and relations of interest. Perhaps the first significant circumstance that strikes the eye, in glancing at the table, is the very unequal deal with which nature has distributed matter among the ninety odd[10] known elements. One-half the lithosphere, and one-quarter of the atmosphere are made up of the element oxygen.

The eight most abundant elements of the earth's crust (oxygen, silicon, aluminum, iron, calcium, sodium, potassium and magnesium)—the only ones whose amounts are over 1 per cent—constitute together over 98 per cent of the earth's crust. These, with hydrogen, titanium, carbon and chlorine—twelve in all—make up 99.5 per cent; thus leaving only one-half of one per

---

[9] S. Arrhenius, Worlds in the Making, 1908, p. 108. See also Young, Astronomy, 1904, p. 475.

[10] Uncountable isotopes aside.

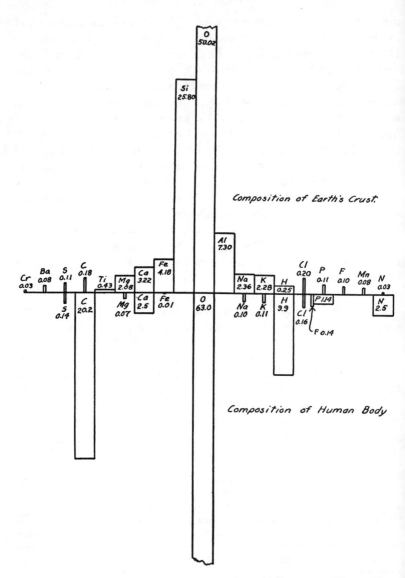

FIG. 42. COMPARISON OF COMPOSITION OF EARTH'S CRUST AND HUMAN BODY

Figures indicate percentages

cent for all the other elements, among them some quite indispensable for our existing civilization.[11]

Relation to Composition of the Organism. Of the elements specifically significant for the living organism, only one, oxygen, is present in great abundance. Carbon, hydrogen and nitrogen, the principal "organic elements," are among the less abundant constituents of the globe. On the whole it may be said the living organisms are composed of comparatively rare elements. We are, indeed, earth-born, but yet not altogether common clay.[12] This is well brought out

TABLE 17

Average composition of human body

	POUNDS	PER CENT
Oxygen	97.20	63.03
Carbon	31.10	20.20
Hydrogen	15.20	9.90
Nitrogen	3.80	2.50
Calcium	3.80	2.50
Phosphorous	1.75	1.14
Chlorine	0.25	0.16
Fluorine	0.22?	0.14?
Sulphur	0.22	0.14
Potassium	0.18	0.11
Sodium	0.16	0.10
Magnesium	0.11	0.07
Iron	0.01	0.01
Total	154.00	100.00

in the chart figure 42, which shows, side by side, the average composition of the known terrestrial matter, and, in comparison, the approximate composition of the human body. This latter is not exactly a representative sample of the totality of living matter (see tables 17

[11] H. S. Washington, Jour. Franklin Institute (1920), vol. 190, p. 7. The figures have been slightly modified in accordance with the latest data of F. W. Clarke and H. S. Washington, Jour. Natl. Acad. Sci., 1922, vol. 8 p. 114.

[12] Indeed, taken literally the expression "common clay," as applied to man, is an extreme case of poetic license; for aluminum and silicon—the chief constituents of clay, and taking second and third place in rank of abundance among the components of the earth's crust, are both present only in traces in the human body.

TABLE 18

*Composition of living organisms**

ATOMIC WEIGHT	HEAT COMBUSTION PER GRAM	ELEMENT	SYMBOL	PLANTS	ANIMALS
				Elements invariably present in living organisms	
	calories				
1.008	34.702 (H₂)	Hydrogen	H		*Hydrogen, carbon, oxygen, and nitrogen—"H, C, O, N"—are essential and of chief rank* in all life processes; forming, with sulphur, practically all plant and animal proteins and, with phosphorus, forming the nucleoproteins
12.005	8.08	Carbon	C		
16.00	0.143	Oxygen	O		
14.01		Nitrogen	N		
31.04	5.747	Phosphorus	P	In nucleoproteins and phospholipins	In nucleoproteins and phospholipins; in some brachiopods; in blood; and in vertebrate bone and teeth
32.06	2.22	Sulphur	S	In most proteins, 0.1 to 5 per cent	In most proteins, 0.1 to 5 per cent
39.10	1.745	Potassium	K	Abundant in marine plants, especially "kelps" (larger *Phæophyceæ*); activity of chlorophyll depends on it	In blood, muscle, etc.
24.32	6.077	Magnesium	Mg	Present in large quantities in *Corallinaceæ* (a family of calcified red algæ	Present in echinoderms and alcyonarians; present in all parts of vertebrates, especially in bones
40.07	3.284	Calcium	Ca	Present in large quantities in certain algæ (chiefly marine)	In all parts of vertebrates; abundant in bones and teeth
55.84	1.353	Iron	Fe	Essential in the formation of protoplasm; present in chlorophyll	Essential in the formation of protoplasm, and in the higher animals; essential in hemoglobin as an oxygen-carrier

23.00	3.293	Sodium?	Na	Believed essential to all plants, but not demonstrated; found in marine plants, especially Phæophyceæ	Present in all animals; abundant in blood and lymph
35.46	0.254	Chlorine?	Cl	Present in many plants; believed by some to be essential; abundant in marine algæ, especially in the Phæophyceæ	Present in all animals; abundant in blood and lymph; present in the gastric juice.
28.3		Silicon?	Si	Found in all plants; present in large quantities in the Diatomaceæ, both fresh-water and marine; in form of "silica" constitutes 0.5 to 7 per cent of the ash of ordinary marine algæ	Present in radiolarians and siliceous sponges; also in all the higher animals
				Elements frequently present in living organisms	
126.92	0.1766	Iodine	I	In marine plants, especially the "brown algæ," Phæophyceæ; in Laminaria and Fucus; also in some Gorgonias	Essential in the higher animals (thyroid)
54.93		Manganese	Mn	In some plants	In most animals in very slight proportions
79.92		Bromine	Br	In marine plants, especially the "brown algæ," Phæophyceæ; in some Gorgonias	In some animals in very slight proportions
19.0		Fluorine	F	In a few plants	In some animals—constituent of bones and teeth; in shells of mollusks and in vertebrate bones

TABLE 18—*Continued*

ATOMIC WEIGHT	HEAT COMBUSTION PER GRAM	ELEMENT	SYMBOL	PLANTS	ANIMALS
	calories			Elements rarely present in living organisms	
27.1		Aluminum†	Al	In a few plants	In a few animals
74.96	1.463	Arsenic†	As		In some animals
137.37	0.952	Barium†	Ba	In a few plants	
11.0		Boron	B	In some plants	
58.97		Cobalt†	Co	In a few plants	
63.57	0.585	Copper†	Cu	In a few plants	Traces in some corals; essential in some lower animals as oxygen-carrier
207.20	0.243	Lead†	Pb	In some plants	Traces in some corals
6.94		Lithium	Li	In a few plants	
58.68		Nickel†	Ni	In some plants	In some animals
226.0		Radium†	Ra	In some plants	
87.63	1.497	Strontium†	Sr	In a few plants	
65.37	1.291	Zinc†	Zn	In a few plants	In a few animals; traces in some corals

The exceedingly rare occurrence of cerium, chromium, didymium, lanthanum, molybdenum, and vanadium is in all probability merely adventitious.

†Commonly regarded as poisons when present in *mineral* (ionic) forms, even in small proportions.

and 18) but will serve well enough for the present pupose.   The chart brings out very pointedly the selective character of the organism's activity in gathering to itself the substance of its body.   Thus carbon, which both in function and in relative quantity figures so prominently in living matter, appears as an insignificant little block in the chart of the earth's crust.   A similar contrast, if not quite so extreme, is seen in the case of nitrogen.   With aluminum and silicon the comparison works the other way about—very plentiful in the earth's crust, these elements are practically absent from the human body.[13]

Taking the mother earth as a whole, and the organism as a whole, it certainly cannot be said that there is much evidence of "inheritance

TABLE 19

*Composition of the salts in sea water and in blood serum in per cent**

		SEA WATER	BLOOD SERUM
Sodium	Na	30.59	39
Magnesium	Mg	3.79	0.4
Calcium	Ca	1.20	1
Potassium	K	1.11	2.7
Chlorine	Cl	55.27	45
Sulphate ion	SO_4	7.66	
Carbonate ion	CO_3	0.21	12
Bromine	Br	0.19	
Phosphoric acid	P_2O_5		0.4

* Maccallum, Trans. Roy. Soc. Canada, 1908, II, p. 145.

of parental characters" in their respective compositions.   Still, resemblance is not wholly lacking.   This becomes evident if we compare, not the entire organism with the whole of the earth's crust, but the blood of a mammalian, for example, with the water of the ocean.   This comparison is made in table 19 and figure 43.   The likeness thus seen, imperfect as it is, can hardly be ascribed to accident.   The fact is,

[13] Silica furnishes, however, the skeletal support in a variety of living forms (radiolaria, sponges, plants).   Cf. G. Bunge, Physiological and Pathological Chemistry, 1902, p. 23–24.   For a detailed discussion of the distribution of the chemical elements in organic nature see Vernadsky, Revue Gén. Sci.   The reader interested in this phase of the subject should not fail to acquaint himself with this article, which came to the writer's attention too late to be given more than this passing note here.

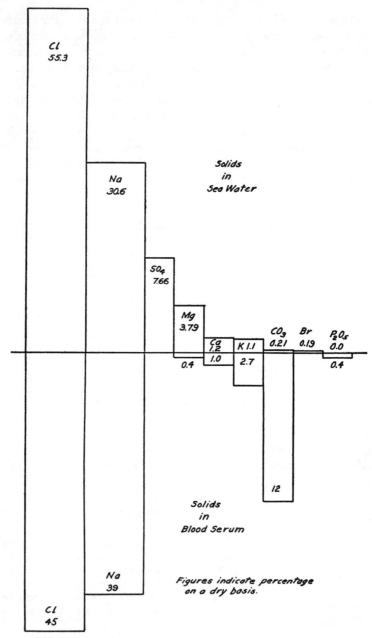

FIG. 43. COMPARISON OF SEA WATER AND BLOOD SERUM

as pointed out by Palitzsch,[14] that aquatic species are in such intimate contact, both at their body surface, and more particularly in their gills, with the surrounding water, that the latter might almost be considered continuous with their bloody fluids, so that sea water may justly be "placed in the same category as the other physiological fluids." "Frederiq[15] has shown that the amount of sodium chloride in the blood of crustacea varies, and all but corresponds, with the density of the water in which the creature has been kept." More highly organized aquatic species have made themselves in greater degree independent of the salinity of their environment;[16] and finally, it would appear, when the marine ancestors of terrestrial vertebrates emerged from the sea and adventured life on dry land, they packed, as it were, a portion of their saline environment in their baggage, and took it along with them on their excursion as an essential part of their *milieu intérieur*. And to this day, according to this view, we ourselves carry about with us in our arteries and veins, if not a portion of the actual ocean, at least a roughly approximate replica of its brine. For, as L. J. Henderson[17] remarks: "Not only do the body fluids of the lower forms of marine life correspond with sea water in their composition, but there are at least strong indications that the fluids of the highest animals are really descended from sea water." Some such indications may be seen in the reflections (conceived from a slightly different point of view) of G. Bunge,[18] "I am convinced that the remarkably high percentage of salt in vertebrate animals, as well as the desire to take salt with our food, can be satisfactorily explained only by the theory of evolution." In support of this consideration Bunge points out that in the weathering of rocks by the action of rain-water charged with carbonic acid, the sodium is dissolved and carried off as carbonate, while the potassium largely remains behind in combination with silica. The sodium carbonate being washed to

[14] Comptes-rendus, Laboratoire de Carlsberg, 1911, vol. 10, part I, p. 93. See Chapter I, footnote 19.

[15] Arch. de Zool. Exp. et Gén., 1885, Ser. 2, vol. 3, p. XXXV; see also D'Arcy Thompson, Growth and Form, 1917, p. 127.

[16] Compare D'Arcy Thompson, loc. cit., p. 127–130; Claude Bernard, Introd. a l'étude de la médecine exp., 1855, p. 110 as quoted on p. 17 (and footnote 20) of Chapter I.

[17] The Fitness of the Environment, 1913, p. 187.

[18] Loc. cit., 1902, p. 101–103.

the sea undergoes double decomposition with the alkali earth chlorides, these latter being deposited as carbonates (limestone and dolomite) while the sodium remains in solution as salt.   Thus sea water is rich in sodium chloride and poor in potassium, while on dry land the balance is essentially reversed.[19]   Plants and invertebrate animals, Bunge points out, contain little sodium, unless they live in a highly saline habitat, in or near the sea, or on salt steppes.   Yet the land vertebrates are all remarkably rich (comparatively) in salt, in spite of the scanty supply around them.

Is not the large amount of sodium chloride found in the present inhabitants of dry land another proof of the genealogical connection which we are forced to accept from morphological facts?   There is no doubt that each of us in his individual development has come through a stage in which he still possessed the *chorda dorsalis* and the branchial arches of his sea-dwelling ancestors.   Why may not the high average of salt in our tissues be also inherited from them?

Support for the supposition thus suggested is seen by Bunge in the fact that the younger a vertebrate is in its individual development, the more salt does it contain.   Furthermore, cartilage contains the highest percentage of sodium of all the tissues of our body, and is also the tissue of greatest antiquity.   The human skeleton is originally composed of cartilage, which is replaced, for the most part, by bone as the individual matures.

These are facts which lead most readily to the interpretation that the vertebrates living on dry land originally came from the sea, and are still continuing to adapt themselves to their present surroundings, where they can get but little salt.   We prolong this process of acclimation by taking advantage of the salt strata which have been left on the land by our primeval element, the salt flood.

Chemical Correlation in Soil and in Organism.   Our ancestral resemblance to the soil from which we spring is also exhibited by evidence converging from a different source.   H. S. Washington,

---

[19] This observation must be accepted with some caution.   Compare Whitney, Science, 1922, vol. 56, p. 218.   "Until we determine the actual loss, through chemical denudation, of silica, alumina, iron, potash and other electrolytes in the colloidal state, carried by rivers, we are in no position to even speculate as to whether erosion is a selective process which might change the chemical composition of the soil."

in his studies on The Chemistry of the Earth's Crust, already cited, draws attention to the fact that in the rocks soda and iron tend to be associated together as a pair on the one hand, and potash and magnesia on the other. This is well brought out in the diagram figure 44, reproduced from Washington's memoir, in which it is seen that the points representing the analysis of a number of rock samples tend to group themselves about the diagonal of the square, indicating that

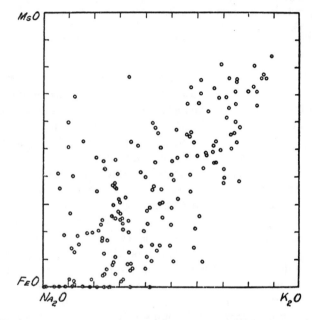

FIG. 44. CORRELATION IN THE OCCURRENCE OF Na, Fe AND K, Mg IN ROCKS

A large number of analyses here plotted show a marked tendency to array themselves along the diagonal, showing that high percentage of Na is commonly associated with high percentage of Fe; K and Mg follow a similar relation. After H. S. Washington.

high content of soda goes together with high content of iron, but with low potash and low magnesia; and *vice versa*. The point of special interest to us here in the present connection is that to which Dr. Washington draws attention in the words:

Curiously enough, the same correlation between these two pairs of elements, soda and iron, and potassium and magnesium, seems to hold good in the organic world. This is apparently shown by the following facts: In autotrophic plant metabolism potash is an essential element, as is also magnesium, in that chlorophyll (which in the leaves acts as the carbon-transferring substance) is a magnesium salt of a complex organic acid, while sodium and iron are generally toxic toward (at least the higher, gymnospermous and angiospermous) plants. On the other hand, sodium, rather than potassium, is the alkali metal essential to the higher animals, salt being a very necessary article of diet (in part because of its chlorine, and in part because of its sodium, content), and sodium chloride is present in the blood plasma; and at the same time, hemoglobin and its derivatives (which act as oxygen carriers, and are analogous to chlorophyll in plants) are iron salts of organic acids closely related to that of chlorophyll; while, similarly potassium and magnesium are more toxic toward the higher animals than are the other pair.

This singular parallel must not, of course, be looked upon as an instance of resemblance due to anything of the nature of inheritance of ancestral traits in the biological sense. Rather must it be connected in our minds with the fact that systems composed of the same fundamental substances, will display certain analogies through interplay, in them, of the same chemical affinities.

Accessibility of Valuable Earth-Constituents. Such a comparison as has been made above of the relative abundance of the several elements in the living organism and in the environment from which it draws its supplies, would be misleading if attention were not drawn to another factor aside from abundance, which enters strongly into play in the quest for the necessities of life. More important than mere abundance is *accessibility*. For, a substance may be present in comparatively large quantities, and yet be difficult to lay hold of, either on account of its wide dispersal in dilute form, or for other reasons. On the contrary, a comparatively rare substance may be procurable with relative ease, if it occurs segregated in concentrated or otherwise readily accessible form. Perhaps the most telling illustrations of this are to be found in industry. The element copper for example is found only to the extent of about $\frac{2}{1000}$ per cent in the earth's crust. Yet it is one of the most important metals in the arts, and is not ordinarily thought of as particularly rare. This is because, in those regions where it does occur, it is found in concentrated form, either as native metal, or as rich ore. Other instances are readily cited. Tin, lead and zinc are all rarer than copper, and each rarer than its precursor, in the order named. Still rarer are silver, tungsten, gold, bromine and platinum, all of which find important use in

TABLE III.—*Periodic classification of the elements.*

Row	Group 0	Group 1	Group 2	Group 3	Group 4	Group 5	Group 6	Group 7	Group 8
1		H 1							
2	He 4	Li 7	Gl 9.1	B 11	C 12	N 14	O 16	F 19	
3	Ne 20	Na 23	Mg 24.4	Al 27.0	Si 28.3	P 31	S 32	Cl 35.5	
4	A 39.9	K 39.1	Ca 40.1	Sc 45	Ti 48.1	V 51	Cr 52.1	Mn 55	Fe 55.9, Co 59, Ni 58.7
5		Cu 63.6	Zn 65.4	Ga 70	Ge 72.5	As 75	Se 79.2	Br 79.9	
6	Kr 82.9	Rb 85.5	Sr 87.6	Yt 88.7	Zr 90.6	Cb 93.5	Mo 96		Ru 101.7, Rh 103, Pd 106.5
7		Ag 107.9	Cd 112.4	In 115	Sn 118.7	Sb 120.2	Te 127.5	I 126.9	
8	Xe 130.2	Cs 132.9	Ba 137.4	La 138.9	Ce 140.3				
9				Rare earth metals.					
10						Ta 181	W 184		Os 191, Ir 193.1, Pt 195.2
11		Au 197.2	Hg 200.6	Tl 204	Pb 207.1	Bi 209			
12	Nt 222		Ra. 226		Th 232.5		U 238.2		

FIG. 45. PERIODIC CLASSIFICATION OF THE ELEMENTS, SHOWING DIVISION INTO PETROGENIC ELEMENTS, ABOVE THE ZIGZAG LINE, AND METALLOGENIC ELEMENTS, BELOW THE LINE

After H. S. Washington

the arts.   But the mode of occurrence of these substances is such that they can be gathered or mined with comparative ease.   It has been pointed out by H. S. Washington that the elements, as arranged in Mendeleeff's table, naturally fall into two groups divided by a zig-zag line, as shown in figure 45.   Above this line are the *rock elements* or petrogenic elements, that enter into the principal rock-forming minerals (and also, the gases of the atmosphere).   Below the line are the *ore elements* or metallogenic elements, which commonly occur in concentrated form as ores and as native metal.

Now man's industrial activities are merely a highly specialized and greatly developed form of the general biological struggle for existence; and this same feature of accessibility and of concentration in segregated supplies (ores and the like), which is a prime condition for the very existence of some of our industries, is also involved, in closely analogous manner, in the more primitive life processes. Our fields demand fertilizers bringing ammonia, nitrates, potash, phosphates, etc., in suitably concentrated form, if they are to bear a harvest commensurate with the needs of a modern community. And this again is merely an accentuated example of the still more primitive needs of the unsophisticated flora and fauna of virgin nature. Of scattering, dissipating processes there are plenty.   Rain and snow wash most of what is soluble, and much that is not, into the rivers and out to sea.   Our own activities in modern intensive agriculture bring each year to the land a highly concentrated diet of fertilizers, which in the very act of cultivation are scattered and diluted many thousand times.   And our modern sewage system is deliberately wasteful of vital substances, which it discharges into streams and out to sea.   All this dissipation must in some way be balanced if the régime is to continue.   Thus the circulation of matter in nature must not only provide for the mere *presence* of certain substances on which the maintenance of life depends, but it must furnish them in suitable *concentration* and, generally, in available form.   It must, therefore, in many cases include, as a definite step, a segregating or concentrating process[20] as well as simple motion through a cycle.

We shall have occasion to note concrete illustrations of this in the separate consideration of the circulation of the several elements, to which we now proceed.

[20] The significance of this from the point of view of energetics will engage our special consideration in a later section.

CHAPTER XVI

THE CIRCULATION OF THE ELEMENTS—THE WATER CYCLE

> The great Sea-water finds its way
> Through long, long windings of the hills;
> And drinks up all the pretty rills
>   And rivers large and strong:
>
> Then hurries back the road it came—
> Returns on errand still the same;
> This did it when the earth was new;
> And this for evermore will do
>   As long as earth shall last.
>
> —*Wordsworth.*

The ancients, totally blind as they were perforce to the fine details of material transformations revealed by the search light of modern chemistry, nevertheless recognized in its broad features the cycle of life, the circulation of the elements in nature. "Dust thou art, and unto dust shalt thou return," we read in an old book of wisdom. Heracleitus (536 to 470 B.C.), promulgator of the famous doctrine πάντα ρεῖ has a more detailed, if not more accurate conception of the cycle of Nature, which he formulates in these terms:

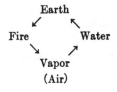

```
            Earth
          ↙      ↖
     Fire           Water
          ↘      ↗
           Vapor
           (Air)
```

The human mind was not yet schooled, then, to polish the facets of this rough gem, and bring out the sharp-edged truth as we see it today

```
         Solid
       ⌐    ↖
  Heat  by    Liquid
       └    ↗
         Vapor
```

But all honor to the minds that discerned through the mists of dawn the bold features of the landscape to be revealed in the sunlight of later day. Today we recognize not four elements, but over ninety, not counting those modern variants, the isotopes. And we follow in much detail not one cycle, but, as particularly pertinent to life, five major cycles—the circulation of water, carbon, oxygen, nitrogen and phosphorus. This was noted already at the conclusion of Chapter XIV, but the discussion of the cycles was deferred to give space to a preliminary survey of the scene in which these cycles churn the planet's surface in their age-long duty.

We are now prepared to take up the thread where we broke off; we turn our attention first to the water cycle.

Water Requirements of Human Body. We do not ordinarily class water as a food, though we partake of it by the same channel that gives entrance to the materials commonly so classed, and although the lack of water, if we are by any circumstance deprived of this substance, is felt even more acutely than an interruption in the adequate supply of food. The fundamental basis for this distinction, its origin in the unsophisticated mind, is undoubtedly the fact that we have a separate sense of thirst, distinct from the signals of hunger and appetite originating from nutritive demands of the body. And this naïve, unsophisticated distinction is entirely in accord with the reasoned analysis of the respective functions of water and of food in the narrower sense. It is undoubtedly just because of this difference in function that thirst and hunger have been developed as separately recognized sensations. Water acts merely as a vehicle; unlike the food, which undergoes extensive and complicated reactions within the economy, water leaves the body essentially as it enters it, unchanged chemically, though charged (in part) with substances in solution.

It would be a gross error, however, to suppose that water, because it functions thus in accessory capacity, and escapes the more intimate transmutations of metabolism, can be lightly regarded in making a survey of the participation of the several elements in the cycle of nature. It must be remembered that water constitutes as much as 60 per cent of the total mass of the human body, for example, and a still greater proportion of the substance of most of our food-stuffs, as shown in table 20.

Thus an adult human being consumes per diem about 3 liters of water of which about 1 liter is contained in his solid food. In point of fact he consumes about 5 pounds of water for every pound of dry solid matter ingested. It is thus seen what an important item water is in the daily economy of the human organism.

The excretion of water by the kidneys, lungs, intestine and skin is somewhat in excess of the intake. The excess of the outgo over the intake is formed in the body by the oxidation of hydrogen organically combined.[1]

Water Requirements of Plants. Rainfall as a Limiting Factor. In the economy of most plants the traffic of water is of even greater importance[2] than in man and land animals generally, and

TABLE 20

Moisture content of some common foods

	PER CENT		PER CENT
Beef (fresh)	43–65	Sugar granulated	0
Fish	40–71	Cabbage	78
Eggs	66	Cucumbers	81
Butter	11	Potatoes	63
Whole milk	87	Tomatoes	94
Cheese, Cheddar	27	Strawberries	86
Wheat flour	12	Walnut, California	1
White bread	35		

indirectly the moisture needs of plants are, of course, of fundamental importance also to the animal population feeding on the vegetable growth of the soil, so that the water supply of a territory

[1] L. J. Henderson (The Fitness of the Environment, p. 133) estimates that a man weighing 60–70 kgm. excretes daily:

	grams
Water	2500–3500
Carbon dioxide	750– 900
All other substances	60– 125

and that water is, accordingly, three-fourths and carbon dioxide one-fifth of the total excreted. The proportion of water excreted from kidneys, skin, lungs and intestines, is given by Kirk (Physiology, p. 208) as $1:0.5:0.22:0.09$, or $11.5:5.75:2.5:1$.

[2] L. J. Henderson, loc. cit., estimates that of the materials ingested by ordinary green plants, more than nine-tenths is water, and carbon dioxide at least five sixteenths of the remaining tenth.

may function as the basic limiting factor of the total life which that territory is able to support. A study of these relations with particular reference to the human population of the United States, has been made by W. J. McGee, who remarks:[3]

Hellriegel in Germany and King in this country have shown that crop plants require for their growth a quantity of water, measured by transpiration, averaging from 300 to 600 (with a mean of about 450) times the weight of the plants after drying; and common field experience indicates that, in addition to the moisture passing through the plants, the soil requires an even larger quantity to maintain a texture suitable for crop growth—much of which passes away through evaporation and seepage. On this basis "the agricultural duty of water" in this country has been formulated as the production of one-thousandth part of its weight in average plant crop. Reckoning human food and drink on this basis, and assuming that meats require (chiefly in the growth of plants used as feed for the animals) ten times the quantity of water represented in vegetal food, it appears that the adult who eats 200 pounds each of bread and beef in a year consumes something like 1 ton of water in drink and the equivalents of 400 tons in bread and 4000 tons in meat, or 4401 tons in all—figures corresponding fairly with the results of intensive agriculture in arid districts. Accordingly, the "duty of water" considered in relation to human population may be stated roughly as the maintenance of a human life a year for each 5 acre-feet used effectively in agriculture.

Now mainland United States (i.e., the chief body of our territory, exclusive of Alaska and the insular possessions) comprises something over 3,000,000 square miles, or somewhat less than 2,000,000,000 acres of land; yet the annual rainfall—the sole original source of fresh water—averages barely 2½ feet (30 inches), or hardly 5,000,000,000 acre-feet. So while the land area, if peopled to the density of Belgium (over 640 per square mile,) would carry a population of 2,000,000,000, the water supply suffices for only 1,000,000,000.

The conclusions of McGee may have to be modified in point of detail, and some of his figures may perhaps have to be revised; but the general principle underlying his reflections attract our attention. The moisture needs of the living population (all species included) are a large and fundamental item in biological economy; whether this item proves the ultimate limiting factor of population growth, as McGee suggests, is a question whose answer must be sought in

[3] Science, 1911, vol. 34, p. 429; Yearbook of the Department of Agriculture, 1910, pp. 169–176; Bureau of Soils Bull. 71 (1911), pp. 7–14; World's Work, 1912, vol..23, p. 443. Compare also L. J. Briggs, The Water Requirements of Plants, U. S. Department of Agric., Bureau of Plant Ind., Bulletins 284, 285.

terms of Liebig's Law of the Minimum; a dearth of other essentials may make itself felt before the limit of available moisture is reached.

The Sources of Supply. Such, then, in broad outline, are the moisture needs of organic nature; as such they have existed, in greater or less degree, for millions of years, and have been satisfied, and will continue long to be satisfied, from a source essentially inexhaustible because constantly replenished by the return flow: The great reservoir is the ocean, with its 302 million cubic miles of water, and an evaporating surface of over 144 million square miles. Annually there rise from this into the atmosphere about 63,300 cubic miles of water, to which some 22,800 more are added by evaporation from the land, making a total of 86,100 cubic miles. This figure also represents the total precipitation in rain, snow, etc., but of the total about 56,700 fall back directly into the ocean, and only the balance, 29,400 is available for the needs of the land. It has been noted that the evaporation from the land is about 22,800 cubic miles. The difference between this and the precipitation on land, the balance of 6500 cubic miles, is the drainage from the land to the ocean by rivers.

No attempt will be made to estimate what proportion of the precipitation on l   derived from evaporation over the sea, and what proportion comes from the land itself. Some idea of the relation, however, can be formed from a consideration of the difference or the ratio of the rainfall within the area drained by rivers and the amount actually discharged by them into the sea. John Murray[4] has collected information on this subject, with the result shown in table 21, which covers 33 of the world's principal rivers. It will be seen that the total rainfall in the area of these rivers is 10,186 cubic miles, the discharge to the sea is 2182 cubic miles, leaving a difference of 8004 cubic miles unaccounted for. A certain portion of this perhaps represents seepage, but the bulk must correspond to water re-evaporated from the land and from inland waters. It will be observed that for the 33 rivers combined the proportion of the discharge to sea to the total rainfall is about one-fifth. For individual rivers the ratio varies widely, between the extreme of 0.58 (Rhone) and 0.027 (Nile). Naturally the climate very materially affects this figure.

[4] Scottish Geographical Magazine, 1887, vol. 3, p. 76.

There is also a circulation of waters of the sea in very large dimensions. According to L. J. Henderson[5] the Gulf Stream in the Straits of Yucatan carries 200 million tons per second,[6] travelling

TABLE 21

Showing the drainage area, annual rainfall, annual discharge, and ratio of discharge to rainfall, of 33 rivers in different parts of the world

POSITION OF MOUTH OF RIVER	RIVER	DRAINAGE AREA	ANNUAL RAINFALL	MEAN ANNUAL DISCHARGE	MEAN RATIO
		square miles	*cubic miles*	*cubic miles*	
50–60°N.	Rhine	32,600	19,500	10,100	2,049
	Oder	51,100	14,700	2,500	5,803
	Niemen	36,450	10,355	3,783	2,737
	Vistula	65,800	19,908	5,657	3,508
40–50°N.	St. Lawrence	565,200	338,967	87,312	3,904
	Danube	320,300	198,736	67,511	2,746
	Po	27,100	23,887	13,322	1,794
	Volga	592,300	152,384	43,736	3,484
	Seine	23,250	10,266	5,469	1,877
	Rhone	34,850	22,439	14,066	1,724
	Dnieper	197,450	56,093	22,195	2,527
	Loire	42,600	18,210	7,810	2,332
	Dniester	30,950	8,792	3,274	2,685
30–40°N.	Yang-tse-kiang	689,100	408,872	125,043	3,421
	Hoang-ho	387,150	117,711	28,591	4,159
	Nile	1,293,050	892,120	24,334	30,998
	Pei-ho	65,000	22,354	1,650	13,551
20–30°N.	Mississippi	1,285,300	673,064	125,603	5,446
	Rio Grande	232,300	113,655	12,676	8,966
	Indus	360,050	104,416	26,032	4,886
	Ganges	588,450	549,791	43,263	16,169
10–20°N.	Magdalena	92,900	116,746	59,451	1,964
	Irawali	181,950	180,849	82,298	2,256
	Kistna	81,300	61,025	14,776	4,137
	Godavery	154,850	95,924	16,841	5,708
0–10°N.	Orinoco	429,700	603,397	122,242	4,936
Equator	Amazon	2,229,900	2,833,830	527,951	8,009
0–10°S.	San Francisco	212,900	218,459	22,197	9,842
	Congo	1,540,800	1,213,044	419,291	3,213
20–30°S.	Orange	267,150	50,913	21,875	2,327
30–40°S.	Olifant	14,300	2,472	0,679	3,639
	De La Plata	994,900	904,687	188,740	6,091
	Uruguay	151,000	130,890	32,136	4,073
Total.....................		13,272,000	10,186,460	2,182,485	

[5] The Fitness of the Environment, 1913, p. 182.

[6] Across any cross-section of the stream, presumably; the statement is not clear on this point.

with a mean velocity of about 80 miles per day.   This circulation in
the ocean has of course no direct part in the water cycle of the organic
world, but indirectly is most important on account of its climatic
effects.

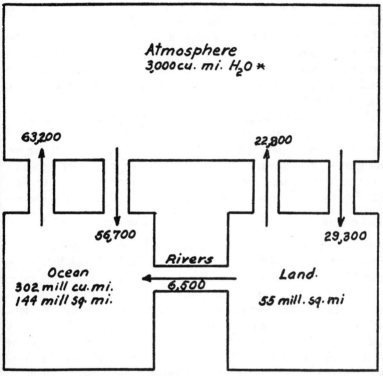

FIG. 46. CIRCULATION OF THE ELEMENTS IN NATURE.   THE WATER CYCLE

Water Cycle Diagram.   The principal figures relating to the
circulation of water on the globe are exhibited in diagrammatic form
in figure 46, which tells the story more effectively than words.   It
may here be added in explanation that the 3000 cubic miles of

moisture contained in the air are practically restricted to the lower 6 miles or so of the atmosphere. For the rest, this moisture is unevenly distributed, as everybody knows from personal weather observation. Water vapor and condensed water differs in this respect from the other permanently, gaseous constituents of the atmosphere. (See table 12 and figures 40, 41.)

Fraction of Total Water Circulation Taking Part in Life Cycle. Only a fraction of the total circulation of water actually passes through the organic cycle. We may make an attempt as follows to obtain a rough idea of the order of magnitude of the fraction thus concerned.

If the entire land surface were cultivated to produce crops at the rate adopted as standard by W. J. McGee, the growth produced (figured in dry weight) would be $\frac{1}{1000}$ of the rainfall. Furthermore, this growth would evaporate, by transpiration, about 500 times its own weight of water, (this is assuming one crop per year). It would therefore evaporate just about one-half the annual rainfall. But the total evaporation on the land is $\frac{22,800}{29,300}$ = three fourths of the annual rainfall on land, the remaining fourth being drained to sea by rivers. Hence, of the water evaporated on land, one-half times four-thirds = two-thirds is evaporated by plants and thus takes direct part in the organic cycle. In comparison with the evaporation by plants, that from animals is undoubtedly negligible, especially in view of the coarseness of our data. If we put the evaporation on land as one-fourth of the total evaporation, we finally arrive at the value one-sixth as that fraction of the total water in circulation, which takes actual part in the organic circulation.

Desert areas cannot materially alter this estimate, since they contribute but little to either side of the account, both evaporation and life being meagre or absent. In some measure this remark also applies to frigid wastes of the polar regions, where the low temperature makes for comparatively low evaporation (a factor counter-balanced, it is true, in some degree, by the extensive cover of ice and snow). For temperate zones McGee's figure for cultivated fields is undoubtedly too high to apply as an average for the entire land. In the tropics, on the other hand, it is perhaps not excessive. On the whole the fraction one-sixth computed as above is probably too high, but perhaps it serves to give us an idea of the order of magnitude involved.

Another estimate leading to a materially lower result, is obtained as follows: If we accept Engler's estimate that one-fiftieth of the atmospheric carbon dioxide, that is to say, 4.4×10^{10} metric tons, takes part in the organic cycle; and we adopt the figure given by L. J. Henderson[2] that the water taken up by plants, is about 11 times the CO_2 which they absorb, we obtain, as a very rough estimate of the water engaged in the organic cycle, an amount of 5×10^{11} metric tons, or, in round numbers, 120 cubic miles. This, then, is about $\frac{1}{700}$ of the total annual circulation of water, or about $\frac{1}{250}$ of the total rainfall on land.

CHAPTER XVII

THE CARBON DIOXIDE CYCLE

Behold how great a matter a little fire kindleth.—St. James.

If the lamp of life is a poetic symbol, it is an image essentially true to fact. Not only is life, in particular animal life, largely a combustion process: like the flame, life reaches out for fuel, and with the power gained, strains again for more. Like the flame it consumes, and it spreads. And as the fire sends out sparks, of which many die, but a few, falling upon favorable ground, flare up as a second generation, in reproduction of the parent flame; so the living creature scatters its seed, some to die, but some also to live again the life of the parent. "But," someone perhaps will remark, "a fire may start without preëxisting flame; whereas all life is itself begotten of life." Is this distinction really so fundamental? In nature undisturbed by man the starting of a fire spontaneously is a rare event; and that, after all, is the most that we can say positively regarding the origination of life from the non-living—it is either so rare or so unobtrusive[1] an event as to have escaped our observation. No doubt it took man many thousands of years to acquire the art of lighting a fire, may not in the lapse of time a second Prometheus arise to teach us also how to kindle the torch of life? Let us not delay his coming by closing our minds to the possibility.[2]

---

[1] Compare F. J. Allen's view, as presented by L. L. Woodruff in The Evolution of the Earth and its Inhabitants, 1919, p. 102: "Life at this stage was of the humblest kind, since there were no definite organisms, only diffuse substances trading in energy, and between this stage and the evolution of cellular organisms an immense period elapsed." If this picture of the beginning of life is true to fact, the process was unobtrusive; probably, if we were shown a specimen of such elementary "living" matter, we should not recognize it as such. All this is in accord with what has been said in an earlier chapter regarding the definition of life. If we continue to use the word life, this is merely a matter of convenience and does not imply any departure from the point of view set forth in the opening chapters. See also p. 19.

Be that as it may, the fundamental fact remains that slow combustion, oxidation as the chemist calls it, is a dominant feature in the physiology of animal life, and that the leading rôles in this action are played by the elements carbon and oxygen.

In our method of securing our supply of these elements there is a certain dyssymmetry. Carbon we eat in our meals; oxygen we breathe in in respiration. But in function the two elements stand in essentially symmetrical relation; the two together and impartially furnish us with the requisite energy for our life activities. Thus we must regard oxygen as food as much as carbon. This fact deserves a passing note, since it is sometimes stated that assimilation of inorganic food is a characteristic of plants, as distinguished from animals. The statement rests on an arbitrary and wholly gratuitous exclusion of oxygen from our list of foods. It just so happens that there is one item on the animal's *menu*, namely, oxygen that is gaseous and is spread broadcast; does not therefore have to be hunted and captured. Toward this the animal assumes the same attitude which, presumably, plants adopt toward all their foods: he takes it in unconsciously. This touch of plant nature which we recognize in ourselves should serve to give us a sympathetic insight into the "psychology" of plants. At the same time it reminds us once again of the essentially arbitrary character of the division of organisms into two classes, animals and plants. One and the same organism possesses both animal and plant characteristics, and this is true even of that most highly specialized of all animals, the human being. In view of the symmetry in function that exists between carbon and oxygen, and the inseparable relation

---

[2] It is easy to strike a match, but this is merely a way of borrowing the efforts of others, those who have made the match possible, and those who have manufactured it. How many city dwellers could, by their unaided efforts, start a fire where none was before? Anyone who, in an emergency, may have been forced to attempt the feat will appreciate how among the ancients "the spark of fire was zealously guarded and soon invested with sacred attributes . . . . The chief function of the vestal virgins in Rome was to keep the perpetual fire; and in the Catholic church today with its never extinguished light we have the last survival of what was once a social custom. . . . " Another curious survival of this custom is quoted by R. A. Seligman (Principle of Economics, 1908, p. 69): "Whenever the location of gas works is changed the fire is transferred by a brand from the old to the new building. Under no consideration would a new fire be started."

in which they stand in the life processes of the organism, we shall consider jointly, in this chapter, the circulation of carbon on the one hand, and of oxygen on the other.

The Carbon Cycle. A very particular interest attaches to the carbon cycle. Carbon is the organic element *par excellence*, whose absence from any chemical substance stamps this forthwith, by common if somewhat arbitrary consent, as inorganic: whose presence affords the soil and season for the growth of what might be termed the tropical jungle in the domain of chemistry. For in the compounds of carbon nature seems to have run riot, in a revel of creative versatility, as if vying to set a record unapproached elsewhere in all the realm of chemistry, for number, variety and complexity of her children. Other elements—oxygen, nitrogen, phosphorus, sulphur, iron, indeed play a significant rôle in life processes; but the indispensable bond that ever links all other ingredients in organic unity is carbon. Furthermore, carbon is preëminently the energy carrier, the standard coin of the organic real, in which both the first cost of installation, of anabolic tissue building, and also the running cost of operation, of metabolism, is defrayed.

Indescribably complex—far beyond the understanding of the organic chemist of today—as are the metamorphoses that carbon undergoes in the economy of the organism, its source and its gate of entry into the organic cycle are comparatively simple. Some two and a half million million tons (2.2×10^{15} kgm.) of carbon dioxide, in the air, and perhaps twenty to twenty-five times this amount contained in the waters of ocean, lakes and rivers, these constitute the store from which all life ultimately draws its supply.

Of this vast store, according to an estimate made by C. Engler,[3] about one-thousandth part actually takes part in the cycle of life. The total carbon locked up in living organisms, which would be a measure, in a way, of the spread of life on our globe, is difficult to gage even roughly. One hardly knows how much or how little significance to attach to an estimate by A. G. Högbom[4] that the total quantity of carbon in all living matter is of about the same order as that contained in the atmosphere, namely, 6×10^{11} metric

[3] Linck, Kreislaufvorgänge in der Erdgeschichte, 1912, p. 6; Engler, Über Zerfalls-prozesse in der Natur.

[4] Clarke, Data of Geochemistry, 1920, p. 49.

tons; an amount which, spread over the entire surface of the globe, would cover it with a film of carbon 1 mm. thick, or with a film of living matter about ½ inch thick.

The organic carbon cycle, reduced to its simplest terms, is a closed chain of three links.

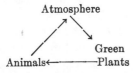

Green plants, under the influence of sun light, absorb CO_2 from the atmosphere and convert it, with elimination of oxygen, into the many and complex compounds of the plant substance.[5]   Animals consume plants (directly or indirectly) as food, and in the course of the operations of their typically active lives (as compared with the typically passive, sessile existence of the majority of plants) they reoxidize the carbon reduced in the photosynthetic plant processes, and return CO_2 to the atmosphere, thus completing the cycle.

In actual fact this simple fundamental cycle is complicated by a number of influences.   The decay of dead animals and plants adds a comparatively small item to the discharge of CO_2 into the atmosphere.   Plants are somewhat more resistant to complete decay than animals, and one result of this is the accumulation of notable

[5] To discuss here the chemistry of photosynthesis in plants would lead us too far afield.   Very important advances have been made recently in this field of biochemistry.   It must suffice here to refer to the original literature of which the following articles may be mentioned: E. C. Baly, Photosynthesis, Nature, March 16, 1922, p. 344.   Report of discussion on photosynthesis at the British Association Meeting, Nature, December 23, 1922, p. 856.   I. M. Heilbron, The Photosynthesis of Plant Products, Nature, April 14, 1923, p. 502.   O. Baudisch, On the Formation of Organic Compounds from Inorganic by the Influence of Light, Science, April 20, 1923, p. 451. O. Baudisch, The Influence of Light on Inorganic Matter and Life Processes, Jour. Industrial and Eng. Chemistry, May, 1923, p. 451.   J. C. Bose, Effect of Infinitesimal Traces of Chemical Substances on Photosynthesis, Nature, July 21, 1922, p. 95.   Baly, Heilbron and Parker, Photochemical Production of Formaldehyde, Nature, September 1, 1923, p. 323.   J. H. Mathews, Trends in Photochemical Research, Jour. Ind. and Eng. Chem., September, 1923, p. 885.

quantities of reduced carbon in the form of peat and coal. This process of fossilization is slow, and would not in itself, in any short period, materially affect the carbon cycle. It has, however, furnished the occasion for a phenomenon which, judged in a cosmic perspective, represents a purely ephemeral flare, such as must ultimately appear utterly insignificant in the geological calendar, if duration alone is considered; but which to us, the human race in the twentieth century is of altogether transcendent importance: The great industrial era is founded upon, and at the present day inexorably dependent upon, the exploitation of the fossil fuel accumulated in past geological ages.

We have every reason to be optimistic; to believe that we shall be found, ultimately, to have taken at the flood this great tide in the affairs of men; and that we shall presently be carried on the crest of the wave into a safer harbor. There we shall view with even mind the exhaustion of the fuel that took us into port, knowing that practically imperishable resources have in the meanwhile been unlocked, abundantly sufficient for all our journeys to the end of time. But whatever may be the ultimate course of events, the present is an eminently atypical epoch. Economically we are living on our capital; biologically we are changing radically the complexion of our share in the carbon cycle by throwing into the atmosphere, from coal fires and metallurgical furnaces, ten times as much carbon dioxide as in the natural biological process of breathing. How large a single item this represents will be realized when attention is drawn to the fact that these human agencies alone would, in the course of about five hundred years, double the amount of carbon dioxide in the entire atmosphere, if no compensating influences entered into play. In point of fact the percentage of carbon dioxide in the atmosphere exhibits remarkable constancy and there are several very large items, in addition to those already touched upon, both on the ingoing and outgoing side of the account. The case of man has been singled out for mention here merely because our knowledge of the human population and economy enables us to make a reasonably close estimate of his contributions. The quota supplied by the remaining animal species can hardly even be guessed at. But probably the greatest source of atmosphere CO_2 are volcanoes and mineral springs. Cotopaxi alone has been credited with an annual discharge of two million tons of the gas.

On the debit side there is first of all the item of consumption by plants. E. H. Cook,[6] from very uncertain data, computes that leaf action alone more than compensates for the production of carbon dioxide, consuming about one-hundredth of the total atmospheric oxygen in a year. Jost[7] computes that if the entire land area were planted with sun flowers, about 6.5×10^{11} tons of CO_2 would be absorbed per annum. Forests would be considerably less efficient, and would take care of about 2.8×10^{10} tons per annum, or, say in round numbers one-hundredth of the atmospheric carbon dioxide. An older estimate, by Liebig, puts the annual output of the soil of Central Europe at 2.5 tons of dry organic matter per hectar, or, say 1 ton per acre. Allowing 40 per cent carbon in such organic matter we find for the total annual production of carbon in plants 13,000 million (1.3×10^{10}) tons. This is about ten times the world's annual coal consumption, and about one-fiftieth of the total carbon in atmospheric carbon dioxide. Arrhenius points out that if all this carbon fixed by plants were deposited in peat bogs, the atmosphere would be depleted in half a century. But, of course, only a small proportion of the bodies of plants are thus "horded" and removed from the organic life cycle.

A figure of perhaps greater interest, because based upon observations of processes actually going on in a selected portion of the universe, is given by W. R. G. Atkins. From the observed change in the hydrogen ion concentration in the water of the English Channel, this author has calculated that 250 metric tons of organic carbon (figured as hexose) were produced per square kilometer between July and December. From similar observations made at Port Erin, Moore found a production of 300 metric tons per square kilometer during the six months that included the vernal maximum of diatom production.[8]

An important item among the withdrawals from the atmosphere is the absorption of carbon dioxide in the weathering of rocks, with replacement of silicates by carbonates. A. G. Högbom reckons this item as about balancing the reproduction of carbon dioxide in the

[6] F. W. Clarke, loc. cit., p. 48; Phil. Mag., 5th ser., vol. 1882, p. 387.
[7] Pflanzenphysiologie, 1913, p. 151.
[8] Journal of Marine Biol. Assoc. October, 1922, vol. 12, no. 4, Nature, January 27, 1923, p. 132.

combustion of coal. Its accumulated record is seen in the sedimentary rocks, which, according to F. W. Clarke,[9] contain 30,000 times as much as CO_2 as are today present in the atmosphere.[10] Sterry Hunt "illustrates the effect of weathering by the statement that the production from orthoclase of a layer of kaolin (china clay) 500 meters thick and completely enveloping the globe would consume 21 times the amount of CO_2 now present in the atmosphere." Chamberlin and others estimate that it would take about 10,000 years to consume the present amount of atmospheric CO_2 by the weathering of rocks. Loss of CO_2 by peat formation may be estimated at the same figure. The formation of CO_2 by the burning of coal would, according to these estimates, cover the loss by weathering and peat formation combined, seven times over.

Finally, there is the great reservoir of the ocean, in equilibrium with the atmosphere, and absorbing, under present conditions, some 18 to 25 times as much CO_2 as it leaves in the air above it. Thus the sea acts as a vast equalizer; of every ton of CO_2 thrown into the atmosphere by volcanoes, or by coal fires, for example, the ocean ultimately receives directly or indirectly, about 1900 pounds, only the balance of 100 pounds remaining in the atmosphere. It is thus seen that even extensive contributions from the lithosphere have but a slight effect upon the atmospheric store, and fluctuations are in this way ironed out and moderated. Arrhenius[11] points out, moreover, that at the present time the carbon dioxide content of the air over the ocean is on an average 10 per cent lower than over land. From this, and the fact that generation of CO_2 by coal (and probably also from volcanoes) has in late years been increasing, he concludes that the air is, at the present epoch, becoming richer in this gas.

[9] Loc. cit., p. 48. See also C. Shuchert, The Evolution of the Earth and its Inhabitants (Yale Press, 1919), p. 52.

[10] Högbom's figure, quoted by Arrhenius (Worlds in the Making, 1908, p. 54), is 25,000 for limestones and dolomites. Am. Jour. Sci., 3d ser, 1880, vol. 19, p. 349. Clarke, loc. cit, p. 48.

[11] Loc. cit., p. 54. Arrhenius' figure differs somewhat from the one given above. He supposes that the sea takes up five-sixths of the CO_2 thrown into the air, i.e., 1 ton would yield up 1667 pounds to the ocean, leaving 333 pounds in the air.

As to which side of the account shows a net balance, in the carbon cycle, we have no certain knowledge. Arrhenius builds his conception of the future industrial development of our race on the expectation that the atmosphere is gaining in carbon dioxide, under the present régime of "evaporating" our coal mines, as it were into the air. On the other hand, if our atmospheric CO_2 is of volcanic origin, and the balance is maintained today with the aid of discharge from the lithosphere, then the ultimate extinction of the earth's plutonic fires would bring in its train the depletion of the atmosphere and secondarily the extinction of life. "The cessation of volcanism would signify the end of life on the globe." A similar position is taken by C. Schuchert,[12] who further remarks:

We should add that if there were again as much life as there is at present, all the carbon of the atmosphere would be in the living plants and animals, and, if such a condition were possible death would come to them all . . . . Life and its abundance at any time are conditioned by the amount of this gas (CO_2) present in the atmosphere.

This remark of Schuchert's is suggestive as illustrating in concrete manner the relative amounts of carbon concerned in the life balance. It is, perhaps, somewhat misleading in making no mention of the equalizing influence of the ocean which has been noted above. In point of fact, if all the CO_2 in the air were withdrawn, a nearly equal amount would rise from the ocean to take its place.

A summary, in graphic form, of the principal relations in the carbon cycle noted in the preceding paragraphs, will be found in figure 47, which should aid in giving a comprehensive picture of the situation.

The Oxygen Cycle. The organic oxygen cycle is, of course, directly related to the carbon cycle, although other features also enter into operation in regulating the oxygen balance of the atmosphere. The complementary relation between animals (essentially oxidizers of carbon) and plants (essentially reducers of carbon dioxide) is indeed a biological fact of fundamental importance at the present stage of evolution. But if we look back through the vista of ages, to the time before the advent of life, such as we know it, our curiosity is aroused as to the origin of the atmospheric carbon

[12] The Evolution of the Earth and its Inhabitants, 1919, p. 52.

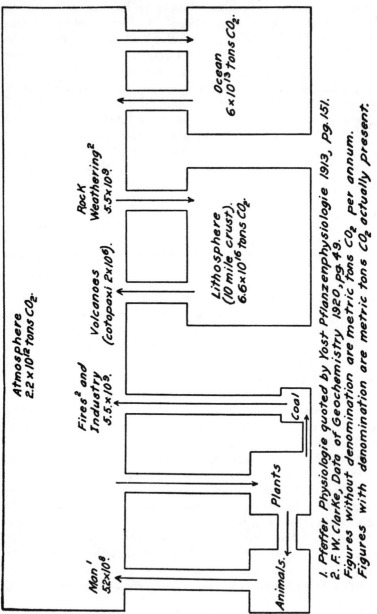

1. Pfeffer Physiologie quoted by Yost Pflanzenphysiologie 1913, pg. 151.
2. F. W. Clarke, Data of Geochemistry 1920, pg. 49.
Figures without denomination are metric tons CO_2 per annum.
Figures with denomination are metric tons CO_2 actually present.

FIG. 47. CIRCULATION OF THE ELEMENTS IN NATURE. THE CARBON CYCLE

dioxide and oxygen. Various views have been upheld on this subject. F. W. Clarke[13] remarks:

It is likely that carbon dioxide has been added to the atmosphere by volcanic agency, in some such manner as this: Primitive carbon, like the graphite found in meteorites, at temperature no greater than that of molten lava, reduced the magnetite of igneous rocks to metallic iron, such as is found in many basalts, and was itself thereby oxidized. Then, discharged into the atmosphere as dioxide, it became subject to the familiar reactions which restored it to the lithosphere as coal or limestone.

Arrhenius,[14] referring to Koehne's reflections on this subject, points out that the atmosphere contains about 1.2×10^{15} tons of oxygen, an amount which roughly[15] corresponds with the mass of fossil coal in the sedimentary rocks. "The supposition appears natural, therefore, that all the oxygen of the air may have been formed at the expense of atmospheric carbon dioxide. Probably all the oxygen of the air owes its existence to plant life."

F. W. Clarke resumes the views of a number of investigators as follows:[16]

C. J. Koehne assumed that the primitive atmosphere contained no free oxygen, and he has been followed by T. L. Phipson,[17] J. Lemberg,[18] J. Stevenson,[19] and Lord Kelvin.[20] Lemberg and Kelvin, however, do not go to extremes, but admit that possibly some free oxygen was present even in the earliest times. Lemberg argued that the primeval atmosphere contained chiefly hydrogen, nitrogen, volatile chlorides, and carbon compounds; the oxygen which is now free, being then united with carbon and iron. The

---

[13] F. W. Clarke, loc. cit., p. 55.

[14] Worlds in the Making, 1908, p. 58.

[15] The correspondence is rather distant if we accept Engler's estimate of the world's coal reserves, namely, 3×10^{12} tons, containing 75 per cent carbon. See Linck, loc. cit., p. 37. Engler's estimate is probably low. The World Almanac, 1921, p. 201, gives 7.5×10^{12} tons. This would correspond to 1.5×10^{13} tons oxygen, as against 1.2×10^{15} tons in the atmosphere. It is true that these estimates of coal reserves cover only such coal as it would pay to mine.

[16] F. W. Clarke, loc. cit., 1921, p. 56.

[17] Chem. News, 1893, vol. 67, p. 135. Also several notes in vols. 68, 69, and 70. For Koehne's work see Phipson's papers, 1893–1894.

[18] Zeitschr. Deutsch, geol. Gesell, 1888, vol. 40, pp. 630–634.

[19] Philos. Mag., 1900, 5th ser., vol. 50, pp. 312–399; 6th ser., 1902, vol. 4, p. 435; 1905, vol. 9, p. 88; 1906, vol. 11, p. 226.

[20] Ibid., 1899, 5th ser., vol. 47, pp. 85–89.

liberation of oxygen began with the appearance of low forms of plant life, possibly reached a maximum in Carboniferous time, and has since diminished. Stevenson's argument is much more elaborate, and starts with an estimate of the uncombined carbon now existent in the sedimentary formations. In the deposition of that carbon, oxygen was liberated, and from data of this kind it is argued that the atmospheric supply of oxygen is steadily increasing, while that of carbon dioxide diminishes. The statement that no oxygen has been found in the gases extracted from rocks is also adduced in favor of the theory. First, an oxidized crust and no free oxygen in the air; then processes of reduction coming into play; and at last the appearance of lower forms of plants, which prepared the atmosphere to sustain animal life. The arguments are ingenious, but to my mind they exemplify the result of attaching excessive importance to one set of phenomena alone. It is not clear that due account has been taken of the checks and balances which are actually observed. At present the known losses of oxygen seem to exceed the gains. For example, C. H. Smyth[21] has estimated that the oxygen withdrawn from the air by the change of ferrous to ferric compounds, and so locked up in the sedimentary rocks, is equal to 68.8 per cent of the quantity now present in the atmosphere.

G. Bunge[22] also supports the view that atmospheric oxygen is continually diminishing, becoming bound by the ferrous oxide resulting from the decomposition of silicates. Accumulation of carbon dioxide in the atmosphere, at any rate under present conditions, is also assumed by S. Arrhenius, as has already been remarked.[23]

[21] Jour. Geology, 1905, vol. 13, p. 319.
[22] Text book of Physiological and Pathological Chemistry, 1902, pp. 16–17.
[23] See Jour. Franklin Inst., 1920, vol. 190, pp. 114–121.

CHAPTER XVIII

THE NITROGEN CYCLE

If the demand becomes insistent enough, we cannot doubt that methods will be devised which will give us the desired results. To question that would be to admit that man has neared the culmination of his evolutionary career and is preparing to bequeath the mastery of the earth to his successor, whoever that may be.—*G. W. Martin.*

Natural Demand and Supply. The proportion of nitrogen to carbon in the human body is 1:3, in the atmosphere it is 5,500:1. A human adult contains in his body about 42 pounds of nitrogen, and over 50 pounds of carbon. Over every square foot of the earth's surface rises a column containing some 1500 pounds of nitrogen, and only about 1/4 pound of carbon. The demand and the supply of these two elements appear, therefore, at first sight, to be altogether out of all proportion favorable to nitrogen. Yet, in point of fact, the practical problem of securing an adequate supply for the sustenance and expansion of life is incomparably more complex in the case of nitrogen than in the case of carbon. The reason for this somewhat remarkable inversion is to be seen in the fact that nitrogen is readily accessible as food for living organisms only when it occurs in certain chemical combinations, and nitrogen thus combined is far from plentiful. It has been estimated by T. H. Norton that this available or "nomadic" nitrogen—i.e., that which takes part in the migration through the organic cycle—amounts to only about two one-millionths of the total nitrogen of the atmosphere, or, say, to about 8×10^9 tons. In fact, nitrogen is today probably the chief of those limiting factors[1] which, in accordance with Liebig's law of the minimum, establish the bounds for the extreme expansion of living matter upon the earth. At the same time the circumstance of the chemical idiosyncrasies of the element nitrogen introduces a certain complexity into the nitrogen cycle, which strikes the eye at a glance in the charts, figures 48 and 49, exhibiting the essentials of the nitrogen

---

[1] Compare G. Bunge, Physiological and Pathological Chemistry, 1902, p. 17; Grinnell Jones, Qu. Jour. Economics, 1920, vol. 34, p. 394.

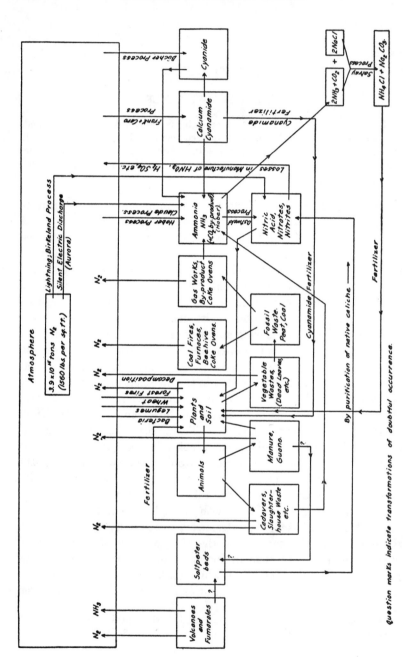

Question marks indicate transformations of doubtful occurrence.

Fig. 48. Circulation of the Elements in Nature. The Nitrogen Cycle

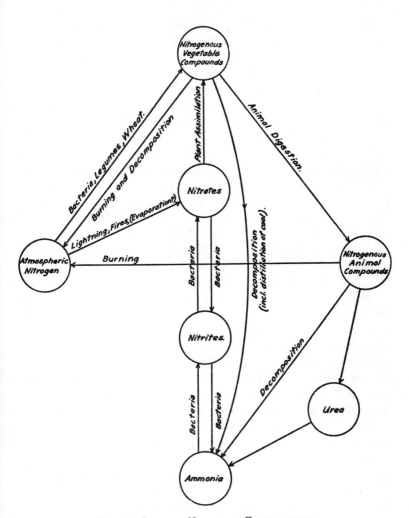

FIG. 49. ORGANIC NITROGEN CIRCULATION

cycle.   Figure 48 shows in broader outline the main feature of the cycle, while figure 49 exhibits in greater detail especially those stages in the cycle that are most intimately associated with life agencies.[2]

[2] For details on this phase of the subject the reader must be referred to the special literature. A good summary, fairly detailed and complete, yet concise, will be found in R. Huber, Zur Stickstoff-Frage, Bern 1908 pp. 1–16.

Gate of Entry into Nitrogen Cycle. The natural gateway for the entry of atmospheric, elementary nitrogen, into the organic cycle is a narrow one. So far as at present known, only a limited class of organisms possess the faculty of "fixing" this element, that is, taking it in its gaseous state from the atmosphere and converting it into the condensed (liquid or solid) form, in which only it has common acceptation as coin of the organic realm. The organisms known to take part in this natural process of nitrogen fixation are three, namely certain bacteria having their habitat in the soil; certain leguminous plants (peas, beans, clover, alfalfa), working in conjunction, in symbiosis, with nitrogen-fixing bacteria lodged in tubercles upon their roots; and, thirdly, the wheat plant has recently been shown to possess the independent faculty of assimilating nitrogen from the air. This recent demonstration,[3] of course, suggests the ready question whether after all, a number of other plants may not be similarly endowed. This remains as a matter for further investigation, but it is improbable that we shall have occasion to change materially our present impression, namely, that the natural avenues by which elementary nitrogen gains admission from the atmosphere into the cycle of life are rather narrowly restricted. As to other avenues opened up by the man, these will be considered presently.

Leak of Nitrogen out of Circulation. While there is thus a narrowly restricted class of vegetable organism through which nitrogen trickles in a thin stream from the elementary supply in the atmosphere into the life cycle, the majority of plants derive the supply for their biological needs from ready formed nomadic nitrogen in the soil, that is to say nitrogen combined in the form of ammonium salts, nitrites and nitrates. These substances are subject to oxidation and reduction in the soil under the influence of various bacteria, as indicated in the chart figure 49. The result of these changes is that a certain fraction of the nomadic nitrogen is continually leaking out of the circulation and joins the general reservoir of free nitrogen in the atmosphere. This is only one of a number of items on the losing side of the balance sheet. Other items will be found in following up the details of the two charts already

[3] C. B. Lipman and J. K. Taylor, Science, November 24, 1922, p. 605. These authors report that in their experiments wheat plants assimilated 13 to 21 per cent of their nitrogen content from the air.

referred to. There is loss in the autumnal leaf fall of deciduous plants; in the decay of dead plants, or in their fossilization as peat, lignite and coal. Forest fires, and the burning of wood and coal; the distillation of coal for illuminating gas; the oxidation of coal in metallurgical furnaces, the coking of coal in ovens of the so-called beehive type; all these are operations in which a greater or less proportion of the combined nitrogen in the coal is liberated into the air in the free, unavailable form. In view of the great loss which this represents in the economy of our food resources, the highest importance attaches to the modern drift away from the beehive coke oven to the by-product oven, in which the major part of the nitrogen in the coal is recovered as ammonia.

TABLE 22

Fraction, of total output of coke in the United States, produced in by-product ovens

YEAR	PER CENT	YEAR	PER CENT	YEAR	PER CENT
1890	0	1910	17.1	1917	38.6
1900	5.3	1915	33.8	1918	46.0
1905	10.7	1916	35.0	1919	56.2

These by-product ovens were introduced in 1893. It is estimated that during the period from 1893 to 1910 alone, through the continued use of the old beehive type coke oven, over 9,300,000 tons of ammonium sulphate were wasted, representing, at the prices then prevailing, a value of 558 million dollars. In addition to this must be reckoned a further loss in the resulting field crops. Had all the nitrogen wasted in the beehive ovens been spread as fertilizer on the field, this would have increased the crops some 20 per cent.[4] An idea of the extent and significance of the healthy modern drift towards replacement of the beehive by the recovery coke oven may be gathered from table 22, reproduced from an article by Grinnell Jones in the Quarterly Journal of Economics, 1920, vol. 34, p. 402. H. E. Fischer, writing in the Journal of the Franklin Institute, 1920, vol. 190, p. 191, remarks that if all the coal in the United States were used as coke, and the ammonia recovered in the process, this alone would

[4] This and other data regarding nitrogen losses here set forth are drawn, largely, from an article by J. D. Pennock in the Journal of Industrial and Engineering Chemistry, 1911.

furnish one million tons of ammonia, which corresponds to about one-half the world's total production of nitrogen compounds.

Returning to the chart (fig. 48) and continuing to trace the progress of nitrogen in the organic cycle, we note next that combined nitrogen is absorbed from plants by animals in their food. It is rejected from the animal economy in part as excretory matter (manure, etc.), in part in the bodies of dead animals, in so far as these are not themselves consumed as food. A large item here, in the economics of the human community, is the refuse from slaughter houses. Certain portions of this are recovered for various uses (glue, leather, etc.). Some is made into fertilizer. Much of it goes to waste, and thus gives opportunity for another leak of nitrogen out of the life cycle to the elementary form in the atmosphere. It is difficult to form any estimate of the extent of this loss, but there can be no doubt that it represents a waste of hundreds of tons of nitrogen daily. Much also is lost from the other item of animal waste materials, not a little of the loss being occasioned by modern methods of sewage disposal in large cities. Such methods represent, from the standpoint of agricultural economy, a luxury, which however, will be thought worth the price if the means are at hand to make good the loss from other sources. Those portions of animal refuse which are placed on the soil of crop-bearing fields and pastures return, at least in part, into the organic cycle.

Accessory Sources of Combined Nitrogen. It is of course absolutely essential for the continuance of the life cycle that the losses of combined nitrogen which have been noted should in some way be compensated by equal or greater accessions to the total amount of nomadic nitrogen. One source of such compensating revenue has already been noted, namely the direct assimilation of elementary nitrogen from the atmosphere by a narrowly restricted class of plants. There are two other natural sources. Volcanoes and fumaroles belch notable quantities of ammonium chloride into the air; nitric acid is also formed by the action of lightning, while ammonia is produced by the passage of the silent electric discharge (aurora) through the atmosphere. Arrhenius[5] estimates that the amount of nitrogen annually bound in this way amounts to about 1.4×10^9

[5] S. Arrhenius, Worlds in the Making, 1908, p. 144. See also Haber, Zeitschr. f. Angew. Chemie, 1910, p. 685.

metric tons, or one part in 3 millions of the total atmospheric nitrogen. The products are washed into the soil by the descending rain, together with more or less of the same substances that have escaped into the atmosphere from the ground and are thus restored to the soil. Estimates which have been made of the quantities involved

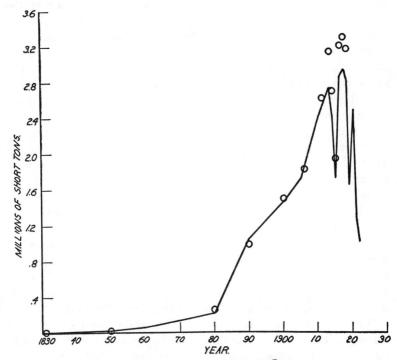

FIG. 50. THE RISE OF THE SALTPETER INDUSTRY

are somewhat conflicting, but on the whole the gains of the soil in this way are held to exceed its losses.[6]

The stages and agencies so far reviewed may be collectively designated as those constituting the "natural nitrogen cycle," as distinguished from a group now to be considered, which are charac-

[6] F. W. Clarke, loc. cit., 1920, p. 52; Linck, Kreislaufvorgänge, 1912, pp. 6-7. It has also been put forward (Schönbein) that a certain amount of nitric acid is formed in the evaporation of moisture from the earth (Bunge Physiological Chemistry, 1902, p. 11). But this is doubted by Ostwald. (Grundlinien der Anorganischen Chemie, 1912, p. 384.)

terized by human interference with the course of nature. It is hardly necessary to point out that such a distinction between natural and artificial agencies is merely a convenient use of brief terms; the fact must never be lost sight of that man himself is very essentially part of nature, and that his development, whether physiological, psychological, sociological, economic, or what not, is part of the great process of nature.

Human Interference in Nitrogen Cycle. Man's earliest conscious, purposive intervention in the nitrogen cycle dates from antiquity, and primarily consisted merely in taking more or less pains, in an empirical way, that the nitrogenous waste material of animal economy be, as far as possible, restored to the soil. Perhaps the first recorded use of fertilizers not derived from current wastes of domestic animals is the exploitation of guano by the Incas, which dates from antiquity, and was brought to the notice of Europe by de la Vega in 1604. It seems to have aroused no interest until attention was again drawn to it two hundred years later by von Humboldt and by Justus Liebig, and large scale importations of guano into Europe began soon after this. A greater event in the history of agriculture was the opening up, in 1831, of the Chilean nitre beds. Without this source of saltpeter the modern development of intensive agriculture, and the consequent growth of population in all civilized countries, would have been at the least greatly hampered. The rapid rise of the saltpeter industry is clearly exhibited in table 23 and the corresponding graph figure 50.

While our chief interest here is in the agricultural use of Chile saltpeter, its consumption in the industries is altogether too extensive to be passed by without mention. J. D. Pennock[7] gives the figures shown in table 24 for the relative amounts of saltpeter consumed in different uses.

It should be observed that Pennock's figures relate to peace time conditions. Even so, nearly one-half the consumption is taken up in the manufacture of explosives. Nitrogen thus employed is, of course, lost to the life cycle. A certain loss also occurs in refining of the caliche (native saltpeter), and in the production of nitric acid and sulphuric acid[8] therefrom.

[7] J. D. Pennock, Jour. Industr. and Eng. Chem., 1911, p. 172.
[8] When manufactured by the Chamber process.

TABLE 23

Growth of the saltpeter industry

	SHORT TONS		
	(I)	(II) Sodium nitrate	(III) Nitrogen on basis of 15.65 per cent
1830	800		
1831		112	17.5
1850	22,800	22,350	3,498
1880	222,559	257,060	40,230
1890	1,050,119	998,970	156,339
1900	1,471,500	1,490,950	233,334
1906	1,795,000	1,835,190	287,207
1911	2,482,000	2,624,250	410,695
1913	2,730,000	3,055,800	478,230
1914	2,422,000	2,715,050	424,900
1915	1,728,000	1,935,140	302,850
1916	2,868,000	3,210,008	502,370
1917	2,955,000	3,319,920	519,570
1918	2,821,000	3,170,106	496,120

The figures in column I are the Chilean nitrate production, as given by Parsons and Petit, Brokers. The figures in colums II and III, from 1831 to 1911 inclusive, represent the World's consumption of saltpeter according to Génie Civil, vol. 62, p. 192. The figures from 1913 to 1918 in colums II and III represent the total production of Chilean and Indian nitrate, according to Grinnell Jones, Jour. Frankl. Inst., 1920, vol. 134, p. 398. The precipitous drop in the Chilean production in 1915 was due to a blockade established by the Germans during the early stages of the World War. See Fig. 50, in which circles indicate production, the drawn out curve consumption.

TABLE 24

Distribution of Chili saltpeter consumption in the United States in 1910 among different uses

	PER CENT
In manufacture of fertilizer....................................	13
In manufacture of dyestuffs....................................	12
In general chemistry...	10
In glass...	4
In explosives..	41
In nitric acid...	9
In sulphuric acid..	6
Unaccounted for...	5
	100

Origin of Nitre Beds.   The origin of the nitre beds is uncertain. The presence of boron in the deposits, and the association of this element with ammonia in volcanic emanations, have been regarded by some as evidence that the saltpeter is of ultimately volcanic origin. Others have ascribed it to organic sources, such as altered guano deposits.   But whatever be their origin, this is certain, that the saltpeter beds represent an accumulation of ages, and that the present rapid rate of consumption is out of all proportion with the rate of formation of the deposits.   In other words, here, as in the case of coal, we are living on our capital, and must prepare ourselves for its impending exhaustion.[9]   It is true that our other sources of combined nitrogen—notably ammonia from coke ovens—supplement our drafts upon the nitre beds, and thus help to defer the day of scarcity. But coal itself is a limited stock, and other sources of combined nitrogen seem quite inadequate for the needs which we have developed under the stimulation of temporarily bountiful supplies. It is a peculiarity of living substance that in times of plenty it tends to grow beyond the bounds compatible with ultimate stability; it overshoots the mark so to speak; the curve along which it approaches its equilibrium is very apt to be humpbacked, or it may be oscillatory.[10]   The prospect of a period of actual diminution (not mere marking time) to follow upon a period of exuberant prosperity, is one that an organism gifted with foresight must look upon with disquietude.   Such foresight may, then, lead an organism so gifted, to make efforts to provide for untoward future exigencies, either by laying by supplies, in times of plenty, for times of stress; or by devising means, if possible, to increase, by new measures, the supplies which, under the old régime, would presently fall short of requirements.   Man has not always made a display of brilliant foresight, but in this instance, in making ready for the exhaustion of the nitrate supply, he has taken time by the forelock, and all indications are that long before the emergency arises he will have made himself

[9] The probable date of this exhaustion has been variously estimated. Little value can be attached to positive statements.   More significant, perhaps, is the negative report made in 1913 to the Chilean Government by the Inspector General of Nitrate Deposits: "There is no fear of the Chilean nitrate deposits being exhausted for two hundred years" (Grinnell Jones, loc. cit., p. 401).

[10] Compare what has been said on this subject in Chapter XI.

ready to meet it. For the last decade has seen the development, to full industrial capacity, of several processes for the fixation of atmospheric nitrogen, its conversion into compounds directly or indirectly adapted to enter the cycle of nomadic nitrogen. For details regarding these modern industrial developments the reader must be referred to the technical literature.[11] It must suffice to indicate here very briefly the nature of the several processes.

1. **The Birkeland and Eyde Process,** is essentially man's imitation of the production of nitric acid by lightning. Air is passed through an electric arc fanned out into a broad disc by a magnetic field. The process is commercially viable only where very cheap power is available, and has been developed mainly in Scandinavia, with the use of water power.

2. **The Cyanamide (Frank and Caro) Process** effects the absorption of atmospheric nitrogen by calcium carbide in the electric furnace. The product can be employed directly as a fertilizer, or can be made to yield ammonia and other nitrogen compounds.

3. **The Haber Process** effects the synthesis of ammonia from nitrogen and hydrogen under pressure (100 to 200 atmospheres) in the presence of a catalyst. An allied process is that of Claude, which works at very high pressure (1000 atmospheres).[12]

4. **The Bücher Process,** which has not yet passed beyond the experimental stage, yields cyanides; these can also, if the market warrants it, be made a source of ammonia.

A highly significant development is the union of the Haber ammonia process with the Solvay process, whereby the carbon dioxide obtained as a waste product in the manufacture of the hydrogen for ammonia synthesis, is utilized in the production of sodium carbonate; while, on the other hand, the formation of large quantities of the nearly worthless calcium chloride waste of the Solvay process, as ordinarily conducted, is avoided. Inasmuch as "soda ranks second only to sulphuric acid among all chemicals in magnitude of output (1,390,628 short tons in the United States in 1918) and fundamental importance, ... this (combination of the Haber and the Solvay processes) may well prove to be the most

[11] See for example the articles by G. H. Fischer and Grinnell Jones already cited.

[12] H. E. Fisher, Jour. Franklin Inst., 1920, vol. 190, p. 201.

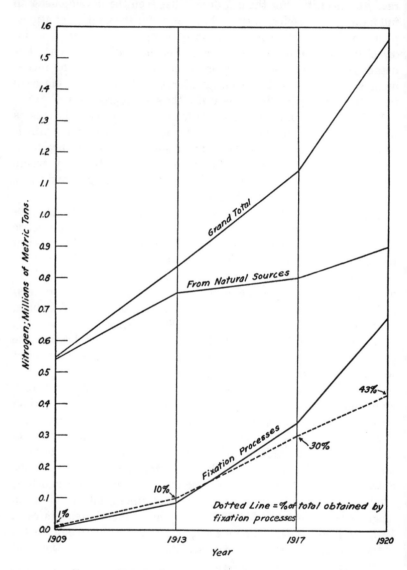

FIG. 51. THE RISE OF THE FIXED NITROGEN INDUSTRY

significant development in industrial chemistry of the present decade."[13]

5. The Ostwald Process. A subsidiary process bridging the gap from the product (ammonia) of the processes of the Haber and Frank and Caro types, to the market requirements of nitric acid (nitrate and nitrites), is the Ostwald process for the catalytic oxidation of ammonia.

The Meteoric Rise of Nitrogen Fixation Industries. In the period during and immediately following the World War the situation in the nitrogen industries was abnormal, production being temporarily activated to fever heat, inasmuch as nitrogen compounds are among the most indispensable of war materials. Thus it came about that the development of nitrogen fixation had for its immediate motive not so much the constructive spirit of the arts of peace, providing for the future needs of men, as the malice and forethought of the conspirators of war. The conflict left on our hands, upon the conclusion of the armistice, both completed and unfinished manufacturing plants in excess of immediate needs in times of peace. Legislative difficulties also hampered well-designed efforts to convert these plants to industrial use. These are temporary conditions; although one may not be able to foresee exactly how, in detail, these industries will finally adjust themselves, there can be little doubt that from now on synthetic nitrogen compounds will continue to be drawn in increasing amounts from the atmosphere into the life cycle. The phenomenal growth of this infant industry within the past ten or twelve years is forcibly brought out in the graph (fig. 51) and the corresponding table 25. It will be observed that in 1909 only about 1 per cent of the world's needs in combined nitrogen were satisfied from the new-born industry. In 1917 its contribution had swollen to 30 per cent, and by 1920 the capacity of existing plants was adequate to furnish 43 per cent of the world's requirements.

This extraordinary development is something much more than a fundamental new departure in industry. It represents nothing less than the ushering in of a new ethnological era in the history of the human race, a new cosmic epoch. In the short span of a dozen years—geologically speaking in an instant—man has initiated transformations literally comparable in magnitude with cosmic

[13] Grinnell Jones, loc. cit., p. 414.

TABLE 25

World's resources in nitrogen products, showing the meteoric rise of the nitrogen fixation industry*

Pre-war and post-war period contrasted

SOURCE OF SUPPLY	1912			1920		
	Output in long tons of product	Output in metric tons of nitrogen	Percentage of total output	Productive capacity long tons of product	Productive capacity metric tons of nitrogen	Percentage of total productive capacity
Chile nitrate industry (assumed 95 per cent product).	2,586,975	411,329	57.5	2,966,061†	471,000	30.2
By-product industry (sulphate assumed 24.5 per cent ammonia)............	1,229,773	272,007	38.0	2,015,440	413,000	26.6
Fixation industry:						
a. Cyanamide (assumed 18 per cent N)............	126,538	22,435	3.1	1,777,000	325,000	20.9
b. Nitrate of lime and arc process products (assumed 13 per cent N)............	75,000	9,907	1.4	290,400	38,300	2.5
c. Synthetic ammonia......	Nil	Nil	Nil	1,503,000	308,000	19.8
Total of fixation industry..	201,538	32,342	4.5	3,570,400	671,300	43.2
Grand total...............	4,018,286	715,678	100.0	8,551,900	1,555,300	100.0

*From Statistical Supplement to the Final Report of the Nitrogen Products Committee of the British Ministry of Munitions, 1921, J. A. Harker.

†The figure inserted here to represent maximum capacity of the Chile nitrate industry is the maximum war output in a single

processes. Accepting Arrhenius' liberal estimate of the total quantity of combined nitrogen washed down to the soil in the annual rain fall over all continents of the globe, namely 400 million tons, it is seen that the new industry even now is capable of furnishing a supplementary supply equal to one six-hundredth of this prodigious quantity.[14]

Economic and Energetic Significance of Concentration. We are, of course, greatly more interested in this six-hundredth which is under our control—and of which a due proportion falls, in consequence, upon our fields in concentrated form—than in the very much larger quantity that nature scatters with sublime indifference on stony places and good soil alike. This is just one of those cases to which reference has already been made in a general way. It is not so much the quantity of the material provided by nature that counts, as its accessibility; and accessibility here means, among other things, suitable concentration. This question did not so obviously project itself into the discussion of the carbon cycle, because the natural source of carbon is atmospheric carbon dioxide, which, being a gas, in the very nature of things spreads evenly, and presents itself unsought, by a spontaneous process, at the mouth of the hungry plant. But the combined forms of nitrogen are for the most part solids or solutions, occurring in definitely localized amounts of greatly varying concentration. The labors forced upon us in our efforts to satisfy the nitrogen needs of our fields are, to be precise, not primarily work of production, but virtually work of concentration; or to be more exact, work of bringing about concentration at the particular locality where it is wanted—by transportation if need be. It is only because we find it easier, in some instances, to produce than to concentrate existing supplies, that we elect the former expedient; just as we may prefer to feed a boiler with a fresh supply of water, rather than to

[14] For land and sea together Arrhenius estimates 1500 million tons of nitrogen in the rain fall.

Note added in correcting proof.

Since the writing of this chapter there have become available Trade Information Bulletins No. 226 and 240 of the U. S. Department of Commerce, which give further and more recent data. In Bulletin 240 J. M. Braham estimates the capacity of the world's nitrogen fixation plants at 496,000 tons for 1923. The reader interested in this topic may also consult J. R. Partington, The Nitrogen Industry, published by Constable, 1924.

return to it the condensed exhaust from the engine. That the mere concentration of existing supplies should at all require the doing of physical work is a circumstance of particular interest, not only in its economic relations,[15] but also, and quite particularly, from the standpoint of energetics. This is a matter that will duly engage our attention in a later section, devoted to the energetics of the several processes that have here been considered in their purely material or stoichiometric aspect.

Meanwhile it is interesting to observe that such localized sources of concentrated supplies as those presented in the Chilean nitre beds virtually function as centers of attraction toward which gravitates a stream of human beings—or their representatives in the form of ships and other conveyances—arriving in search of cargo and going out laden with material. To an ultramundane observer who should survey the scene in suitable perspective, the activities around the nitre beds must appear very like the busy swarming of a colony of ants around the treasure trove of some silvan inhabitant departed this life; who, having completed his earthly career, is now yielding up, in the dissolution of death, such energies as still remain locked up in the carcass. Attractions such as this are, in a sense, merely apparent; they are the outward symptoms of a complicated chain of cause and effect[16] characteristic of the behavior of living organisms. Yet they are often so consistent in their action that it would not be unreasonable to essay a systematic treatment of the movements in a world comprising such centers of attraction and such moving pawns, on the basis of brute tropisms unanalyzed into their ultimate component agencies. Here it must suffice to have pointed out that our highly complex industrial system, our far-flung intricate network of lines of traffic by land and sea, is but a sublimated copy, on a heroic scale, of the hustle and bustle that is going on all around us in nature, in response to attractions, tropisms, determinants of the

[15] A striking illustration of this is cited by Haber (Zeitschr. f. Angew, Chemie, 1910, I, p. 685). If the gold in sea water were extracted and apportioned evenly to all the human inhabitants of the globe, we should all be millionaires three times over; yet it does not pay to as much as begin this extraction.

[16] Commonly accompanied by that anticipatory inversion of the sequence, in time, of effect and cause, which is the earmark of *purposive* action.

moves of an army of checkers over the mosaic of the earth's topography.[17]

Total Circulation Tends to Increase. The study of the nitrogen cycle furnishes us with a first occasion to take note of a phenomenon the full significance of which will become apparent in dealing with the dynamics of evolving systems. It is to be observed that the general trend of man's effort, especially in this new epoch of nitrogen fixation, has been towards drawing into the organic circulation a greater amount of matter, enlarging the wheel of the mill of life, so to speak. There can be little doubt that this trend will continue and increase in the future, and that it is the expression of one aspect of a general law;[18] the other aspect of this law, and its full significance, must be reserved for later discussion, as already intimated.

[17] For a discussion of the natural concentrating processes the reader may be referred to the following articles: A. C. Lane, Nature's Concentrators, Engineering and Mining Journal, 1897, vol. 63, p. 542. J. C. Russell, Concentration as a Geological Principle, Bulletin Geol. Soc. An., 1907, vol. 18, pp. 1–28. E. Blackwelder, The Geologic Rôle of Phosphorus, Am. Jour. Sci., 1916, vol. 62, p. 285. W. Lindgren, Concentration and Circulation of the Elements from the Standpoint of Economic Geology, Economic Geology, 1923, vol. 18, pp. 419–442.

[18] The phenomenon is, of course, closely related to that to which R. Lascaux refers as "une propriété particulière de la vie: celle de l'extension" (La Production et la Population 1921, p. 37). See also A. J. Lotka, Proc. Nat'l Acad. Sci., 1922, p. 47.

CHAPTER XIX

THE PHOSPHORUS CYCLE

There is no coming into being of aught that perishes, nor any end for it
. . . . but only mingling, and separation of what has been mingled.—
Empedocles.

Immobile Elements. The circulation of water, carbon dioxide
and oxygen in nature is greatly assisted by the freely occurring
processes of evaporation, condensation (rainfall) and diffusion. In
the case of nitrogen these processes still give some aid, as in the distribution broadcast of atmospheric nitrogen, and in the formation
and precipitation of nitrogen "fixed" by lightning, etc. In phosphorus we have, on the contrary, a typical example of the *inherently
immobile* elements needful to the living organism—to adopt Liebig's
phrase *(für sich nicht beweglich).* The successive steps in the concentration, diffusion, and reconcentration of this element, as available
for the substance of the organism, accordingly display a characteristic
complexity. Some of the principal items and steps in the phosphorus cycle are set forth in diagrammatic form in figure 52.

Natural Phosphorus Supply of Soils. The virgin soil contains,
in general, a certain natural supply of phosphates. So, for example,
Var Hise[1] reports that the virgin soil of Ohio, Illinois and Wisconsin
contained, to a depth of 8 inches, 2077 pounds of P_2O_5 per acre.
After fifty-five years of cultivation this figure had sunk to 1813 pounds
per acre, a loss of 36 per cent. These figures show the extreme importance of a conservation of our resources of phosphorus. The loss
probably occurs partly through erosion by rain water charged with
carbonic acid, which dissolves phosphates in the soil and in rocks,
and ultimately washes a certain proportion out to sea. To this
unavoidable loss, however, is added a large item of preventable loss
through our failure to ensure that the phosphorus of animal wastes
be returned to the soil. So, for example, farmyard manure contains
over three-fourths of the phosphorus in the feed and bedding supplied
to the animals. It is therefore very essential that this be returned

[1] Ann. Acad. Polit. Soc. Sci., 1909, vol. 33.

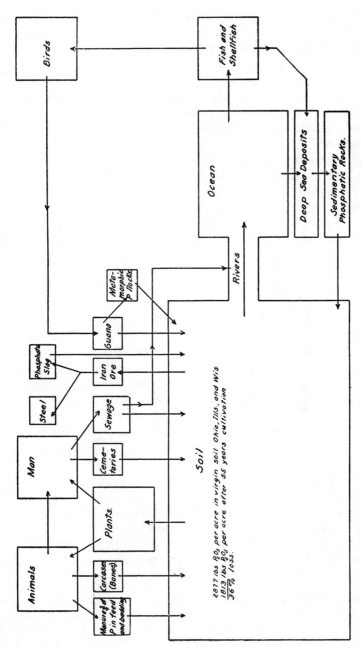

FIG. 52. CIRCULATION OF THE ELEMENTS IN NATURE. THE PHOSPHORUS CYCLE

to the soil as completely as possible. Of the one-fourth of the phosphorus fed to the animals, and not accounted for in the manure, a considerable fraction appears in the bodies of these animals, especially in the bones. These, then, also should find their way back to the soil, as they do to some extent through the practice of using bone meal, either as such, or after conversion into superphosphate,[2] as fertilizer. This practice is materially assisted by the modern methods of meat production on a large scale, with very complete utilization of by-products.

Leakage of Phosphorus from Circulation. The human cadaver is in the great majority of cases returned to the soil in the regular course of events, although under conditions which, obviously do not render it very readily available for crop production. An adult contains about $1\frac{1}{2}$ pounds of phosphorus, or 3.4 pounds P_2O_5. If we allow one-half of this for a "unit of population," i.e., 1.7 pounds P_2O_5, with a death rate of 1.3 per cent per annum, we find that the amount of P_2O_5 annually committed to the cemeteries of the United States is about 1105 tons. This is about the equivalent of 3300 tons of phosphate rock, or about one-thousandth of the annual production of that material in the United States.

But a very much larger amount of waste is occasioned from the human population by the practice of running the sewage from cities into rivers and thus to sea. Van Hise estimates that annually 400,000 tons P_2O_5 or the equivalent of 1,200,000 tons of phosphate rock are thus run to waste. He remarks: "The wide dispersal of the vast quantities of phosphorus which it took the process of nature an indefinite period to segregate, must cease. The loss is irreparable." Much has been done in recent years to comply with this demand.

Phosphate Rock and the Migration of Phosphorus. In the meantime, in our phosphorus economy also, as in the case of the combined nitrogen of the Chilean nitre beds, we are living on our capital. For, as our fields tend to become depleted of phosphorus under intensive agriculture, we restore some of the rarefied element to the tired soil by drawing upon the accumulations of ages, in the form of phosphate rock. As a matter of fact, in this we are welding

---

[2] By treatment with sulphuric acid, which renders the phosphorus more readily available to plants. These are technical details that cannot be entered into here. The reader must be referred to the pertinent agricultural and technological literature.

the closing link in a very remarkable endless chain of nature. For the phosphates washed by the rivers[3] into the sea serve as food to the marine vegetation and indirectly to the fishes and other aquatic species.[4] These act in this case as concentrating agents, the bones and teeth of fish, and some shells of crustacea and molluscs, being comparatively rich in phosphorus.[5] In its further migration the

[3] For details the reader may be referred to an article by E. Blackwelder in the Am. Jour. Sci., 1916, vol. 62, p. 285, from which the following particularly pertinent passage may here be noted: "Of the vast quantity of dissolved mineral matter annually delivered to the sea by the run-off, it is estimated that about 0.45 per cent consists of phosphorus pentoxide. Using the best available figures for the amount of water thus brought to the ocean annually, it is calculated that if the phosphatic material in the form of solid tri-calcium phosphate were loaded into standard railroad cars it would fill a train stretching continuously from Boston to Seattle and would be 7 to 12 times as great as the world's total production of phosphate rock in 1911. Nevertheless, so great is the volume of the oceans, and so vast the area of their floors, that if all this material were deposited in solid form uniformly over the bottom of the sea, it would build annually a layer less than 0.2 mm. thick. Of the phosphorus poured into the sea, so large a proportion is utilized by living beings that the net working balance dissolved in oceanic water constantly averages less than 0.005 per cent, expressed as P_2O_5, or, in other words about 0.18 per cent of the dissolved salts. In this solution, phosphorus seems to have reached the most dilute state in which it exists during the course of its complex migrations. Its subsequent transformations generally tend to ever greater concentration, almost until the cycle is closed upon itself.

[4] Compare also W. Lindgren, Concentration and Circulation of the Elements from the Standpoint of Economic Geology: "In the sea water the blue-green algae concentrate phosphorus, certain mollusks or crustaceans feed on the algae, and other meat-eating mollusks devour the vegetarians. Small fishes eat the mollusks, large fishes eat the small, finally seals and birds swallow the fishes, and so in about six transformations the phosphorus originally contained in the sea-water may come to rest in deposits of guano on desert islands or in accumulations of bones of vertebrate denizens of the sea" (Economic Geology, 1923, vol. 18, p. 431).

[5] In this connection may be noted again a passage from Blackwelder's article, p. 289 (see footnote 3): "As phosphorus ascends in the evolutionary scale of animals, its concentration tends to increase, although irregularly. The protozoan, air dried, contains less than 0.6 per cent P_2O_5. According to Juday quantities of minute crustaceans from Lake Mendota contain in the air-dried condition 1.8 to 2.4 per cent of P_2O_5, or several times that of the protozoans. A Russian biochemist, Sempelovski, found in entire fresh specimens of a cartilaginous fish (the common skate) 0.91 per cent P_2O_5, whereas the average for eight Teleostean fishes with well-developed bones was about 1.5 per cent. Certain brachiopods, such as those of the family *Lingulidae*—form shells of fibro-crystalline tricalcium phosphate—probably either the mineral dahllite or staffelite."

phosphorus here splits into two streams. On the one hand the hard parts of dead fish and other sea animals fall to the bottom and form a phosphatic deposit. So, for example, it is reported that in certain localities a single draft of the dredge has brought up 1500 shark's teeth from the sea bottom. These deposits become further enriched through the replacement of their calcium carbonate by calcium phosphate under the action of the sea water.[6] Subsequently some of the deposits so formed have been raised, in a crust upheaval, above the sea level, so as to form sedimentary strata from which we now derive some of our supplies of phosphate rock.

The other division of the stream in the flow of phosphorus is perhaps one of the most remarkable examples of a cycle in the economy of nature. The fish of the sea are eaten by birds, who flock in great hordes and have their nesting places upon rocky islands and shores.[7] There an accumulation of immense amounts of guano has taken place in the course of centuries and ages. Of this guano some has been returned directly to the land by the agency of man. Other portions, of more ancient origin, have undergone transformation, and have passed into fossil form by reaction with the rock base on which they were in the first instance deposited. This is the origin of a second class of (metamorphic) phosphate rock, which also we mine and spread on our field, so that this loop in the chain also is closed.

Soil Losses of Phosphorus. From this sketch of the migration of phosphorus in nature it is seen that *qualitatively* the path of the element is a closed circulation. Unfortunately the cycle is *quantitatively* quite incomplete. Van Hise, quoting Whitson's investigations, shows that, on a very conservative estimate, the soil of the United States loses annually some 2 million tons of P_2O_5, the equivalent of 6 million tons of phosphate rock. This is about double the total output of our phosphate quarries, and about four times our domestic consumption of that output. It is thus seen that the situation with regard to our supply of phosphatic fertilizers is an exceedingly serious one—it would perhaps not be out of place to say

[6] For a detailed discussion of some of these concentrating processes and related matters the reader is referred to F. W. Clarke, loc. cit., 1921, pp. 132, 495, 502. See also Chapter XVIII, footnote 17.

[7] For an excellent illustrated account of the part played by the Guanay bird in this cycle see R. C. Murphy, Natl. Geogr. Mag. Sept. 4, 1924, p. 279.

an alarming one. For here we have no reserve which we may hope to find means of tapping in the future, such as is presented to us, in the case of nitrogen, by the inexhaustible supply in the atmosphere. Phosphorus is at best a comparatively rare element, constituting only about 0.14 per cent of the earth's crust (see table 16, Chapter XV).

The general and alarming decrease in the crop yield per acre in various states so well described by Mr. James J. Hill,[8] is largely due to the depletion of the soil in phosphorus. . . . . The work (at the Ohio Agricultural Experiment Station[9]) upon different fertilizers shows that for the soils tested in their experiments phosphorus was the controlling element in producing an increase in the cereal crops.[10]

And elsewhere[11] Van Hise remarks:

The average rock contains twenty times as much potassium as phosphorus. Therefore, looking toward the distant future, if we consider ratios, we may unhesitatingly assert that the problem of maintaining the fertility of the soil in phosphorus will be twenty times as difficult as for potassium; but this ratio by no means measures the real difference, for when a deposit contains a moderate percentage of a substance it may be possible to utilize it commercially, whereas, if the percentage falls below this amount it is without value.

Phosphatic Slag as Fertilizer. To the consideration of the migration of the element potassium thus referred to by Van Hise, we shall presently turn our attention. Before leaving the subject of the migration of phosphorus, one secondary source of phosphate fertilizer remains to be noted here, namely, the by-product (slag) obtained in certain processes of steel manufacture, in which the phosphorus contained in the ore (and very objectionable as a constituent in steel) becomes segregated, and is thus eliminated, in the slag. This latter, by suitable processes, is converted into a very serviceable fertilizer.[12]

[8] The Natural Wealth of the Land, and its Conservation. Paper given at the White House Conservation Conference, May 13, 1908.

[9] Ohio State Agr. Coll. Bull. 141, 182.

[10] Van Hise, loc. cit., p. 704.

[11] Idem, loc. cit., p. 701.

[12] For details regarding the use of phosphatic slags as fertilizer the reader may be referred to G. S. Robertson, Basic Slag and Rock Phosphates, Cambridge University Press, 1922.

CHAPTER XX

CYCLES: CONCLUSION AND SUMMARY

The saltness of the sea is due to the numerous springs of water, which in penetrating the earth, find salt mines, and dissolving parts of these carry them away with them to the ocean and to the other seas, from whence they are never lifted by the clouds that produce the rivers.—*Leonardo da Vinci.*

The Circulation of Chlorine and the Alkalis. It will be convenient to consider jointly the migration of the elements chlorine, sodium, and potassium in nature, inasmuch as they are closely connected.

There is a piece of laboratory apparatus known as the Soxhlet Extractor, of which the chemist makes use when he wants to prepare a solution, an extract, of one of the constituents of a mixture of substances. This apparatus, as represented in figure 53, operates on a simple principle. The solvent (water, ether, petroleum spirit, etc.) is placed in the flask A heated by a bunsen flame B, so as to drive vapors of the solvent up through the tube C to the top of a tubular vessel D containing the material M to be extracted. The whole apparatus is open at the top, but escape of vapor is prevented by a condenser tube E cooled by a water jacket F. The vapor condensing in E drips down upon the material M, and dissolves out the substance to be extracted. The condensate accumulates in the vessel D and rises in the syphon tube I until it reaches the top of the syphon, whereupon it drains back into the flask A and is reëvaporated, this cycle being repeated indefinitely as long as desired. Since the vapor of a liquid containing a non-volatile substance in solution is pure solvent, the action continues until practically all the soluble substance has been extracted.

It is almost literally true that we pass our lives in the midst of a gigantic Soxhlet apparatus. The flask is the sea basin; the solvent is the water of the ocean, the rain, and our rivers and lakes. The material extracted is the earth's crust (rocks, soil, etc.). The place of the Bunsen burner is taken by the sun which raises water vapor from the ocean's surface, into clouds which drift over the land.

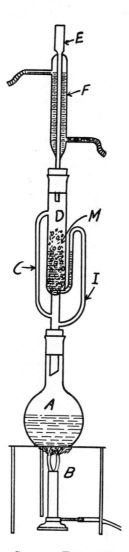

FIG. 53. THE SOXHLET EXTRACTION APPARATUS

The action of this apparatus is closely analogous to the natural extraction of soluble constituents from the earth's crust by the water in circulation through clouds, rain, rivers and the sea, under the influence of the sun's heat.

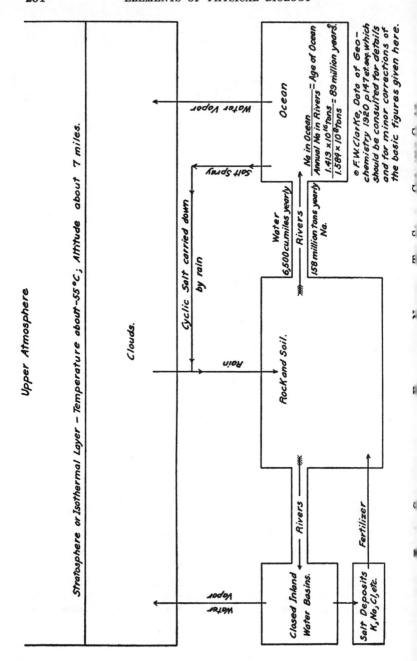

The cold upper atmosphere acts as a condenser (see fig. 54), beyond which no clouds can pass out above. Presently the moisture of the clouds is precipitated as rain over the face of the earth. It drains into rivers and lakes back into the sea, charged now with the soluble constituents of rock and soil. This operation has been going on over and over for ages, with the result that the greater part of the more soluble constituents of the rocks is by this time collected in the ocean, imparting to its water its characteristic salt taste. It is worthy of more than passing note that these relations, in all essentials, were recognized by that universal genius, Leonardo da Vinci, whose remarks on this subject appear at the head of this chapter.

The principal soluble constituents of the earth's crust are the carbonates and chlorides of the alkali metals, sodium and potassium. These, then, mainly take part in the extraction process described. There is, however, an important difference in the behavior of sodium and potassium in this process. In the igneous rocks sodium and potassium are present in very nearly equal proportions (see table 16). Yet the ocean is very much richer in sodium than in potassium (see table 14). What becomes of the potassium?[1] It is a circumstance highly significant for terrestrial life that potassium salts seem to be largely absorbed from their solutions on their passage through soil and clay. Thus the soil would retain a supply of the element so essential for plant growth, while the less vitally important sodium —in other respects so similar to its next kin potassium—has in large part passed on into the ocean.[2]

Nevertheless, potassium is not present in most soils in profusion; under intensive agriculture the soil becomes impoverished in this constituent also, and recourse must be had to sources of potassium salts in concentrated form, the deposits left by the drying up of ancient seas, to make up the deficiency. In this field, also, the World War has materially affected the complexion of agricultural economics. Its influence has been twofold. In the first place, since

[1] In this connection, and for details regarding the circulation of Na, K, Cl, and the related question of the age of the ocean, the reader may be referred to F. W. Clarke, Data of Geochemistry, pp. 136, 137, 145, et seq.

[2] These suppositions must be viewed with a certain caution, as has already been pointed out; see p. 204, footnote 19.

the only areas highly productive of potassium salts were contained within the domains controlled at that time by Germany, it became necessary for the Allies to find other sources of the needed element. One outcome of this was a temporary development of potash recovery from the waste of cement works and other materials. Unfortunately much of the commerce thus started had to be abandoned again when the customary sources of potash became once more available after the close of the war.

The second effect of the war upon the potash situation arises from the political changes which it brought about. The Alsatian potash deposits, formerly controlled by the same monopoly as the German Stassfurt deposits, are now in French domains, and the monopoly is broken.[3]

Some of the quantitative aspects of the migration of chlorine and sodium are shown in figure 54.

The Circulation of Sulphur. Sulphur occurs in abundance in inorganic nature in the form of the sulphates of the alkalies and alkaline earths. Plants assimilate these compounds directly and then form proteids containing about 0.3 to 2 per cent of sulphur. In this form it is assimilated by animals, who excrete the element chiefly in the form of sulphates. These, returned to the soil, complete the cycle.

The Circulation of Iron. The importance of iron in the economy of the living organism is out of proportion to the comparatively small amount of this element actually present in the body. Thus the body of a human adult holds only about 4.5 grams of iron, contained, for the most part, in the red blood corpuscles. The importance of this comparatively small amount of the metal arises out of the fact that it fulfills the essential function of an oxygen carrier, a catalyst as it were, mediating the transfer of oxygen from the air in the lungs to the tissues of the body through the blood stream. Similarly, in plants, the iron is contained chiefly in the chlorophyll, whose catalytic action is a fundamental condition for the assimilation of carbon dioxide from the air. This catalytic action of iron is attributable to the ease with which it passes from ferrous to the ferric condition and vice versa, and plays a significant

[3] G. Jones, Q. Jour. Econ., 1920, vol. 34, p. 392.

rôle not only within the body of the organism, but also in the soil, where it hastens the oxidation of carbonaceous matter, thus rendering carbon once more available for the organic cycle.[4]

Summary of Cycles. In conclusion of this chapter a few remarks and tables regarding the circulation of the elements in general may be offered.

In retrospect we may observe that a characteristic stamp is placed on certain of the elementary cycles by the form in which

TABLE 26

Supply of plant foods in soil

Number of years the supply of several elements would last, utilizing soil to a depth of 7 inches, and producing annually a crop of 100 bushels of corn. Average compositon of soil assumed equal to that of 2110 samples of common rocks in the United States. (C. G. Hopkins, Annual Acad. Sci. 1909, vol. 33, p. 638).

| N | | | | | | | |
Soil	Atmosphere	K	P	Fe	Ca	Mg	S
50	700,000	2,600*	130	200,000	55,000	7,000	10,000

* Assuming stalks returned to the land.

each element occurs or takes part in the circulation. Thus, the gases oxygen and carbon dioxide occur in nearly uniform distribution, so that their migration is free from certain complications that arise in the case of the other elements. Water occupies a position intermediate between the gaseous elements and those which like phosphorus, potash, etc., as solids, are subject to local segregation, and thus introduce problems of transportation in one form or another. As vapor, water drifts with air currents. But owing to the phenomenon of precipitation, water, unlike the permanent gases, is very unevenly distributed, the supply available for life processes being strictly a matter of climatic conditions. Thus, in desert regions, water functions as the limiting factor of life. Nitrogen, although

[4] G. Bunge, Physiological and Pathological Chemistry, 1902, p. 21.

gaseous in the elementary state, is chiefly operative in combined forms, so that its distribution in *available* form, is also a locally varied phenomenon.

All these facts have their influence not only on the primitive flora and fauna as a function of geographic site, but play also an important rôle in those secondary life phenomena which we commonly describe as commerce and trade.

Two tables 26, and 27, are, finally appended, the one giving certain data of interest regarding the Supply of Plant Foods in the

TABLE 27

Rate of participation of the elements in cycles of nature

	METRIC TONS		CIRCU-LATION BY WEIGHT ONE PART IN	AUTHORITY[*]				STANDARD OF REFERENCE
	Annual circulation	Total in Standard of Reference		A.	C.	L.	M.	
H_2O	1.4×10^{14}	1.3×10^{18}	10,000		22, 59	4	434	Ocean
CO_2	4.4×10^{10}	2.2×10^{12}	50	145		7		
O	3.5×10^{10}	1.2×10^{15}	35,000	145		7		Atmosphere
N	1.4×10^9	3.9×10^{15}	3,000,000	144		7		

* Authorities: A. = Arrhenius, Worlds in the Making, 1908; C. = Clarke, Data of Geochemistry, 1921; L = Linck, Kreislaufvorgänge, 1912; M. = McGee, Science, 1911, vol. 134. The numbers in the column "Authority" refer to pages of the works cited.

Soil, according to C. G. Hopkins; the other giving estimates of the Rate of Participation of the Elements in the Cycle of Nature.

It seems hardly necessary to point out that the quantitative estimates cited in these chapters on the circulation of the elements in nature represent only very rough approximations, the best perhaps that can be attained in the present state of our knowledge. As F. W. Clarke[5] remarks, "Such estimates may have slight numerical value, but they serve to show how vast and how important the processes under consideration are." Rough as the data are, they give us, presumably, at least an idea of the order of magnitudes involved. The least that can be claimed for them is, in the words of Clarke[5] once more: "In calculations of this sort there is a certain fascination, but their chief merit seems to lie in their suggestiveness."

[5] F. W. Clarke, Data of Geochemistry, 1920, p. 48.

CHAPTER XXI

MOVING EQUILIBRIA

Aus dieser Untersuchung wird kein Dualismus hervorgehen, sondern eine Wissenschaft, welche Organisches und Anorganisches umfasst, und die den beiden Gebieten gemeinsamen Thatsachen darstellt.—*E. Mach.*

In preceding pages we have considered as examples of biological "equilibria," states that quite obviously can be regarded only as rough approximations to equilibria or steady states; and we have not, so far, examined critically the justification for this attitude. It is desirable to give at least brief consideration to this matter.

It is common custom, in dealing with the relatively simple systems studied in physical chemistry, to assume that a sufficiently slow change in one parameter (e.g., volume) defining the state of the system, brings in its train a succession of states each of which is essentially equilibrium. So, for example, if we slowly raise the piston in a gas-tight cylinder containing X grams of water and Y grams of water vapor at a temperature θ, it is commonly assumed that at every instant the quantities X, Y are such as correspond to equilibrium at the temperature θ.

The Principle of Continuity. The basis of the assumption referred to in the preceding paragraph is rarely if ever discussed. Obviously it is to be sought in the principle of continuity. If the parameter P is constant, at the value P_0, the variables X, Y, . . . defining the state of the system have certain values X_0, Y_0, . . . We tacitly assume that if the parameter P_0 is nearly constant at the value P (that is to say, passes through P_0 in very slow change) then the variables X, Y will have *nearly* the value of X_0, Y_0, . . . Or, in the notation of an earlier section, if

$$\frac{dX_i}{dt} = F_i (X_1, X_2, \ldots P) \tag{1}$$

and if, with $P = P_0 = $ constant

$$F_1 = F_2 = \ldots = F_i = \ldots = 0 \tag{2}$$

259

gives

$$X_i = C_i = \text{constant} \tag{3}$$

then we assume that with

$$P = P(t) \tag{4}$$

where $P(t)$ is a *slowly changing* function of t, we shall have

$$X_i = C_i(t) \tag{5}$$

where $C_i(t)$ is a root of the system of equations

$$F_1(t) = F_2(t) = \ldots = F_i(t) \ldots = 0 \tag{6}$$
$$\text{(for all values of } t)$$

It should be noted that, strictly speaking, this involves a contradiction. For if the velocities F are zero, the variable X cannot be changing. And, in point of fact, the result (5) represents a first approximation which is not in all cases free from significant error.

Higher Approximation. It is possible, in certain cases, to proceed to second, third and higher approximations by successive steps, or, as will be shown, by a single formula. So, for example, for a system in two variables X, Y, we may write, first of all

$$\frac{dX}{dt} = F_1(X, Y, t) \tag{7}$$

$$\frac{dY}{dt} = F_2(X, Y, t) \tag{8}$$

The first approximation here is

$$F_1 = F_2 = 0 \tag{9}$$

$$X = X_1(t) \tag{10}$$

$$Y = Y_1(t) \tag{11}$$

The second approximation we obtain by differentiating (10), (11), so as to obtain the derivatives X_1', Y_1', which, although not zero, are nevertheless small, according to our supposition of a slow change. Substituting these in (7), (8) we find

$$F_1 = X_1'(t) \tag{12}$$

$$F_2 = Y_1'(t) \tag{13}$$

Hence

$$X = X_2(t) \tag{14}$$

$$Y = Y_2(t) \tag{15}$$

And so on, for successive higher approximations. But this process can be contracted into a compact expression. We have

$$\frac{dF_1}{dt} = \frac{\partial F_1}{\partial t} + \frac{\partial F_1}{\partial X}\frac{dX}{dt} + \frac{\partial F_1}{\partial Y}\frac{dY}{dt} \tag{16}$$

$$\frac{dF_2}{dt} = \frac{\partial F_2}{\partial t} + \frac{\partial F_2}{\partial X}\frac{dX}{dt} + \frac{\partial F_2}{\partial Y}\frac{dY}{dt} \tag{17}$$

If we substitute in (16) (17)

$$\frac{dX}{dt} = X_1'(t) \tag{18}$$

$$\frac{dY}{dt} = Y_1'(t) \tag{19}$$

the right hand member must vanish, in view of (9), (10), (11) and we have

$$\frac{\partial F_1}{\partial t} + \frac{\partial F_1}{\partial X}X_1' + \frac{\partial F_1}{\partial Y}Y_1' = 0 \tag{20}$$

$$\frac{\partial F_2}{\partial t} + \frac{\partial F_2}{\partial X}X_1' + \frac{\partial F_2}{\partial Y}Y_1' = 0 \tag{21}$$

from which it is seen that $X_2(t)$, $Y_2(t)$ can be expressed directly as the solution of the system of equations

$$\frac{\partial F_1}{\partial t} + \frac{\partial F_1}{\partial X}F_1 + \frac{\partial F_1}{\partial Y}F_2 = 0 \tag{22}$$

$$\frac{\partial F_2}{\partial t} + \frac{\partial F_2}{\partial X}F_1 + \frac{\partial F_2}{\partial Y}F_2 = 0 \tag{23}$$

Similarly the $(n + 1)^{th}$ approximation is found by writing

$$\frac{d^n F_1}{dt^n} = \frac{d^n F_2}{dt^n} = 0 \tag{24}$$

Special Case. Returning to the general case of n variables, suppose that for all values of $X_1\ X_2\ \ldots\ $ differing appreciably from the equilibrium values, the velocities $\dfrac{dX_1}{dt}$ $\dfrac{dX_2}{dt}$ . . . are very great

as compared with some one of them, say $\dfrac{dXr}{dt}$, except when the X's

are near their equilibrium value. Then we can write, practically

$$F_1(X_1, X_2, \ldots X_r, \ldots X_n) =$$
$$F_2(X_1, X_2, \ldots X_r, \ldots X_n) = \qquad (25)$$
$$\cdot \quad \cdot \quad \cdot \quad \cdot \quad \cdot \quad \cdot \quad \cdot \quad \cdot \quad \cdot \quad \cdot \quad \cdot \quad \cdot$$
$$F_n(X_1, X_2, \ldots X_r, \ldots X_n) = 0$$

where F_r is excluded from the system (25). This defines

$$X_1 = C_1(X_r)$$
$$X_2 = C_2(X_r) \qquad (26)$$
$$\text{etc.}$$

In addition to this we then have the equation

$$\frac{dX_r}{dt} = F_r(C_1, C_2, \ldots X_r, \ldots C_n) \qquad (27)$$

$$= F_r(X_r) \qquad (28)$$

Hence

$$\frac{dX_r}{F_r(X_r)} = dt \qquad (29)$$

which is directly integrable

$$t = \int \frac{dX_r}{F_r(X_r)} \qquad (30)$$

In such case as this, then, that particular change which is much slower than all the others, sets the pace and controls the whole process. It acts as a brake, as a limiting factor.

RADIOACTIVE EQUILIBRIUM

Moving equilibria play an important rôle in evolutionary processes of the most varied type, as emphasized almost *ad nauseam* by Herbert Spencer,[1] though some of the most typical and at the same time most fundamental examples were unknown to him. For, the most exact, quantitatively precise illustrations of moving equilibria are to be seen in the evolution of chemical elements by successive steps

[1] First Principles, Chapter XXII.

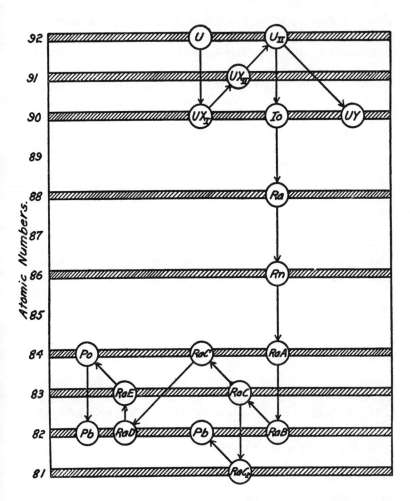

FIG. 55. URANIUM AND ITS PRODUCTS OF RADIOACTIVE DISINTEGRATION

(U = uranium; Io = ionium; Ra = radium; Rn = radon = radium emanation; Po = polonium; Pb = lead.) Each element in the chain is produced from its predecessor either by the emission of an alpha particle, i.e., a doubly charged helium atom, in which case the atomic number is decreased by two units; or by the emission of a beta particle, i.e., an electron, in which case the atomic number increases by one unit.

of atomic disintegration, accompanied, in most cases known to us, by radioactive manifestations. It is not within the plan or compass of this work, to give a detailed account of what has by this time grown into an extensive special field of physical science. It must suffice to refer to the chart (fig. 55) of one of the typical series of radioactive transformation chains, and to state briefly the simple law of transformation of such elements by spontaneous atomic disintegration: The amount of a substance transformed per unit of time is directly proportional to the amount of that substance present, so that if S_i is the ith substance in a transformation chain

$$S_1 \rightarrow S_2 \rightarrow \ldots \rightarrow S_i \ldots \rightarrow S_{i+1} \rightarrow \ldots \qquad (31)$$

and if we denote by X_i the mass of S_i, then we have a system of equation

$$\frac{dX_i}{dt} = \lambda_{i-1}X_{i-1} - \lambda_i X_i \qquad (32)$$

where the coefficients λ are constants, invariable under all conditions to which observation to the present date has extended.

It will be seen that the system of equations (32) is a simple special case of the general form discussed in Chapter VI. Its solution[2] is of the form there indicated, but the simplicity of the differential equations is reflected in the integrals, which here appear as finite series, the expression for the mass of ith substance, being

$$X_i = a_{i,1}e^{-\lambda_1 t} + a_{i,2}e^{-\lambda_2 t} + \ldots + a_{i,i}e^{-\lambda_i t} \qquad (33)$$

The series contains only linear terms, and breaks off at the term in a_{ii}.

If λ_k is (numerically) the least of the λ's, then, evidently, after a sufficient lapse of time the term in λ_k outweighs all other terms, which thus become negligible, so that

$$\frac{X_i}{X_k} = \frac{a_{ik}}{a_{kk}} \qquad (34)$$

The coefficients a are easily determined[3] as functions of the λ's. It is thus found that

$$\frac{a_{ik}}{a_{kk}} = \frac{\lambda_k \lambda_{k+1} \ldots \lambda_{i-1}}{(\lambda_{k+1} - \lambda_k)(\lambda_{k+2} - \lambda_k) \ldots (\lambda_{i-1} - \lambda_k)(\lambda_i - \lambda_k)} \text{ if } i > k \qquad (35)$$

$$\frac{a_{ik}}{a_{kk}} = 0 \qquad\qquad\qquad\qquad \text{if } i < k \qquad (36)$$

---

[2] For a somewhat remarkable method of integration (by a multiple integral), see A. Debierne, Les idées modernes de la Matière, 1913, p. 328.

[3] See, for example, E. Rutherford, Radioactive Substances, 1913, pp. 422, 423.

Thus, after a sufficient lapse of time, the substances S_1, S_2, . . . S_k are always present together in constant proportion, so that we have a moving equilibrium of a very simple type, illustrated graphically in figure 56, in accordance with some of the constants given in tables 28 and 29. The most slowly decaying substance here acts as

TABLE 28

Radioactive equilibrium of radium in contact with its disintegration products on the basis of data in Jour. Am. Chem. Soc., 1923, vol. 45, pp. 872–873

	AMOUNT IN EQUILIBRIUM	$1/\lambda$ = MEAN LIFE
Radium	1.00 ton	2,440 years*
Radon	6.23 grams	5.55 days
Radium A	3.37 mgm.	4.32 minutes
Radium B	30.18 mgm.	38.7 minutes
Radium C	21.91 mgm.	28.1 minutes
Radium D	9.75 kgm.	23.8 years
Radium E	8.08 grams	7.2 days
Radium F†	220.01 grams	196 days

*Half-decay period = $\dfrac{0.69315}{\lambda}$ = 190 years.

†Polonium.

the controlling, slowly variable parameter, and sets the pace with which all the subsequent members in the transformation chain keep step, so that the polygons representing the system in its successive stages are geometrically similar. (Compare fig. 58 on p. 277.)

The second of the two expressions for the ratio a_{ik}/a_{kk} calls for brief comment. If $i < k$, that is to say if the substance S_i precedes, in the transformation chain, the substance S_k which has its lowest disintegration rate, then S_i does not appear at all in the equilibrium. Hence when an aggregation of substances in radioactive equilibrium is found in nature, the substance at the head of the chain (the "parent substance") is always the one of slowest disintegration rate. But, obviously we cannot from this draw any conclusion as to whether or not it is itself a product of disintegration of a pre-parent of more rapid decay rate. Any such pre-parent would, as it were, have been weeded out in the evolution of the system, as being "unadapted" to present conditions, like the extinct species of biology.[4]

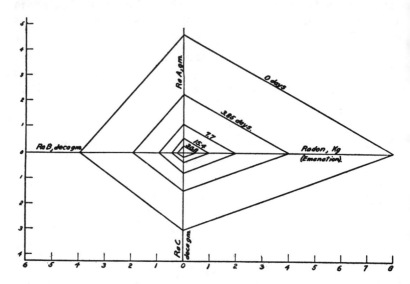

FIG. 56. EQUILIBRIUM POLYGON FOR RADON IN CONTACT WITH ITS DISINTEGRATION PRODUCTS

The successive amounts, at intervals of 3.85 days (half-decay period), of the four substances radon (radium emanation, a gas), radium A, B and C are laid off along the four radial axes. Owing to the wide disparity in the relative amounts of these substances in equilibrium, it is necessary to employ widely different scales to represent these amounts. This must be duly taken into account in construing the diagram. The geometric similarity of successive polygons is the graphic expression of the constancy of the ratio of the several substances. The linear dimensions of successive polygons form a geometric series.

The differential equations representing the course of radioactive transformation are readily solved by direct integration, and there is therefore no necessity to employ the method of successive approximations to determine the moving equilibrium. However, the first

[4] H. Mitchell, Phil. Mag., 1911, vol. 21, p. 40; A. J. Lotka, *ibid.*, 1911, vol. 22, p. 353.

approximation is so simple, that it is commonly applied. Equating the right hand member of (32) to zero we find immediately

$$\frac{X_i}{X_{i-1}} = \frac{\lambda_{i-1}}{\lambda_i} \tag{37}$$

and by an obvious extension

$$\frac{X_i}{X_k} = \frac{\lambda_k}{\lambda_i} \tag{38}$$

It is easily shown that L_i, the reciprocal of λ_i, is the "mean length of life" of an atom of the substance S_i. We may write (38)

$$\frac{X_i}{X_k} = \frac{L_i}{L_k} \tag{39}$$

which expresses the fact that, in first approximation, the amounts of several substances present together in radioactive equilibrium are in the ratio of the respective mean lengths of life.[5] This result can also be read out of (35) if $|\lambda_k|$, the least of the $|\lambda|$'s, is negligible in comparison with all the other $|\lambda|$'s, so that the denominator reduces to the product

$$\lambda_{k+1}\lambda_{k+2} \ldots \lambda_i$$

It is thus seen that the closeness of the first[6] approximation depends on the relative magnitude of λ_k and the remaining λ's. In many chains of radioactive transformation the parent substance is very slow in its disintegration, and the first approximation (giving what Rutherford has termed the secular equilibrium) is exact within the limits of experimental error. But if one of the more rapidly decaying members is isolated and is then allowed to come into equilibrium with

[5] This is a special case of a general law that if all the exponents λ are real and negative, the final stages of the process of evolution are characterized by constancy in the ratios of the Variables x. Compare p. 261, *Special Case;* also, Lotka, A. J., Proc. Am. Acad. Sci., vol. 55, 1920. It should be noted, however, that in the general case, x_i denotes not mass of S_i, but excess of that mass over the equilibrium mass of S_i. In the radioactive equilibrium there is no distinction between X and x, since the ultimate value of both is zero.

[6] For the second and higher approximation, applied to the radioactive equilibrium, the reader may be referred to A. J. Lotka, Proceedings Natl. Acad. Sci., 1921, vol. 7, p. 170.

its own products of disintegration, the error of the first approximation may become appreciable.[7] This is shown, for example in table 29, which exhibits the amounts of radon gas (radium emanation) and its several products of disintegration in radioactive equilibrium. It will be observed that in the case of radium C there is a discrepancy of about 1 per cent between the amount computed by first approximation and the true amount.

Radioactive Chains as Cosmic Clocks. It must be noted that all that has been said above regarding the amounts of the substances present in radioactive equilibrium does not apply to the last link in the chain, the end product. This does not, of course, take part in the equilibrium, but accumulates, if non-volatile, as in the case of lead, or, it may in part escape and be lost to observation, as in the case of helium.

TABLE 29

Radioactive equilibrium of radon (radium emanation) in contact with its disintegration products, on basis of data in Jour. Am. Chem. Soc., 1923, vol. 45, pp. 872–873

	λ (PER SECOND)	$L = 1/\lambda$	EQUILIBRIUM AMOUNT	
			Exact	First approximate
Radon...........	2.085×10^{-6}	5.55 days*	1.000 kgm.	1.000 kgm.
Radium A.......	3.85×10^{-3}	4.32 minutes	0.5416 grams	0.5418 gram
Radium B.......	4.30×10^{-4}	38.7 minutes	4.874 grams	4.849 grams
Radium C.......	5.92×10^{-4}	28.1 minutes	3.552 grams	3.522 grams

*Half-decay period $= 0.69315 L = 3.85$ days.

If the amounts of parent substance and end product are large as compared with the amount of intermediates, the amount of any one end product formed is evidently simply proportional to the amount of parent substance lost by disintegration in a given time. The chain of substances in transformation behaves, in fact, much like a sandglass clock having a number of bulbs and from the accumulation in the end bulb we can obtain an indication of the age of the system, *on the assumption that originally all was in the top bulb,* that initially only the parent substance was present. The application of this principle to radioactive mineral deposits has given us a quantitative time scale in historical geology where before we had to

[7] Compare E. Rutherford, Radioactive Substances, 1913, p. 430.

rest satisfied with a crude chronology recognizing only order of precedence, or at best dealing in exceedingly uncertain estimates of lapse of time. Thus the investigation of radioactivity, remote as it seems from the field of life phenomena, has nevertheless contributed to biology essential information regarding the time that has been available for the evolution of the earth and its inhabitants. The estimate reached upon this basis is that the age of the radium-bearing rocks (uranium ore) examined is at least eight million years, and at most seventeen hundred million years old. For a résumé of various estimates of the age of the earth the reader may be referred to G.

TABLE 30

Geologic time table

After Schuchert

	per cent	FROM BARRELL 1917 ON URANIUM BASIS per cent
Cenozoic...................................	5	4
Mesozoic...................................	12	11
Paleozoic...................................	28	30
Late Proterozoic...........................	15	
Early Proterozoic..........................	15	55
Archeozoic.................................	25	

Schuchert, The Evolution of the Earth and its Inhabitants, 1919' pp. 56 et seq.; 80; and to the Proceedings of the American Philosophical Society, 1922, vol. 61, pp. 247–288. See also E. Rutherford, Radioactive Substances, 1913. Schuchert's estimate is that "geologic time endured about eight hundred million years," distributed among the several geological eras as indicated in table 30.

The Origin of the Elements and the Ultimate Genesis of the Organism. The case of radioactive equilibrium has here been introduced primarily by the way of illustration, as probably the most typical example in nature of a moving equilibrium in a system in the course of evolution. But the matter is also of more material interest to us in our survey of the evolution of the earth as the abode of life. For, as has already been emphasized, we are not only *on* the earth but *of* it; we have thus a two-fold interest in the evolution of its substance —first, as providing the stage upon which our life drama is set; and second, as furnishing the material of our bodies. Of these same elements that make up the earth's crust we also are composed: their genesis is therefore also the first, remote chapter in the genesis of our own bodies. Through the discovery of radioactive chains of elements we hold a clue regarding the fundamental influences that have determined the quantitative chemical composition of our world, and have thus appointed the measure of the supplies available for our needs. Those elements whose genesis is known to us came into being in perfectly definite proportions. Presumably the same is true also of those whose precise mode origin is still unknown. There is good evidence to support this view. We have at present no detailed quantitative knowledge of the laws which determine the value of the decay coefficients λ of the radioactive elements, and which thus ultimately fix their relative abundance in equilibrium. But a significant qualitative relation has been pointed out by W. D. Harkins.[8] When the elements in a radioactive chain are arranged in order of their atomic numbers,[9] and are separated into two groups, those of odd and those of even number, it is found that each even-numbered element is more abundant than the adjacent odd-numbered elements. And, what is of particular significance, the law of relative abundance of odd and even-numbered elements extends also to those elements, regarding whose precise mode of origin we have not, as yet, that sure knowledge which is gained by direct observation within the four walls of the physical laboratory. (See fig. 57.)

[8] Jour. Am. Chem. Soc., 1916, vol. 38, pp. 863, 869; 1923, vol. 45, pp. 1426–1433. Compare also F. W. Aston, Nature, March 15, 1924, p. 394. For other regularities observed in the length of life of radioactive elements see K. Fajans, Radioaktivität (Sammlung Vieweg Heft 45) 1921.

[9] The chemical elements, arranged in ascending order of atomic weights, beginning at hydrogen = 1, may be given ordinal numbers 1, 2, 3, etc., indicating their position in the series. These ordinal numbers have been found to have important relation to the atomic architecture. They have been termed the atomic numbers. The definition here given is not quite exact; in certain places allowance must be made, gaps left for unknown elements, and the several isotopes of one element receive the same atomic number, though differing in their atomic weights. A more precise definition is the following: The atomic number of an element represents the excess of positive over negative charges in the constitution of the atomic nucleus. Each atomic number also represents the place occupied by the element in Mendeléef's table (Jour. Am. Chem. Soc., 1923, vol. 45, p. 868). For further information the reader must be referred to the special literature; of comprehensive works the following may be mentioned: Bragg, X-rays and Crystals; F. W. Aston, Isotopes.

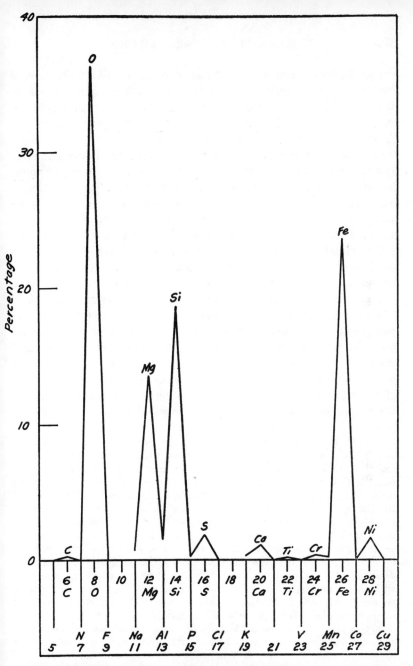

FIG. 57. RELATIVE ABUNDANCE OF THE ELEMENTS

Each element of even atomic number is more plentiful than the adjacent elements of odd stomic numbers. Diagram according to W. D. Harkins, based on analysis of meteorites. (Jour. Am. Chem. Soc., 1916, p. 863.)

But the laboratory is not a prison, and the eye of the physicist is free to sweep the sky, where nature's great smelteries gleam at night. With the aid of the spectroscope he has studied the multitudes of the stars, and has recognized in them a number of distinct stages of evolution. Life's day is far too short to give the observer any opportunity to study directly the evolutionary changes in any one star. But by piecing together the observations made upon the mixed population of stars of different ages, it has been possible to construct with considerable certainty the main stages in stellar evolution, just as the stages of human life could be gathered from a single observation of a mixed population comprising persons of all ages. The evidence points clearly that the elements, such as we know them, are the product of "the general brewing of material which occurs under the intense heat in the interior of the stars." Out of such foundry came our own abode, if we accept the well-considered views of Eddington:[10] "I do not say that the earth was a gaseous body when it first became recognizable as an independent planet, but I am convinced that its material was at one time merged in a completely gaseous sun." And since we are of earth, ours also is the same origin. The hand that writes these words and the eye that reads them alike are composed of the selfsame atoms that came into being, ages and ages ago, in the young sun. Far, far more wonderful than any dream of old

---

[10] A. S. Eddington, *The Borderland of Astronomy and Geology*, *Nature*, 1923, p. 18, also, *The Interior of a Star*, Supplt. to *Nature*, May 12, 1923. The reader who wishes to acquaint himself in greater detail on this subject may refer to Eddingtons's work *Stellar Evolution*. In the interest of unbiassed presentation it must be noted here that T. C. Chamberlin (The Origin of the Earth, 1916) has put forward a theory of the origin of the earth and the planets which is at variance with that sustained by Eddington. On the other hand it is also proper to mention a fundamental objection to theories of cosmogony of the type of that of Chamberlin and Moulton, which is based on the supposition that the luminous stars are formed by the collision of dead suns. "The distances separating the stars are enormous compared with their own dimensions. Sir Frank Dyson once used the illustration of twenty tennis balls distributed at random throughout the whole interior of the earth, to give a model of the density of distribution of the stars. . . . . Taking a very liberal view of the kind of approach that can be held to constitute a collision, it is estimated that a star would suffer a collision about once in a hundred million million years" (Eddington). For a survey of the modern views on this subject see J. Barrell, The Evolution of the Earth (Yale University Press, 1919).

mythology is the story of our creation. Thus was the birth of man prepared in the grey dawn of time; thus the metal of his frame compounded in the flaming furnace of a star. . . . .

TERMINAL STAGES OF THE EARTH'S EVOLUTION

Geophysics and Geochemistry. For the last stages in the evolution of the elements and their chemical combinations we do not look to the stars. We can study them at close quarters in the field and in the laboratory. In this way, with the application of physics and chemistry to general problems of geology, have grown up the sciences of geophysics and geochemisty. Indeed, it naturally might be supposed that on the terrestrial phases of inorganic evolution we should be altogether better informed than on those prior stages, far remote in time and space, which run their course in distant suns. But this is true, at best, only in restricted measure. It is a singular circumstance that, in some ways, we are better informed regarding the physics and chemistry of the stars, of which the nearest, outside the solar system, is twenty-five million million miles distant, than regarding that of our own planet. To say that the earth's surface layers accessible to our direct observation are comparable, scale for scale, to the shell of an egg, is to err on the side of liberality. The deepest burrow into the earth made by human agency, the mine shaft at Morro Velho, Brazil,[11] is $1\frac{1}{5}$ miles (6400 feet) deep or only about $\frac{1}{6500}$ of the earth's diameter. Direct observation can therefore give us at best only the most uncertain information regarding the conditions at even moderate depths. Where the crust has been creased and thrown into folds, subsequent denundation may have exposed layers of some 50 or 60 miles aggregated thickness.[12] But, though this gives us an invaluable record of some of the most significant chapters in the earth's history, it adds little or nothing to our knowledge of conditions of temperature and pressure even at comparatively trivial depths, and regarding chemical composition also it gives us, after all mere surface indications. Indeed, our information on all these points is very largely of a negative character. We know from the earth's average density that the composition of the core must be very different from that of the shell. We know that the temperature

[11] Sir Charles Parsons, Nature, February 19, 1920, p. 677.
[12] G. Schuchert, The Evolution of the Earth, Yale University Press, 1919, p. 67.

gradient observed in boreholes near the surface averages an increase of about 1°F. for every 60 feet (1°C. for every 35 meters) descent, but of the further course of temperature at greater depths we know with reasonable certainty only that it cannot continue at this gradient, which would give a phantastic temperature of 300,000°F. (180,000°C.) at the center. Lord Kelvin's calculations, based on the rate of cooling of the earth, and the more recent figures of the same character given by Van Orstrand, are rendered uncertain in their application owing to the presence of radium, in unknown amounts, evolving heat in its distintegration. Strutt has made the tentative estimate that the temperature rises uniformly to a depth of about 30 miles, and after that remains sensibly constant at 2700°F.

A little more definite is our information regarding the pressure in the earth's interior. A first approximation of its value is found by considering the earth as a fluid. It is thus found[13] that the pressure at the center would be three million atmospheres. In any case there can be no doubt whatever that the pressures reached vastly exceed anything at our command in the laboratory, where a pressure of twenty-four thousand atmospheres, employed by P. W. Bridgman in his researches, stands out as a record achievement, though it corresponds to a depth of rock of only 56 miles.[14]

It must be clear from what has been said above, that all conjectures as to the physical, chemical and subatomic transformations going on in the earth's interior are subject to a very large margin of uncertainty. In this connection it is well to recall the words of F. W. Clarke:[15]

The chemistry of great pressures and concurrently high temperatures is entirely unknown, and its problems are not likely to be unravelled by any experiments within the range of our resources. The temperatures we can command, but the pressures are beyond our reach. . . . . We may devise mathematical formulae to fit determinable conditions; but the moment we seek to apply them to the phenomena displayed at great depths, we are forced to employ the dangerous method of extrapolation, and our conclusions are not verified.

[13] This supposition, in calculating pressures, probably does not err far from the truth. The researches of F. D. Adams (Journal of Geology, February, 1912), P. W. Bridgeman and others have shown that at depths of some 30 miles rocks probably give way like butter to the pressure of the layers above them.

[14] W. D. Lambert, Jour. Washington Acad. Sci., 1920, p. 126. Sir Charles Parsons, loc. cit.

[15] Data of Geochemistry, p. 271.

In these circumstances we can feel but little confidence in inferences based upon our laboratory observations, relating to radioactive and other possible atomic transformations going on at greater depths within the earth. If the degree and character of radioactivity which we observe in the accessible surface layers were to continue throughout the mass of the earth, the amount of heat developed would be much in excess of the observed losses by radiation.[16] Unless therefore, we are to draw the highly improbable inference that the temperature of the earth's mass is steadily rising, we are forced to one of two assumptions. Either the radioactive elements are segregated chiefly in the earth's crust; or, the present rate of heat loss by radiation from the earth does not represent its average rate. This latter is the alternative elected by J. Joly[17] in an original conception. According to this there are alternate periods of accumulation of heat in the solid rocks, followed by periods in which these rocks, having finally become melted, well to the surface in a death-dealing flood of fire. Thus, by convection, a process far speedier than conduction, through the solid rock mass, heat is dissipated until, after sufficient cooling, a second period of quiescence, with a solid earth's crust, is ushered in. And so, in long waves of perhaps some thirty million years duration, the planet alternates between periods of hospitable clemency and periods intolerant of life.

There is, for us living inhabitants of this globe, a certain wildly romantic element, a feature of calamitous tragedy, in the hypothetical picture of the world's history thus summoned up before our imagination.

In its biological aspect how great and wonderful it all is! The living being working out his destiny on this poor raft, unknowing of the fiery ocean upon which this world is floating: unknowing of the inevitable sinking and uplifting which in truth largely controls the destinies of his race. Death-dealing forces all around, and yet the light of life shining age after age upon the earth.

---

[16] Compare V. Moritz, Der Stoffwechsel der Erde, Zeitschr. f. Elektrochemie, 1922, p. 421.

[17] J. Joly, Movements of the Earth's Crust; lecture under the auspices of the Royal Dublin Society, published in Nature, 1923, p. 603. A third possibility is that under the extreme conditions of temperature and pressure prevailing in the earth's interior reversal of the familiar radioactive disintegrations, or similar endothermic processes may go on. (Jour. Natl. Acad. Sci., 1924, p. 89.)

Such conceptions as this, stimulating as they are to the imagination in reconstructing for us an image of the remote past and distant future, must be entertained with reserve, remembering the words of caution quoted above from Clarke's classic work. We must be prepared to consider the possibility that under the extreme conditions of temperature and pressure prevailing at great depths other subatomic transformations than those known to us in the laboratory may occur. Perhaps some evidence of this is seen in the evolution of helium as a component of natural gas, in amounts (up to 1.5 per cent[18]) in excess of anything readily accounted for on the basis of the observed radioactivity of the rocks. And, while the subatomic transformations known to us are exothermic, accompanied by liberation of heat, others undoubtedly are endothermic, associated with absorption of heat. We seem to have *carte blanche*, in the present state of knowledge, in our speculations regarding the net heat balance of the elemental transformations that may be going on under our feet.

On surer ground rest our conceptions regarding the organization of matter, especially in the more superficial layers of the earth, under the action of ordinary physical and chemical influences. That the prime factor effecting the first and fundamental segregation of the lighter elements is flotation under gravity can hardly be doubted; this statement would in fact, be little more than a platitude if we were assured that the elements themselves remain unchanged under the extreme conditions of temperature and pressure prevailing in the earth's interior. Beyond this prime factor the study of mineral and rock formation becomes a complex chapter in applied physical chemistry, the consideration of which is not within the plan of this work. The reader who wishes to follow out further this phase of the subject will find a comprehensive survey of the field in an article *Der Stoffwechsal der Erde*, by V. Moritz, in the Zeitschrift für Elektrochemic, 1922, pp. 411–421; and in the memoir *The Chemistry of the Earth's Crust* by H. C. Washington, which has already been quoted.

Organic Moving Equilibria. Of moving equilibria in the organic world, data are most readily available for the system comprising man and his domestic animals. Here the human race acts as the controlling factor, drawing its dependents after it in its growth. The equi-

---

[18] R. B. Moore, Nature, 1923, p. 91; Cady and McFarland have reported one instance of 1.84 per cent. J. Joly, Radioactivity and Geology, 1909, p. 218.

librium polygon for the principal items of animal husbandry in the United States is shown in figure 58. The geometric similarity of successive polygons is in this case only approximate, the proportion of the several components varies somewhat; except in the case of the sheep population, however, the variation is moderate over the half-century from 1871 to 1921. (Compare fig. 56 on p. 265.)

Aside from the features for the express illustration of which the diagram figure 58 was drawn, it also serves to point once more to the

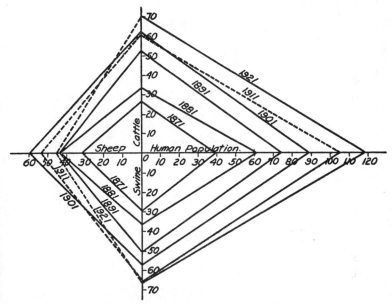

FIG. 58. EQUILIBRIUM POLYGON FOR THE HUMAN SPECIES AND SOME OF THE SPECIES ON WHICH IT DEPENDS FOR ITS FOOD SUPPLY. SCALES READ IN MILLIONS

fact already emphasized, that the concept of evolution, to serve us in its full utility, must be applied, not to an individual species, but to groups of species which evolve in mutual interdependence; and further, to the system as a whole, of which such groups form inseparable part.

It would be conveying a false impression in a very essential respect, to exhibit the example illustrated in figure 58, without a comment in emphatic reservation. Although, in a roughly approximate way, it is true, as shown by the polygon diagram, that in its relation

TABLE 31

World's development, of population Production, vessel tonnage, and Commerce: 1800 to 1918*

YEAR	POPULATION		COMMERCE TOTAL		TONNAGE SAIL AND STEAM		RAILWAYS		TELEGRAPHS		PRODUCTION OF					
											Cotton		Coal		Pig iron	
	Absolute millions	Relative	Absolute millions	Relative	Absolute	Relative	Absolute thousand miles	Relative	Absolute thousand miles	Relative	Absolute million pounds	Relative	Absolute million short tons	Relative	Absolute million tons	Relative
1800	640	100	1,479	100	4,026	100					520	100	11.6	100	0.8	100
1820	780	122	1,659	112	5,834	145					630	121	17.2	148	1.0	125
1830	847	132	1,981	134	7,211	179	0.2	100			820	158	25.1	216	1.8	225
1840	950	148	2,789	189	9,380	233	5.4	2,700			1,310	252	44.8	386	2.7	337
1850	1,075	168	4,049	274	12,334	306	24.0	12,000	5	100	1,435	276	81.4	702	4.7	587
1860	1,205	188	7,246	490	16,600	412	67.4	33,700	100	2,000	2,551	491	142.3	1,227	7.2	900
1870	1,310	205	10,663	721	15,940	396	139.9	69,950	281	5,620	2,775	534	213.4	1,840	11.9	1,487
1880	1,439	225	14,761	998	20,280	504	224.9	112,450	440	8,800	3,601	693	340.0	2,931	18.0	2,250
1890	1,488	233	17,519	1,185	17,461	434	390.0	195,000	768	15,360	5,600	1,077	466.0	4,017	27.2	3,400
1900	1,543	241	20,105	1,359	20,531	510	500.0	250,000	1,180	23,600	6,247	1,201	800.0	6,897	40.4	5,050
1906	1,579	247	27,148	1,854	25,522	634	564.0	282,000	1,200	24,000	7,650	1,471	885.0	7,629	58.7	7,337
1910	1,616	253	33,634	2,274	26,670	662	637.0	318,500	1,307	26,140	9,013	1,733	1,141.6	9,841	65.8	8,225
1911	1,630	255	35,909	2,428	28,298	703	666.0	333,000	1,356	27,120	10,634	2,045	1,309.6	11,290	62.4	7,800
1912	1,643	257	39,570	2,675	29,061	722	683.4	341,700	1,400	28,000	10,301	1,981	1,377.0	11,871	72.8	9,100
1913	1,652	258	40,420	2,733	30,408	755	690.2	345,100	1,462	29,240	10,809	2,079	1,478.0	12,741	77.9	9,737
1914	1,661	260	37,760	2,553	31,674	787	703.5	351,750	1,489	29,780	11,933	2,295	1,346.0	11,603	56.8	7,100
1915	1,672	261	31,302	2,116	31,693	787	717.5	358,750	1,526	30,520	8,805	1,693	1,169.6	10,083	59.0	7,375
1916	1,692	264	46,523	3,146	31,293	777	720.3	360,150	1,564	31,280	9,047	1,740	1,242.9	10,715	71.4	8,925
1917	1,693	265	52,781	3,569	29,805	740	729.8	364,900	1,568	31,360	8,705	1,674	1,317.9	11,361	64.6	8,075
1918	1,699	265	62,802	4,246	31,139	773	732.8	366,400	1,586	31,720	8,845	1,701			62.0	7,750

to certain staples of agricultural production, our population has advanced in a succession of moving equilibria; yet the progress of modern industrial civilization on the whole is essentially the very antithesis of a moving equilibrium conditioned by and following upon the changes of a slowly varying parameter. Quite on the contrary, the development of this age is rather of the nature of a rocket-like ascent with a speed altogether unparalleled in all previous history of organic evolution, and at the cost of rapid depletion of capital resources. Certain aspects of this phenomenon are reserved for consideration in a later chapter. Here it will be sufficiently to the point to draw attention to table 31, reproduced from R. Pearl's essay on *The Population Problem*,[19] which shows the altogether disproportionate increase in the growth of our material accessories in recent years, as compared with that of the population itself.

The human species, considered in broad perspective, as a unit including its economic and industrial accessories, has swiftly and radically changed its character during the epoch in which our life has been laid. In this sense we are far removed from equilibrium—a fact which is of the highest practical significance, since it implies that a period of adjustment to equilibrium conditions lies before us, and he would be an extreme optimist who should expect that such adjustment can be reached without labor and travail. We can only hope that our race may be spared a decline as precipitous as is the upward slope along which we have been carried, heedless, for the most part, both of our privileges and of the threatened privation ahead. While such sudden decline might, from a detached standpoint, appear as in accord with the eternal equities, since previous gains would in cold terms balance the losses, yet it would be felt as a superlative catastrophy. Our descendants, if such as this should be their fate, will see poor compensation for *their* ills in the fact that *we* did live in abundance and luxury.

[19] R. Pearl, Geographical Review, 1922, vol. 12, p. 638.

CHAPTER XXII

DISPLACEMENT OF EQUILIBRIUM

Die Physik wird aus dem Studium des Organischen an sich noch sehr viel neue Einsichten schöpfen müssen, bevor sie auch das Organische bewältigen kann.—*E. Mach.*

In preceding pages we have passed in review some of the principal features of interest presented by systems maintained constantly at or near equilibrium, while one of more of the parameters determining such equilibrium were slowly changing, thus engendering a moving equilibrium.

One might proceed to a consideration, on a more general basis, of the changes brought about in an evolving system through changes of any kind, including rapid ones, in the parameters. In the most general case this would amount to the discussion of a system of differential equations of the form.

$$\frac{dX_i}{dt} = F_i(X_1, X_2, \ldots X_i, \ldots X_n, t)$$

in which the time t entered explicitly into the function F.

It is not proposed to take up the study of this perfectly general case; it must suffice to point to the mathematical literature regarding equations of this form.[1]

But there is another special phase of the general problem which, like the case of *slow* changes, yields with comparative ease to analytical treatment; namely, that special phase which enquires only into the ultimate effect, upon equilibrium, of a given total change in a parameter, leaving aside all questions relating to the path by which the displacement of equilibrium takes place. Such a separate consideration of this special and restricted phase of the general problem is rendered possible by the fact that, in certain cases at any rate, the displacement of the equilibrium is independent of the path of the change, and depends only on the given initial and

[1] See, for example, E. Picard, Traité d'Analyse, vol. 3, 1908, pp. 187, 188, 194, 197; E. Goursat, Cours d'Analyse, vol. 2, 1918, pp. 482, 498.

final values of the parameters whose modification provokes or is associated with the change. So, in physico-chemical transformations ("changes of state") the principle of Le Chatelier enables us to predicate, within certain limits, the *sign* of the displacement of equilibrium conditioned by a change in certain of the parameters upon which the equilibrium depends.

THE PRINCIPLE OF LE CHATELIER

The principle of Le Chatelier is best illustrated by a simple example. Consider the simple chemical reaction

$$2H_2 + O_2 \rightleftarrows 2H_2O + 58.3 \text{ cal.}$$

At high temperatures this reaction is reversible; that is to say, it takes place to some extent in the direction of the upper arrow, but also to some extent in the direction of the lower arrow, and an equilibrium is finally established between these two opposing reactions. Now this is what the Le Chatelier principle tells us:

If we add either H alone or O alone to the system, the equilibrium is shifted in the direction of the upper arrow, that is to say, in such direction as to absorb some of the added constituent.

Similarly, if we heat the system, the equilibrium is shifted in the direction of the lower arrow, that is to say, in the direction of the reaction which *absorbs* heat. The principle, as enunciated by *Le Chatelier*[2] *himself*, is:

Every system in chemical equilibrium, under the influence of a change of any single one of the factors of equilibrium,[3] undergoes a transformation in such direction that, if this transformation took place alone, it would produce a change in the opposite direction of the factor in question.

The factors of equilibrium are temperature, pressure, and electromotive force, corresponding to three forms of energy—heat, electricity and mechanical energy.

The second paragraph of the principle as quoted above, requires special emphasis. It is often omitted, even by authors of the highest

[2] Recherches sur les Equilibres Chimique, 1888, pp. 48, 210; Comptes Rendus, 1884, vol. 99, p. 786; Mellor, Chemical Statics and Dynamics, 1904, pp. 435–436.

[3] It appears that some French writers employ the term "facteur d'équilibre" as synonymous with "intensity factor of an energy." (Cf. F. Michaud, Ann. de Phys., vol. 16, 1921, p. 132.)

repute,[4] with the result that a vagueness is introduced for which Le Chatelier himself cannot justly be made responsible. This vagueness is then often rendered still worse by departures from the original wording, aimed at an extension of the scope of the law to all conceivable systems and "factors," an extension which is gained with a total sacrifice of all validity of the principle. So, for example, if we seek to apply the principle as quoted above, but omitting the restriction of the second paragraph, to the water equilibrium already mentioned, and if we select as "factor" of equilibrium not pressure but volume, the principle would lead us to reason as follows: On *diminishing* the volume of the system, that transformation will take place which, did it take place alone (i.e., at constant pressure), would be accompanied by *increase* in volume; a conclusion which is false. As has been shown by Ehrenfest,[5] the error arises through failure to discriminate, in the application of the principle, between the intensity factor (e.g., pressure) and the capacity factor (e.g., volume) of an energy.

It must appear singular that so obvious a defect of the principle, *as commonly quoted*, should so generally have escaped attention, and should for example, have passed unnoted through seven editions of so excellent a work as Nernst's *Theoretische Chemie*. Ehrenfest points out that the explanation lies in the very vagueness of the principles, which permits it to be construed in each case to suit circumstances. The principle is commonly applied *ex post facto*, and its competence to predict thus escapes any serious test. This, however, is only a partial explanation. After all, the fundamental reason for the tardy recognition, and the still more tardy admission in the general literature, of the weakness of the principle, *as commonly quoted*, must be sought in an inherent weakness of the human mind: by a curious inversion of what might be expected in logical sequence, the last things to receive critical scrutiny are always the fundamental premises of our arguments. This is true both as regards the judgment of the average individual, of the people at large, and often even of the man of very superior intellect. One recalls, in this connection, MacAuley's remarks regarding Dr. Johnson: "How it chanced that a man who reasoned upon his

[4] See, for example, W. Nernst, Theoretische Chemie, 1913, p. 698.
[5] Zeitschr. f. phys. Chem., 1911, vol. 77, p. 735. Cf. also P. Duhem, Traité d'Energétique, 1911, vol. 1, p. 467.

premises so ably should assume his premises so foolishly is one of the great mysteries of human nature."

If such an outwardly slight departure from Le Chatelier's original enunciation as the omission of his second "explanatory" paragraph, thus completely destroys the validity of his principle, what is to be said of such sweepingly vague settings as in the following examples:

The broadest definition of the principle of Le Chatelier is that a system tends to change so as to minimize an external disturbance (W. D. Bancroft, Journal of the American Chemical Society, 1911, p. 92).

Every external action produces in a body or system changes in such direction, that in consequence of this change the resistance of the body or system against the external action is increased. If we regard the faculty of adaptation of animals and plants from the point of view that the organisms undergo, under the influence of external actions, changes which render them more resistant to those actions, then the property of non-living matter which is expressed by the principle of Le Chatelier-Braun may be regarded as a sort of adaptation of such non-living matter (Chwolson, Traité de Physique, 1909, vol. 3, p. 547).

If the equilibrium of a natural complex (system of masses, organism, system of ideas) is disturbed, it adapts itself to the stimulus (Reiz) which causes the disturbance, in such manner that the said stimulus continually diminishes until finally the original or a new equilibrium is again established (J. Löwy, Kosmos, 1911, p. 331).

The last two examples are of particular interest to us here as suggesting application of the principle to biological systems. As a matter of fact, such application of the vaguely formulated principle (in a form in which it would be injustice to link it with the name of Le Chatelier) antedates by many years its enunciation by the French physicist. The following passages in Herbert Spencer's First Principles are pertinent:

Among the involved rhythmical changes constituting organic life, any disturbing force that works an excess of change in some direction is gradually diminished and finally neutralized by antagonistic forces, which thereupon work a compensating change in the opposite direction, and so, after more or less of oscillation, restore the medium condition. And this process it is which constitutes what physicians call the *vis medicatrix naturae*.

This is a conclusion which we may safely draw without knowing the special re-arrangements that effect the equilibration: If we see that a different mode of life is followed after a period of functional derangement by some altered condition of the system—if we see that this altered condition, becoming by and by established, continues without further change, we have no alternative but to say that the new forces brought to bear on the system have been compensated by the opposing forces they have evoked (First Principles, Chapter XXII, *Equilibriation*, 173).

Almost simultaneous with Le Chatelier's publication (1884) is the following pronouncement.

L'être vivant est agencé de telle manière que chaque influence perturbatrice provoque d'elle même la mise en activité de l'appareil compensateur qui doit neutraliser et reparer le dommage (Léon Frédéricq, Archives de Zoologie Exp. et Gén., ser. 2, vol. 3, 1885, p. xxxv).

Now it is not denied that such expressions as this have a certain utility, as describing with fair accuracy a goodly proportion of a class of phenomena to which they relate. But to designate such statements, as "Le Chatelier's Principle," is wholly misleading. That principle, in its exact and narrower formulation is rigorously true, as much so as the laws of thermodynamics from which it can be deduced; it has no exceptions, any more than there is any exception to the law that heat flows by simple conduction from the hotter of two bodies to the colder.

The alleged "principle," as applied to biological systems, lacks the sureness which the true Le Chatelier principle possesses, in its stricter formulations, in physical chemistry. An organism may, by exposure to a certain influence A, become *more* resistant to the influence, as in the case of acquired immunity after an attack of infectious disease, or after habituation to such a poison as arsenic. But, by exposure to another influence B it may become less resistant to B, as in the case of cumulative poisons, or of anaphylaxis. The Le Chatelier principle does not enable us here to predict in which direction the effect will take place in a new and untried case of some influence C.

Conditions of Validity of Le Chatelier's Principle. The question arises why the principle thus breaks down in its application to biological cases of the kind cited. The answer is found by examining the basis on which the proof of the principle rests. Such an examination brings out the fact that one of the necessary conditions for the applicability of the principle is stability of the equilibrium to which application is made. Now the equilibria commonly contemplated in physical chemistry are stable, so that this condition is satisfied. But it is not always satisfied in the equilibrium of the living organism. The organism is, indeed, stable with regard to many of the commonly occurring attacks of its environment. But it is of little consequence to the species whether, for example, the individual organism is stable with regard to the ingestion of a large dose of strychnine, for in nature such ingestion will occur so rarely, if at all, as to influence in no appreciable degree the life of the species. It is not necessary for the stability of the *species*, that the *individual* be stable at all times.[6] In point of fact, we know perfectly well that sooner or later each individual finds itself in a condition of instability, by "accident" or sickness, and dies. An analysis[7] of the basis of the principle of Le Chatelier reveals the fact, among others, that all demonstrations of this principle postulate, as a fundamental characteristic of the systems to which it applies, that they be in *stable* equilibrium. The principle can, therefore be applied at best only with cautious reservation to living organisms, reservation such as, for example, Le Dantec[8] makes: "In studying as closely as possible the consequences of disease in living organisms, *when they survive such diseases*, I have drawn attention . . . . to the fact that all these consequences, such as acquired immunity and the production of antitoxic sera, can be summarized in the principle of Le Chatelier." But with such reservation the principle loses its chief utility, which consists in its power to predict the course of events. Indeed, it might be accused, in such restricted form, of being little more than a tautological platitude, which tells us that if the system or unit in question is stable, then it is stable. This is not quite such a damning accusation as may at first sight appear, for the same can be brought against the principle of the survival of the fittest, which nevertheless has proved supremely fertile in biological research. In point of fact there is a close relationship between

[6] Compare what has been said in the discussion of chemical equilibrium regarding the stability of aggregates composed of individuals, themselves of limited stability, of limited life period (Chapter XII).

[7] Such an analysis, carried out in considerable detail, has been given by the writer in Proc. Am. Acad. Arts and Sci., 1922, vol. 57, pp. 21–37. The importance of the restriction to stable equilibria, in connection with biological systems, has also been pointed out by C. Benedicks, Zeitschr. f. phys. Chemic, 1922, vol. 100, pp. 42–51. A. J. Lotka, Am. Jour. Hygiene, 1923, p. 375.

[8] La Stabilité de la Vie, 1910, p. 24.

the two principles. But it is important to note that the principle of the survival of the fittest is avowedly statistical in character, and is to be applied to organisms in the gross. This is true, also, of the principle of Le Chatelier in physico-chemical systems; its field of application is to aggregates of molecules, not to the individual. But the applications that have been essayed in biology have been made to the individual; such application can at the best yield a judgment of probabilities. In physical chemistry we deal for the most part with stable equilibria. But in biology, as has already been pointed out, though the *races* that come under our observation possess stability *as races* (else they would not have survived to be our contemporaries), it does not follow at all, that each and every individual is at all times in a state of stable equilibrium.

Aside from the limitation in the applicability of the principle to *stable* systems, other limitations appear in such an analysis of its foundations as has been referred to above. So, for example, loose analogy to the physico-chemical equilibrium, as affected by the addition of a quantity of one of the reacting substances, might lead one to draw the erroneous inference that in a community infected with malaria, the introduction of additional malaria parasites would shift the equilibrium in the direction of a higher malaria rate. But there is every reason to expect, on the contrary, that the equilibrium remains unchanged by such addition. For a close analysis of the reason for this divergence in the two cases the reader must be referred to the original paper already cited. It must suffice here to state briefly that this reason is to be found in the existence in the physico-chemical case of equations of constraint, relations between certain variables, and in the absence of analogous relations in the case of malaria.

Extension of Scope of Rigorous Applicability. While the prime result of a searching analysis of the foundations of the Le Chatelier principle is to emphasize rather the restrictions of its scope, yet in certain respects such analysis does furnish a rigorous basis for a certain generalization of its applicability beyond those bounds where its warrant rests on the firm ground of thermodynamics. And this extension of the strict applicability of the principle takes place essentially in two directions. On the one hand the thermodynamic justification, at any rate in the form commonly presented, covers only true equilibria, and does not extend to steady states maintained with constant dissipation of energy. This restriction does not appear in the demonstration of the principle on the broadest grounds that suffice for its establishment,[9] Le Chatelier's principle applies, in certain cases, to steady states of the more general type, as well as to true equilibria.

The second direction in which the analysis, on general grounds, of the principle, enlarges its field of warrant, is in the matter of the kinds of "factors" to which it is properly applicable. It has already been pointed out that, in its physico-chemical application, it must be used with proper discrimination as to the distinction between the capacity and the intensity factor of an energy, as, for example, volume and pressure. It is found, upon analysis, that the applicability of the principle to the effect of a change in pressure, for example rests upon the following fundamental property of the pressure and volume of a system in stable equilibrium.

1. For every value of v, the volume of the system, there is a definite value of p_i, the pressure *which it exerts*, the internal pressure, as we may term it.

2. The volume v increases or decreases according as the internal pressure p_i is greater or less than the external pressure p_e upon the enclosure, that is to say,

$$\frac{dv}{dt} \gtreqless 0 \text{ according as } p_i \gtreqless p_e.$$

3. It can be shown that, given (1) and (2), stability demands that the curves representing the relative between p (ordinates) and v (abscissae) must slope from left to right downwards. For if such a curve slopes in the opposite direction, then the slightest displacement from equilibrium will immediately cause the system to travel with cumulative effect, avalanche-like, along the pv curve further and further away from the starting point.[10]

[9] For justification of this and other statements made in these paragraphs the reader is referred to the author's paper already cited. It may be remarked that Ehrenfest (loc. cit.) expresses the belief that such broader scope belongs to the principle, but he does not support his impression with proof.

[10] It is interesting to note that an upward slope, from left to right, occurs in the middle limb of the van der Waals' pv curve of a gas. But this limb represents an unstable state which is never realized, the gas, instead of following this part of the curve, partially condenses and traces a horizontal straight line for the pv relation.

Now these fundamental properties (1), (2) and (3), of a capacity and an intensity factor of an energy[11] are shared by certain parameters that have no direct or simple relation to energy whatsoever; and since the applicability of the principle depends upon these properties, it will extend to such other parameters possessing them. As an example may be mentioned the relation between area a occupied by a population, and the rent per unit area R_i that an (average) individual is willing to pay. If R_i is greater than R_e, the rent at market rate, the individual will move into a more spacious apartment, and a will increase, and vice versa; so that

$$\frac{da}{dt} \gtreqless 0 \text{ according as } R_i \gtreqless R_e$$

On the other hand the curves representing, in rectangular coordinates, the relation between rent and area available per head, necessarily slope from left to right downward. If it were true, as sometimes stated, that the more a man has, the more he wants, economic equilibrium would be an unstable condition.

This example is presented here with reservation. There may be various complications in practice that may form obstacles to the simple application of the principle indicated. But it will serve to show how a perfectly rigorous justification may exist for the application of the principle of Le Chatelier outside the field of plain energetics and thermodynamics. Where, and only where such justification can be clearly shown to exist, there it will be permissible and useful to apply the principle. Applications made broadcast, without prior examination of the parameters involved, perhaps without any thought at all of reasonable parameters, are of little if any worth.

One other word of caution must be said, for which the example of area and rent will furnish a suitable illustration. Before we apply

[11] Owing to the custom of counting heat *absorbed* by a system as positive, but work done *upon it* as negative, the relation analogous to that of (2) takes the form, in the case of heat energy,

$$\frac{dQ}{dt} \lesseqgtr 0 \text{ according as } \theta_i \lesseqgtr \theta.$$

where Q is the quantity of heat absorbed by the system at a temperature from a source at the temperature θ. Here the $Q\theta$ curves slope upward from left to right. Cf. A. J. Lotka, loc. cit., p. 36.

the principle to any particular parameter, we must be sure that the contemplated change will modify this parameter alone, and not also at the same time others that are in principle, if not in physical fact, to be regarded as independent. So, for example, one reason why the example of area and rent was presented above with express reservation is that, ordinarily at any rate, it may be difficult or impossible to modify the area of a population without modifying at the same time certain other features, such as the supply of nutriments furnished in the soil, etc.

On the whole, so far, it must be said that the result of a careful analysis of the principle of Le Chatelier yields negative results, so far as practical application to biological systems is concerned. The chief conclusion is that great caution must be exercised in employing the principle. This result may be somewhat disappointing, but it is for that none the less important. Facts are stubborn things; it seems a pity to demolish the idol of a pretty generalization, but in such things we cannot permit the wish to be father to the thought. And the idol is not wholly demolished—in fact his hitherto doubtful title to certain domains has been established on a clear basis. But his province must be recognized as very definitely bounded.

DISCUSSION OF DISPLACEMENT OF EQUILIBRIUM INDEPENDENTLY OF LE CHATELIER'S PRINCIPLE

In view of the limitations in the field of strict applicability of the principle of Le Chatelier, we are in general forced to consider separately each particular case of displacement of equilibrium. How such cases may be treated may be exemplified by the following two instances.

Case 1. Displacement of Equilibrium between Food and Feeding Species. Consider a species S_2 of mass X_2, which requires for its (equilibrium) sustenance of a mass k_2X_2 of food. Let this food be derived exclusively from the slain bodies, of total mass $d_1 X_1$, of a species S_1. Let a fraction ϵ of all the deaths in S_1 be those caused by S_2 feeding upon S_1. Then

$$k_2X_2 = \epsilon d_1X_1 \tag{1}$$

$$\frac{X_1}{X_2} = \frac{k_2}{\epsilon d_1} = \alpha \tag{2}$$

It is generally in the interest of the species S_2 to reduce this ratio to a minimum, especially in such a case as that of a domestic species S_1, kept by man (S_2) to provide him with flesh food. For the species S_1 itself consumes food, and is thus directly or indirectly a tax upon the system. In fact, the species S_1 is merely a sort of food factory for S_2, and the less of S_1 is required to produce the requisite amount of food k_2X_2, the more efficient is S_1 as a food factory.

We may therefore enquire what the formula (2) tells us regarding the efficiency of S_1 as a food producer.

It will be observed that the ratio $\alpha = \dfrac{X_1}{X_2} = \dfrac{k_2}{\epsilon d_1}$ may be reduced in two ways by operating upon the species S_1 (operating on S_2, it might be reduced by diminishing k_2; but we will exclude this from consideration); an increase in either ϵ or in d_1 will bring about this result of reducing α. Now ϵ would be increased if the species S_2 helped to protect S_1 from its other enemies. This, of course, is one of the obvious expedients employed by man toward his domesticated sources of sustenance.

But the species S_2 may also operate to reduce the ratio $\alpha = \dfrac{X_1}{X_2} = \dfrac{k_2}{\epsilon d_1}$ by increasing d_1, and it may do this in several ways.

We may write

$$d_1X_1 = d_1N_1m_1 \tag{3}$$

$$= d_1N_1m_1'j_1 \tag{4}$$

where N_1 is the number of the population of S_1, m_1 the mass per head of this living population, m_1' the mass per head of the individuals slain by S_2, and j is a factor, namely $\dfrac{m_1}{m_1'}$. Evidently d_1j is the death rate per head in the population S_1; to simplify matters we may assume that j is (nearly) unity, so that d_1 represents directly the death rate per head in S_1.

It is evidently possible to increase d_1, the death rate per head in S_1, without disturbing the equilibrium, provided that the birth rate b_1 is increased in equal amount. There are several ways of accomplishing this. The most obvious is systematic breeding. We may briefly consider the analysis of an ideally simple case in point.

Let b_1 be the natural birth rate per head and d_1 the death rate per head, in a population of N_1 individuals of a food species S_1.

Of the total deaths, let pN_1 occur through various other causes, while qN_1N_2 are due to the destruction of S_1 by the species S_2 that feeds upon S_1.

In equilibrium, then, we have

$$b_1 - d_1 = b_1 - qN_2 - p = 0 \tag{5}$$

$$N_2 = \frac{b_1 - p}{q} \tag{6}$$

Furthermore, let the species S_2, when in equilibrium, consume ζN_2 individuals of species N_1, so that

$$\zeta N_2 = qN_1N_2 \tag{7}$$

$$N_1 = \frac{\zeta}{q} \tag{8}$$

Now let S_2 "cultivate" the species S_1, so that the birth rate of the latter is raised from b_1 to $b_1 + \sigma N_2$.

The conditions for equilibrium now are

$$b_1 + \sigma N_2' - qN_2' - p = 0 \tag{9}$$

$$N_2' = \frac{b - p}{q - \sigma} \tag{10}$$

$$N_1 = \frac{\zeta}{q} \text{ as before} \tag{11}$$

The effect of this cultivation, then has been, in this case, to leave the population of S_1, the food species, unchanged. But the feeding species S_2 has increased in the ratio $\dfrac{q}{q - \sigma}$.

This result could hardly have been foreseen by the aid of the principle of Le Chatelier.

In this argument it has been supposed, as a first approximation, that q is a constant. In point of fact q will no doubt be somewhat modified when the species S_1 is "cultivated" by S_2. The effect of such modification of q would then be superimposed upon the effect derived in the argument set forth above.

Case 2. Change of Circulation through Moving Cycles. Among the moving equilibria in nature an important class are those which arise in systems traversed by matter in cyclic transformations.

Consider a very simple example of a cyclic transformation chain, such as that in which, of three components S_1, S_2, S_3, the first becomes converted into the second, the second into the third and the third returns to the first, after the pattern:

$$S_1$$
$$S_3 \longleftarrow S_2$$

We may write the equations of the transformation

$$
\left.
\begin{aligned}
\frac{dX_1}{dt} &= F_1(X_1,\ X_2,\ X_3) = g_3 X_3 - g_1 X_1 \\[2mm]
\frac{dX_2}{dt} &= F_2(X_1,\ X_2,\ X_3) = g_1 X_1 - g_2 X_2 \\[2mm]
\frac{dX_3}{dt} &= F_3(X_1,\ X_2,\ X_3) = g_2 X_2 - g_3 X_3
\end{aligned}
\right\}
\tag{12}
$$

where in the most general case g_1, g_2, g_3 are each of them a function of X_1, X_2, X_3.

When a steady state is established, so that the derivatives $\dfrac{dX}{dt}$ vanish we have, evidently

$$X_1:X_2:X_3 = \frac{1}{g_1}:\frac{1}{g_2}:\frac{1}{g_3} \tag{13}$$

from which it is seen that, in the steady state, that component is most abundant, which has the slowest proportional rate of decomposition, the smallest g. This smaller g acts as a "bottle neck"[12] in the cycle, causing material to accumulate in front of it. It acts as a brake, as a limiting factor, upon the rate of circulation through the system.

---

[12] I am borrowing this term from the language of efficiency engineers, who employ it to denote a point, in a consecutive series in industrial operations, at which the progress of work is arrested by a local "limiting capacity."

If the total mass of S_1, S_2 and S_3 is in some way fixed, so that we put $X_1 + X_2 + X_3 = M =$ const., we have, evidently, for a steady state

$$X_1 = \frac{1/g_1}{1/g_1 + 1/g_2 + 1/g_3} M = \frac{g_2 g_3}{g_1 + g_2 + g_2} M \qquad (14)$$

Similarly

$$X_2 = \frac{g_1 g_3}{g_1 + g_2 + g_2} M \qquad (15)$$

$$X_3 = \frac{g_1 g_2}{g_1 + g_2 + g_3} M \qquad (16)$$

The *circulation I*, i.e., the mass circulating through the system per unit of time, is evidently given by

$$I = g_1 X_1 = g_2 X_2 = g_3 X_3 = \frac{g_1 g_2 g_3}{g_1 + g_2 + g_3} M \qquad (17)$$

and

$$\frac{\partial I}{\partial g_1} = \frac{g_2 g_3 (g_2 + g_3)}{(g_1 + g_2 + g_3)^2} M \qquad (18)$$

$$= \frac{g_2 g_3}{g_2 + g_3} M \text{ approx., if } g_1 \text{ is small} \qquad (19)$$

Furthermore,

$$\frac{\partial I}{\partial g_1} \bigg/ \frac{\partial I}{\partial g_2} = \frac{g_2 g_3 (g_2 + g_3)}{g_1 g_3 (g_1 + g_3)} \qquad (20)$$

Hence

$$\frac{\partial I}{\partial g_1} \gtreqless \frac{\partial I}{\partial g_2} \text{ according as } g_2 \gtreqless g_1 \qquad (21)$$

Hence, to increase the circulation, the best effect, other things equal, is obtained by seeking to increase the smallest g.

This result, also, the Le Chatelier's principle seems incompetent to predict.

Some Significant Cases of Instability. It lies in the nature of things that a special interest attaches to stable states and stable systems. They represent the lasting features in the changeful landscape of nature—that is what we mean by stability. They are the survivors in the struggle for existence.

But the class of unstable states and systems is not without a special interest of its own. Departures from stability, so far from forming insignificant exceptions, are found to play an important rôle both in normal and in pathological life processes.

The body does not always react in the direction of a restored equilibrium when exposed to a disturbing influence. The opposite type of reaction is sufficiently frequent to give occupation and means of livelihood to a distinct profession, whose business it is to prevent this adverse type of reaction from proceeding to the point where it sets a limit to life. A particularly pernicious form of this adverse reaction to influence tending to disturb the life equilibrium is that known among medical men as the *vicious circle*. A departure from equilibrium, instead of stimulating a compensating response, provokes a further departure in the same direction, with cumulative effect. If this process goes on only to a certain point and then stops, there may be little or no damage sustained. But conditions may arise which, by their very nature, produce a continued accumulation of deviations from the stable equilibrium position, until the limits compatible with the continuation of organized life processes are exceeded. So, for example, a person exposed to hardships through adverse economic conditions, suffers from malnutrition; this lowers his resistance to bacterial infection; he contracts tuberculosis; there is a loss of appetite, and malnutrition not only is accentuated, but may become fixed even if better economic conditions are provided. And now a closed cycle, a "vicious circle," is established, and the disease grows like an avalanche tumbling down a slope,[13] gathering weight at each revolution of the cycle, on the downhill path to dissolution, thus

[13] A condition analogous to that represented by the middle (ascending) limb of the van der Waals' curve for the relation between pressure and volume of gas.

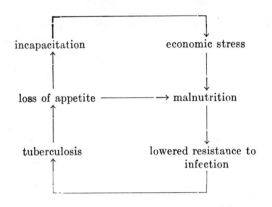

TABLE 32

*Association of high blood pressure (20 mm. Hg or more above average for age)
with "over-weight" among 6,284 white males**

AGE GROUP	WEIGHT	NUMBER EXAMINED	PROPORTION IN EACH AGE GROUP SHOWING SYSTOLIC BLOOD PRESSURE 20 MM. Hg OR MORE ABOVE NORMAL		
			Per cent	Difference	Probable error of difference
All ages	(a) 20 per cent or more over-weight..............	2,033	15.7	9.6	0.600
	(b) Normal weight†	4,251	6.1		
Under 25	(a)	39	5.1	−0.5	2.563
	(b)	269	5.6		
25–34	(a)........................	475	11.2	6.7	1.035
	(b)........................	1,594	4.5		
35–44	(a)........................	832	10.7	6.7	0.803
	(b)........................	1,442	4.0		
45–54	(a)........................	468	22.4	14.2	1.477
	(b)........................	691	8.2		
55 and over	(a)........................	219	32.0	8.9	2.772
	(b)........................	255	23.1		

* Statistical Bulletin Metropolitan Life Insurance Company, July, 1923,
p. 8 and a forthcoming study by Prof. I. V. Hiscock, Yale University.
† Five per cent above or below average weight for age and height.

Cumulative Cycles Simulating Orthogenesis. As another instance of a vicious circle we may perhaps regard certain cases of what has sometimes been termed orthogenesis, or determinate variation. These are cases in which the evolutionary drift seems to be

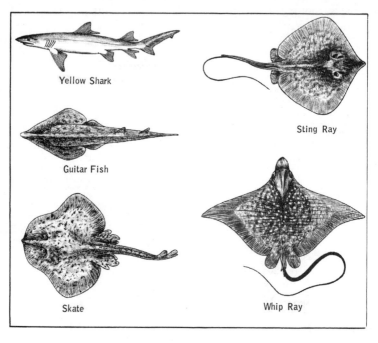

Skate   Whip Ray

FIG. 59. THE YELLOW SHARK AND SOME OF HIS RELATIVES

A group of fishes showing progressive flattening of the body accompanied by thinning out of the tail. Evolution would seem to have been guided, here, rather than by inherent tendency (orthogenesis) than by any utility of the resulting lash-like appendage. But the series may also be interpreted as the product of a cumulative cycle under the influence of some glandular control of growth.

referable, not to extrinsic causes, not to the selecting or other influence of the environment, but to a fatalistic tendency inherent in the organism itself, drawing the race on in a definite direction, for weal or for woe. So, it may be, the extinct races of giant reptiles were swept on upon a tidal wave of unremitting growth, until their cost of living exceeded their earning capacity, until their very strength proved their fatal weakness; unable to gather, in a day's run, sufficient food to fill their monstrous paunch, they became the victims of their colossal ambition; their carcases remained enshrouded in the rocks, monumental wrecks by the wayside, where the caravan of evolution has passed on. . . . .

But there is another view which may account for this chapter in Natural History, as has been pointed out to me by Mr. J. B. S. Haldane in correspondence the gist of which is, briefly, as follows: The large reptiles of the secondary age had large pituitary glands. It was probably the secretion of these that determined their large size. Now a large animal has a high blood pressure—a fact which is exemplified, in a way, in statistics of clinical observations on human material, witness table 32 p. 295. With high blood pressure there would be a tendency for the capillaries to leak. The thing that stops them leaking is pituitrin. Thus selection will tend to increase the pituitary gland in large animals. Unless it is possible for variations to arise increasing the output of pituitrin but not that of the anterior lobe, successive generations will tend to become bigger and bigger, till they ultimately perish of hyperpituitarism.[14]

Sometimes, it seems, the trend of evolution by a cumulative cycle may be grotesque rather than pernicious. This might well be the explanation of such singular vagaries as those observed, for example, in a group of fishes related to the shark. This series (fig. 59) (to which my attention was drawn by Mr. J. T. Nichols of the American Museum of Natural History) exhibits progressive flattening of the body accompanied by thinning out of the tail, until the latter is reduced to a mere lash. Here some gland controlling growth may have become increasingly active in response to selection operating on some useful quality, and meanwhile some secondary effect had to be taken into the bargain, regardless of utility.

But cumulative cycles do not always work toward destruction or toward mere caprices devoid of utility. The effect of gathering momentum is equally potent in the constructive sphere. Perhaps the most striking examples of this have occurred in the realm of

[14] Somewhat similar views have been expressed by A. H. Sturtevant, Science, 1924, vol. 59, p. 579.

mental phenomena. The eye[15] and the hand have probably contributed more than any other single circumstance to the evolution of the human mind up to its present level. The possession of an agile member gave opportunity for exercise of the mental faculties, this in turn reacted towards increased development of the tactile sense and manipulative skill of the hand, and so on in a cumulative cycle.

A similar "cumulative cycle" has probably had a large part in developing our faculty of speech. In the present stage of our development, we find it almost indispensable, in *thinking*, to use *language*, a vehicle whose primary function would seem to be the transmission of thought from one individual to another, and which would seem wholly superfluous in the traffic of thought within the precincts of one mind, as money currency is needless in the give-and-take within the same household. Which, then came first, thought, or language? Neither, of course, can claim clear precedence. They must have developed together, in mutual stimulation. The habit of communicating thoughts to others must have reacted upon the thinker and made him more perfect, first as a thinker, and then again, in turn, as a communicator of thought, as a speaker; and so, in a species of cycle, not vicious but benign, thought promoted speech and speech furthered thought, in an endless chain of cause and effect, such as that which we witness in the somewhat useless but rather entertaining spectacle of a cat chasing its tail, or (to turn from the fine to the useful arts), in the economically more significant performance of the donkey urged to unwonted productive effort by the hope of catching up with that elusive wisp of hay dangled by the driver before the poor beast's nose. Cause and effect are so intermingled in a chain of alternations that they have become indistinguishable.

To cite in third place a more modern instance, the mutually fertilizing influence upon each other of pure and applied science falls into the same class of benign cycles. Here also cause and effect are so intermingled that the relative merits of the two not very clearly separated branches of scientific endeavor are hardly

[15] Cf. G. H. Parker, Proc. Am. Phil. Soc., 1922, vol. 61, p. 107; also G. Elliot, Nature, 1923, vol. 112, p. 443.

a subject for profitable debate. If, as some[16] hold, "the final justification of science is the power it creates for the use of mankind," then we must call to remembrance that this "power must be created before it is used."[17]

The instances cited should be sufficient to demonstrate how effectively resourceful nature makes use, in her economy, of instability, with its cumulative potency, as a *progressive* force; as well as of stability, the essentially conservative element in evolution. Indeed, we, of the human race, have good reason to be mindful of this fact, for the wholly unparalleled rapidity of our scientific and industrial evolution in past decades is itself the most brilliant example of instability and its cumulative power as a factor in evolution.

[16] The writer is not among these, if by final justification is meant the only sufficient justification. No one would think of demanding such justification for art. Why require it of science? Such an attitude towards her is like that of the man who, having received repeated favors from his fellow, begins to acquire the habit, and to look upon such favors as due to him, and as the sole justification for the other's existence.

[17] C. S. Minot, Science, 1911, p. 119.

CHAPTER XXIII

The Parameters of State

In dealing with any natural phenomenon—especially one of a vital nature, with all the complexity of living organisms in type and habit—the mathematician has to simplify the conditions until they reach the attenuated character which lies within the power of his analysis.—*Karl Pearson.*

Little has been said, so far, of the parameters P employed to define the state of the systems under consideration. In the earlier chapters these parameters have, in fact, been largely eliminated from discussion by restricting the treatment to the case of evolution under constant parameters P; subsequently the special cases of evolution with slowly changing P's, and the influence upon *equilibrium alone* of changes of unrestricted kind in the P's have been discussed; but all of this from a general standpoint, without giving much thought to the particular nature and properties of these parameters. It is desirable now to give some attention to this hitherto neglected phase of the subject.

The simplest, and in many respects a very illuminating example of the nature and function of the parameters P is furnished in the thermodynamic treatment of physical systems. Here we are accustomed to the use of such parameters as pressure, temperature, surface tension, etc., to define the state of the systems under consideration.

Topographic Parameters. Obviously there is much latitude in the choice of such parameters; for if any parameter P can be employed to define the state of a given system, any single-valued function $F(P)$ of that parameter will also serve, though certain selections of parameters may be found much more advantageous in practice than others. In particular, it is found, in systems amenable to thermodynamic treatment, that P's can be so selected that they appear as the intensity factors of an energy.[1] This selection has actually been made in the example cited above. Or, alternatively, any one of the P's so selected, can be replaced by

---

[1] Helmholtz, Die Thermodynamisch-chemischen Vorgänge 1882 (Ges. Abh., vol. 3, p. 958); P. Ehrenfest, Zeitschr. f. phys. Chemie, 1911, p. 234.

the extensity factor of an energy. So, in place of the pressure p we can introduce the volume v, these two parameters being connected by a functional relation of the form.

$$v = \varphi(p, X_1, X_2, \ldots X_n) \qquad (1)$$

The parameter v (volume) is almost the simplest type imaginable of a *topographic* parameter. In many systems commonly considered in physical chemistry the only way in which the topography of the system plays any appreciable rôle in the processes going on therein is through the volume defined by the boundaries of the system. Even the shape of the boundary is in most cases immaterial.

In the systems in which organic evolution is proceeding, the situation is very different. In one respect the topographic parameters are often, in this case, even simpler than in the physico-chemical example, namely in this, that living organisms (except aquatic species) make their excursions, extend their activities, essentially in a space of two dimensions—the earth's surface, or at least a rather thin shell near that surface. Hence we are interested in areas rather than volumes; in place of a parameter v, volume, we may expect to find figuring in the discussion a parameter a, area.

But aside from this slight simplification (which does not always apply), the influence of topography in systems in the course of organic evolution is immeasurably more complex than in the simple physico-chemical systems that form the chief subjects of study in the laboratory and in theory. Indeed, the conditions presented in nature are so complex that we can hardly hope to construct any systematic mathematical analysis of this phase of the subject, except by the expedient of dealing in somewhat radical abstractions, such as evolution "in a uniform environment" or, perhaps, in an environment reproducing in very greatly simplified form some of those principal geographic features that are typical of our globe.

There is something unsatisfactory in such abstractions that seem rather far remote from conditions actually met in nature. But it must be remembered that such abstractions are a necessary, and, as experience has abundantly shown, a very effective aid to our limited mental powers, which are incompetent to deal directly with unexpurgated nature in all its complexity. Neither should it be forgotten that the worker in the laboratory, though he may seem to be nearer to nature, himself is dealing essentially in abstractions.

When the physical chemist investigates a chemical reaction in a constant temperature bath, he is not copying nature, where constant temperature is an exception, but is deliberately establishing an "unnatural" situation. He does this in order to separate the influence of one factor upon the course of events from that of a multitude of others; feeling confident that when he has gained an insight into the workings of such a simplified and, in a sense, unnatural system, he will be the better equipped to understand, or at least to make a further study of more complicated systems, approaching more and more nearly those occurring in nature. It is precisely the same principle which justifies us, in "substituting an ideal, upon which it is possible to operate, for intractable reality,"[2] when we essay the systematic treatment of natural processes by mathematical analysis. So, for example, Karl Pearson in his memoir on Random Migration treats among others the case in which "breeding grounds and food supply are supposed to have an average uniform distribution over the district under consideration;"[3] and the simple case of "migration into a cleared rectangular area," etc. Somewhat similar topographic simplicity is assumed as the basis of studies of Brownlee on the Mathematical Theory of Random Migration and Epidemic Distribution. We shall have occasion to refer to these studies again in another connection. It is not intended to follow up this phase of the subject here.

Neither will any attempt be made to sketch here even in outline the empirical side of the subject, our observational knowledge regarding the dependence of life in its various forms upon the parameters of state. There is a ripe and extensive literature available on this special phase of biology, which it is unnecessary to duplicate here. It will suffice to refer to standard works on geographical biology and to general ecology.[4]

[2] Nature, 1922, p. 764.
[3] Draper's Company Memoirs, Biometric Series III, 1906.
[4] The following may be mentioned: A. Engler and O. Drude, Die Vegetation der Erde, Sammlung pflanzengeographischer Monographien (a cyclopedic work in many volumes). A. F. W. Schimper, Clarendon Press, 1903, Plant Geography. E. Warming, Clarendon Press, 1909, Oecology of Plants. A. R. Wallace, 1876, The Geographical Distribution of Animals. F. E. Beddard, 1895, Textbook of Zoogeography. H. Gadow, Cambridge University Press, 1913, The Wandering of Animals. E. L. Trouessart, 1922, La Distribution Géographique des Animaux.

In physico-chemical systems the topographic parameter v (volume) is the capacity factor of an energy, as had already been noted; and associated with v is what may be termed a *conjugate* parameter p_i (pressure), which is the *intensity* factor of the energy in question, i.e., that factor which determines the direction of any change in the capacity factor v, according to the scheme

$$\frac{dv}{dt} \gtreqless 0 \text{ according as } p_i \gtreqless p_e \tag{2}$$

where p_e is the external pressure.[5]

The Intensity Law in Organic and Economic Systems. Is there anything corresponding to the relation (2), the *Intensity Law*, as it has been termed, in the case of the topographic parameter a (area) which enters into the definition of the state of a system in the course of organic evolution? This matter has already been referred to, in a way, in discussing the Principle of Le Chatelier. It was there noted that, in the case of human population *area* and *rent* are related to each other in accordance with a scheme of the type (2). More generally, supply and demand in economics stand in a relation of this type, and accordingly present a certain analogy to the capacity and intensity factors of an energy—an analogy which, by some writers, has been construed as actual identity in kind, *prices* having, by these writers, been identified with the intensity factor of an "economic energy." Now energy is a perfectly definite, measurable thing, of definite dimensions. Those who thus speak of a special form of "economic energy" should be prepared to give us at least some indication how this energy is to be measured, in the customary units of energy. No such indication is forthcoming. On

---

[5] The relation (2) is essentially the Helm-Ostwald *Intensity Law*. Although this law is not as universal as its sponsors would make it appear, yet it has a certain field of utility. For a critique of this law see M. Planck, Eight Lectures on Theoretical Physics, Columbia University Press, 1915, p. 11. The form of the relation (2) may be taken as the definition of a pair of conjugate parameters. However, the definition must be made a little more general to cover certain cases. We shall say that G, g are conjugate parameters if either

$$\frac{dG}{dt} \gtrless 0 \text{ according as } g_i \gtreqless g_e \tag{1}$$

$$\frac{dG}{dt} \gtrless 0 \text{ according as } g_i \lesseqgtr g_e \tag{2}$$

the contrary, as we shall see in dealing with the dynamics of evolution, the economic equivalent of a form of energy (which is something quite different from its mechanical equivalent), is not constant but variable—though it tends to approach, or to fluctuate about, a certain value.

On the mistaken identification of prices and related economic quantities with the intensity factor of an energy, some authors have sought to build a system of biodynamics (social dynamics).[6]   The analogy which certain conjugate parameters of the perfectly general kind bear to intensity and capacity factors of an energy present the opportunity for such efforts, which are, in themselves, well worth while.   But it must not be forgotten that the result of such efforts can be only a species of quasi-dynamics, something analogous to, but not identical with, the dynamics of physical forces. Just what the relation between such quasi-dynamics and true dynamics may be, is a separate problem, to which we shall have occasion to give some attention in the section devoted specifically to the dynamics of life-bearing systems.

The paying of rent in coin of the realm is, of course, a phenomenon peculiar to the human species.   But the peculiarity is one of mode of manifestation rather than of inherent quality.   We may speak of the rent per unit area that the representative individual is willing to pay as a measure or at least an index of the "population pressure."   Now this population pressure—this willingness to sacrifice effort for the sake of gaining elbowroom—is present quite independently of our peculiar method of expressing it in terms of rent.   It exists also among other species, though we may lack so convenient a gauge for it as we have, in our own case, in rent.   We shall see later how at least a quantitative conception of such biophysical (economic) entities as population pressure and the like can be gained on a general basis, which applies to species other than human.

[6] Compare G. Helm, Die Lehre von der Energie, 1887, pp. 72 et seq.; Ostwald, W., Energetische Grundlagen der Kulturwissenschaften, Leipsic, 1909, p. 155.   Die Philosophie der Werte, Leipsic, 1913, pp. 260, 314–317, 326, 328. Among other writers who touch on the subject of the relation of economic value and price to energy are: Budde, Energie und Recht, Leipsic, 1902, p. 56; Winiarski, "Essai sur la Mécanique Sociale," Revue Philosophique, 1900, vol. 49, p. 113.   See also J. Davidson, Qu. Jour. Economics, August, 1919, p. 717.

For the present, without making here a closer analysis of the conjugate parameters a, ρ, (area, rent or population pressure) it will suffice to point out that the mere existence of the relation

$$\frac{da}{dt} \gtreqless 0 \text{ according as } \rho_i \gtreqless \rho_e \tag{3}$$

may give into our hand the means of drawing certain conclusions regarding the behavior of the system, *quite independently of the intimate nature of these quantities, a, ρ.* In illustration of this it is only necessary to refer once more to the discussion of the principle of Le Chatelier in Chapter XXII.

Distant Analogy to Gas Law. Again, still without any searching analysis of all the physical implications of the parameters a and ρ, we may note certain facts regarding the relation.

$$a = \psi(\rho, X_1, X_2, \ldots X_n) \tag{4}$$

which connects the conjugate parameters a, ρ, just as pressure p and volume v, in physico-chemical systems, are connected by the relation

$$v = \varphi(p, X_1, X_2, \ldots) \tag{5}$$

This latter, in the simple case of a gas takes the form

$$v = m \frac{RT}{p} \tag{6}$$

or, since $\frac{m}{v}$ is the density d

$$\frac{p}{d} = RT \tag{7}$$

= constant, at constant temperature

Let N be the total number of a (human) population, a the area occupied by it, and Ni the total income of the population. Let ρ be the rent per unit area; and let the population spend a fraction R' of its income on rent. Then evidently

$$\rho a = NR'i \tag{8}$$

Putting $\dfrac{N}{a}$ = population density = d' we have

$$\frac{\rho}{d'} = R'i \tag{9}$$

It will be seen that there is a certain analogy between the formulae (8), (9) as applied to the relation between rent (population pressure) and area occupied by a population, on the one hand, and the formulae (6), (7) as applied to the relation between the pressure p and the volume v of a gas. The analogy is particularly close if the income per head i, and the factor R' are constant as a changes. The former may be true, approximately, if the inhabitants of area a derive their income from some extraneous source quite independent of this area. It will not be true, even in rough approximation, if the inhabitants derive their income from the produce of the area a itself. It is not the author's intention to emphasize unduly mere analogies. Nevertheless, the one here presented seems worthy of passing notice. Compare also E. Woodruff, Expansion of Races.

The actual relation between population density and rent or land value is a subject of great economic interest. Research in this subject is in progress under the auspices of the Institute for Research in Land Economics, Madison, Wis., but has not, at this time of writing, matured to published results.

Law of Urban Concentration. An empirical law of urban concentration was pointed out some years ago by F. Auerbach (Petermanns Mittheilungen, 1923, p. 74). Arranging in order of magnitude the cities of a given country, he found that the product of population and ordinal number (rank) was approximately constant. Thus, plotting rank against population, he obtained a hyperbolic curve, or, plotting the product of these two quantities, he obtained, roughly speaking, a straight line. For some of his curves the reader must be referred to the original publication.

The illustration (fig. 60) shows the graph obtained by plotting the logarithm of the population of the cities of the United States (1920) against the logarithm of their respective rank. In the higher ranks only every fifth city has been plotted. It will be seen that, excepting cities of rank 4, 5 and 6, the plot does approximate quite closely to a straight line. The slope of this line, however, is not exactly unity, as demanded by Auerbach's law, but 0.93, so that the actual law of urban concentration in the United States, in 1920, was, within the limits indicated, given by

$$PR^{0.93} = 5,000,000$$

where P denoted the population of the city of rank R.

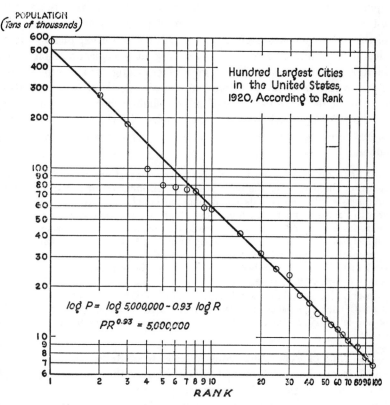

FIG. 60. LAW OF URBAN CONCENTRATION

Graph obtained by plotting as ordinates, on logarithmic scale, Population of United States Cities, and as abscissae the corresponding Rank (in order of magnitude), also on logarithmic scale.

It may be left an open question how much significance is to be attached to this empirical formula. We shall meet with a similar relation in Chapter XXIII in dealing with Willis' theory of Age and Area.

The Biological Background of Population Pressure. In the preceding paragraphs we have accepted it as a fact that there is at any rate some degree of relation between population density and the "desire for expansion" which finds expression, in the human species, in the willingness to spend a certain fraction of the income upon ground rent or its equivalent in interest and taxes upon real estate. It is not proposed to attempt here any searching analysis of the precise physical significance of this desire for expansion. But that it is ultimately referable to very cogent biological and physical factors is self-evident. The degree of crowding of a group of organisms affects both its death rate (mean length of life) and also its rate of reproduction, as well as, no doubt other significant vital functions. As Pearl and Parker[7] remark, in their paper on the influence of population density upon rate of reproduction in Drosophila:

It has long been known that degree of crowding of organisms in a given space, or the density of the population, has an influence upon various vital processes of the individuals composing the population. In the matter of growth Semper[8] and before him Jabez Hogg[9] showed that volume of water apart from food and other conditions has an influence upon the rate. This subject has again been studied recently by Bilski.[10] Farr[11] showed that there is in man a definite relation between population and death rate. This old work of Farr has recently been gone over carefully and confirmed by Brownlee.[12] Drzwina[13] and Bohn show that a particular concentration of a toxic substance, just lethal for a single individual in a given volume of water (working with such organisms as infusoria, planarians, hydra, tadpoles, etc.), will be sub-lethal if several individuals are present in the same fixed volume of water.

Influence of Population Density on Rate of Reproduction. Pearl and Parker[14] have determined experimentally the relation between rate of reproduction and the density of a population of Drosophila (fruit flies) in a universe of constant volume (glass bottle). This

[7] R. Pearl, and S. Parker, Proc. Natl. Acad. Sci., vol. 8, 1922, p. 212.

[8] K. Semper, Animal life as affected by the natural conditions of existence. Fourth Edition, London, 1890.

[9] Cited from Semper, loc. cit.

[10] F. Bilski, Pflüger's Arch., vol. 188, 1921, p. 254.

[11] W. Farr, Decenn. Suppl. Reg. Gen., 1861–1870.

[12] J. Brownlee, Jour. Roy. Stat. Soc., vol. 82, 1919, pp. 34–77; vol. 83, 1920, pp. 280–283.

[13] A. Drzwina and G. Bohn, C. R. Soc. Biol. Paris, vol. 84, 1921, pp. 917–919.

[14] R. Pearl and S. Parker, Proc. Natl. Acad. Sci., vol. 8, 1922, p. 212.

relation is found to resemble in form Farr's law for the death rate D in a human population of density d:

$$\log D = \log a + k \log d \qquad (10)$$

in which a and k are constants.   Pearl and Parker found

$$\log y = 1.54 - 0.008x - 0.658 \log x \qquad (11)$$

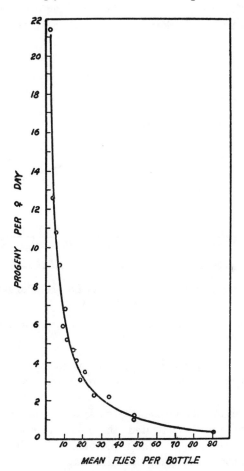

FIG. 61. RELATION BETWEEN RATE OF REPRODUCTION IN DROSOPHILA (FRUIT FLY) AND DENSITY OF MATED POPULATION

The circles indicate observed values; the drawn-out curve is computed according to equation (11). After Pearl and Parker.

where y denotes the number of imagoes per mated female per day, and x denotes the mean density of the mated population (measured as flies per bottle) over a sixteen-day period. The results obtained by Pearl and Parker are exhibited graphically in figure 61, the small circles denoting observed values, and the drawn-out curve values computed by the formula cited above. It should be noted, however, that in Farr's law the coefficient k of log d is positive, whereas in the Pearl and Parker formula it is negative; death rate in-

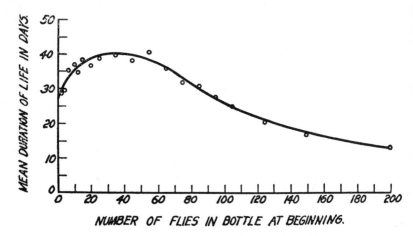

FIG. 62. RELATION BETWEEN MEAN LENGTH OF LIFE AND POPULATION DENSITY IN DROSOPHILA

The curve is a freehand smoothing of the observations indicated by the small circles. After Pearl and Parker.

creases with population density, whereas rate of reproduction, in this series of experiments, was found to decrease as the density increases.

Influence of Population Density on Duration of Life. The same authors have also investigated the relation between population density and duration of life in Drosophila.[15] Their results are shown graphically in figure 62. The smoothed curve exhibits a very interesting feature. While crowding unmistakably diminishes

[15] R. Pearl and S. Parker, Am. Jour. Hygiene, vol. 3, 1922, p. 94; Amer. Naturalist, vol. 56, 1922, p. 312.

the average length of life, as one would naturally expect, the curve does not fall continuously from left to right, but has a maximum. The flies do not thrive best when they have the most ample space per individual; there is an optimum density which is best suited to their needs for company or for some other obscure factor supplied by a certain moderate amount of crowding.

TOPOGRAPHIC PARAMETERS DURING PERIOD OF DIFFUSION

Willis' Theory of Age and Area. As regards the influence of those topographic parameters which define the boundaries of the system, a special case arises during that period in the life of a body of organisms, when its spread has not yet extended to those boundaries. Certain aspects of the phenomena presented during this *period of diffusion* have been made the subject of a painstaking study, conducted with much originality of view, by C. J. Willis.[16] One may not agree in all points with Dr. Willis' conclusions, but the material of fact collated by him is in itself significant and of value. As Prof. W. Bateson in a review of this book remarks: "To have hit on a new method of investigating even a part of the theory of evolution is no common achievement, and that the author has done this cannot in fairness be denied." Dr. Willis' principal thesis is essentially this, that the area occupied by a biological species is a measure of its antiquity in evolution. To be more precise, and to quote the author's own words:

"The area occupied at any given time, in any given country, by any group of allied species at least ten in number, depends chiefly, so long as conditions remain reasonably constant, upon the ages of the species of that group in that country, but may be enormously modified by the presence of barriers, such as seas, rivers, mountains, changes of climates from one region to the next, or other ecological boundaries, and the like, also by the action of man and other causes."

The thesis, thus stated, is "well hedged" with qualifications. Professor Bateson remarks: "Every evolutionist agrees that, *apart*

[16] Age and Area: A Study in Geographical Distribution and Origin of Species; Cambridge University Press, 1922. For review see Nature, 1923, p. 30; Science Progress, January, 1923, p. 474.

from disturbing elements, area is a measure of age.[17] . . . . **We**
are, however, asked to believe that in practice this mode of estimating the age of a species is, on the whole, trustworthy; that
endemic species and varieties in general can and must be for the
most part accepted as new starters in evolution, and not as
(remnants of) survivors."

Dr. Willis supports his views by observations gathered chiefly in
Ceylon and New Zealand. His evidence is not altogether convinc-
ing. Professor Bateson in the review already quoted remarks pointedly: "On any theory of evolution endemics (and rare species) must
be in part novelties and in part relics; but why, apart from the
theory of Age and Area, we should believe that endemics are in
such great majority novelties I do not clearly understand, for though
we know little of origins, we are certain that myriads of species
have become extinct. It is surely contrary to all expectation that
the process of extinction should be in general so rapid, and the final
endemic phase so short that the number of species in that final
stage should be so insignificant." Referring to the same point A.
G. Thacker remarks: "Species and genera do die out, and therefore there are diminishing ranges as well as expanding ranges.
. . . Dr. Willis thinks that very few of the small range species
are, in fact, decreasing." For a further critique of the theory of
Age and Area the reader may well be referred to the two reviews
already cited, while Dr. Willis' own presentation of his case will be
found expanded in detail in his book *Age and Area,* Cambridge
University Press, 1922. Quite recently (I add this in correcting
proof) Prof. G. V. Yule has lent his able advocacy to Willis'
theory in an extensive paper published in the Phil. Trans. Roy.
Soc., 1924, vol. 213, Series B, pp. 21–87. Some of the assumptions
underlying Professor Yule's argument do not seem to commend
themselves to the critical reader, in particular his supposition that

[17] "For this and other reasons Dr. Willis' findings seem hardly competent
to furnish a basis of attack against any otherwise established or suggested
theory of evolution. On this point Dr. Willis himself does not seem wholly
consistent, for though he advises in one place that it would be 'wiser to abandon natural selection' as the general principle that has guided evolution, in
another place he admits that 'nothing can come into lasting existence without
its permission.' This admission is all that any thoughtful adherent of any
theory of evolution asks." A. G. Thacker, The Dynamics of Distribution,
Science Progress, 1923, vol. 17, p. 474.

the number of new species *thrown* is independent of the number of individuals.

Turning from the theoretical and debatable portion of Dr. Willis' contribution, to the factual material presented by him, we are confronted by a number of very remarkable relations, such as those represented graphically in figure 63. In this drawing ordinates represent the number of genera in the several natural families of plants and animals indicated, and the corresponding abscissae represent the number of species in each genus plotted. So, for example (fig. 63), of the family Compositae 1143 genera were noted, as follows:

> 446 genera of 1 species
> 140 genera of 2 species
> 97 genera of 3 species
> 43 genera of 4 species
> 55 genera of 5 species
> etc.

An examination of these drawings clearly brings out the following facts: The monotypic genera, with one species each, are always the most numerous, commonly forming about one third of the whole group; the ditypics, with two species each, are next in frequency, genera with higher numbers of species becoming successively fewer. Set out graphically as in figure 63, the genera exhibit what Dr. Willis calls a "hollow curve" of frequency (in point of fact a hyperbola of the generalized type), and, as Professor Bateson remarks, there is no gainsaying the fact that these curves, though collected from miscellaneous sources, have a remarkable similarity. Perhaps more striking still is the relation established in figures 64, 65, and 66. The quantities plotted here are of the same character as in figure 63, but they are plotted on a doubly logarithmic scale, with the remarkable result that the graphs obtained are in close approximation straight lines. Thus if x denotes the number of species in a genus, and y denotes the number of genera comprising x species, we have

$$\log x + a \log y - b = 0 \qquad (12)$$

or

$$xy^a = \text{const.} \qquad (13)$$

that is to say, the variables x and y are connected by a hyperbolic[18] relation. It should be noted that this relation covers a wide variety of cases, including both plants and animals.

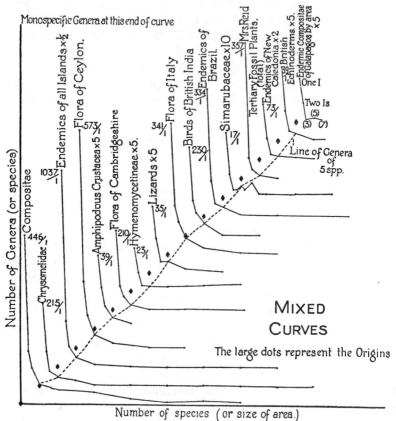

Mixed hollow curves. The numbers (thus 446/1) at the beginning of each are the numbers of monotypes.

By courtesy of Nature

FIG. 63. HYPERBOLIC CURVES OBTAINED BY PLOTTING AS ORDINATES THE NUMBER OF GENERA HAVING 1, 2, 3, . . . n SPECIES, AND AS ABSCISSAE THE NUMBER n OF SUCH SPECIES

The last curve above shows as ordinates the number of species of endemic compositae in the Galapagos Islands, as abscissae the corresponding areas over which such species have spread. After J. C. Willis.

---

[18] Of the general type into which the conic hyperbola $xy =$ const. falls as a special case.

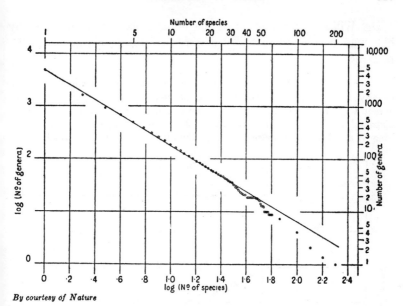

By courtesy of Nature

FIG. 64. RELATION BETWEEN NUMBER AND SIZE OF GENERA OF ALL FLOWERING
PLANTS, PLOTTED LOGARITHMICALLY

After J. C. Willis

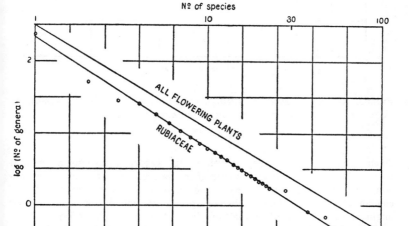

By courtesy of Nature

FIG. 65. RELATION BETWEEN NUMBER AND SIZE OF RUBIACEAE, PLOTTED
LOGARITHMICALLY

After J. C. Willis

Dr. Willis' interpretation of the remarkable curves obtained by him may be quoted in his own words (Nature, February 9, 1924, p. 178):

If species of very limited area and genera of one species (which also have usually small areas) are, with comparatively few exceptions, the young beginners in the race of life, and are descended in general from the species of wider dispersal and the larger genera, and if the number of species in a genus is, broadly speaking, a measure of its age, the idea at once suggests itself that a

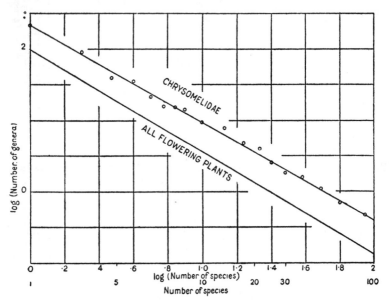

FIG. 66. RELATION BETWEEN NUMBER AND SIZE OF GENERA OF CHRYSOMELID
BEETLES, PLOTTED LOGARITHMICALLY

After J. C. Willis

given stock may be regarded as "throwing" generic variations much as it throws offspring, so that the number of genera descended from one prime ancestor may be expected to increase in geometric ratio or according to the law of compound interest. The number of species descended from one ancestor might be expected to follow the same form of law with a more rapid rate of growth. On such a very rough conception it is found that the form of frequency distribution for sizes of genera should follow the rule that the logarithm of the number of genera plotted to the logarithm of the number of species gives a straight line.

It follows from the conception stated that the excess of the slope of the line over unity should measure the ratio of the rate of increase of genera to that of species. The slope should always, therefore, lie between the limits 1 and 2, for a slope of less than unity would have no meaning, and a slope exceeding 2 would imply that generic variations were more frequent than specific variations. Hitherto no exception has been found to the required rule. One group of fungi tested (Hymenomycetineae) gave a line with a slope very little exceeding unity (1.08), but the figures found for flowering plants lie between the narrow limits 1.38 and 1.64, with an average of about 1.43. Snakes and lizards both give a figure very near 1.50, and the Chrysomelidae about 1.37.

For further details the reader must be referred to Dr. Willis' book *Age and Area*, and to a paper by E. S. Pearson, in *Biometrika*, August, 1923, vol. 15, of which the following passage, part of that author's conclusions, may be quoted:

There is no doubt that these principles represent a certain aspect of the process of evolution, but I believe that Dr. Willis has stressed their importance beyond the limits which the evidence of observation will bear. They cannot explain everything, and we have seen that in many cases results which we are led to predict with their assistance are scarcely borne out, while in other cases recurrent distributions can also be accounted for on different hypotheses.

Climatic Parameters. The state of a physico-chemical system is commonly described in terms of its temperature (in addition to pressure, etc.). Without attaching any deep significance to the analogy, it may be remarked that systems in which organic evolution is under way commonly require, as essential parameters to define their state, the statement of sundry quantities that describe climatic conditions, such as temperature, humidity, precipitation, light, etc. The influence of these upon the course of events must form an essential part of the study of evolution in life-bearing systems.

The investigations of the influence of temperature upon metabolic processes—an approximate doubling of reaction velocities for every 10°C. rise in temperature—we shall here note only very briefly as belonging rather to the field of biochemistry than to the more strictly ecological studies in which we are here interested. More in the line of our immediate interests are certain data gathered in oceanographic researches, which have already furnished us with much illustrative material. The influence of light, temperature, and

CO₂ concentration is discussed by G. W. Martin in his paper already cited.[19]   He remarks:

Plants on land receive the full benefit of the sun's rays as we know them. Plants living under water receive only a portion of the rays that reach the land. Part of the light that strikes the water is reflected, and the part that penetrates the water is gradually absorbed in passing through that medium, the red and yellow rays first, the blue and violet last.   This differential absorption is reflected in the curious and well-known distribution of marine algae according to color—the green kind growing in shallow water, the brown in an intermediate zone, and the red in the deepest water, although there are, of course, numerous exceptions to this general rule of distribution.   Another property

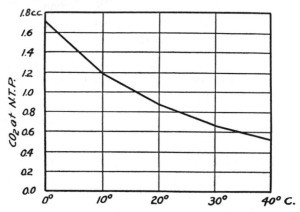

FIG. 67. SOLUBILITY OF CARBON DIOXIDE IN WATER, EXPRESSED IN VOLUMES OF CO₂ MEASURED AT NORMAL TEMPERATURE AND PRESSURE, PER VOLUME OF WATER

After G. W. Martin

of light is that it is refracted by water, and the greater the angle at which the rays strike the water, the greater will be the refraction.   In the tropics, where the rays are practically vertical, the amount of refraction is insignificant, but in high latitude, where the rays strike the water at a sharp angle, the refraction is marked, as a result of which the rays are bent into a more nearly vertical direction, thus increasing their penetration in depth, and partly compensating for the unfavorable angle at which they strike the water.   Helland Hansen was able to show that in the Atlantic Ocean south of the Azores, on a bright summer's day, light is abundant at a depth of 100 meters, still including at that depth a few red rays.   At 500 meters the red rays have completely disappeared, but blue and ultra-violet rays are still plentiful, and may be detected at 1000

[19] G. W. Martin, Scientific Monthly, 1922, p. 456.

meters, but have completely disappeared at 1700 meters. It is not probable, however, that under the most favorable conditions photosynthesis may be carried on at depths greater than 200 meters.

Temperature is less directly important in the sea than on the land since there is no great danger of injurious extremes being reached. Indirectly, its importance lies in the fact that carbon dioxide is much more soluble in cold water than in warm (see fig. 67) and it is probably this, rather than the direct influence of temperature, which accounts for the fact that the most luxurious development of plant life is in the colder waters of the earth.

Among laboratory investigations of the influence of "climatic parameters," under controlled conditions, may be reckoned the work of R. Pearl and S. Parker in their studies "On the Influence of Certain Environmental Factors on the Duration of Life in Drosophila."[20] In these experiments it was found, for example, that certain species of flies, kept in bottles closed by a single layer of silk bolting cloth ("ventilated bottles"), had 10 per cent longer life, on an average, than similar flies kept in bottles whose neck was plugged with cotton wool.

PARAMETERS OF STATE AND THE ANALYTICAL CONDITION FOR EQUILIBRIUM

In the fundamental equations both of the Kinetics and of the Statics of material transformations, as set forth in earlier chapters, the coefficients are in general functions of the parameters of state, and it is only on the supposition that evolution is proceeding under essentially constant conditions of topography, climate, etc., that these coefficients could be treated as constants.

Furthermore, since these same coefficients enter into the analytical conditions for equilibrium, as set forth in Chapter XII, these conditions must be read in the sense that they hold true when certain specified parameters of state are held constant. If another set of parameters, instead, is held constant, the equilibrium conditions will retain the same form, but the values of the coefficients will change accordingly. This is precisely analogous to the state of affairs regarding the thermodynamic conditions for equilibrium. Generally it can be said that in equilibrium the thermodynamic potential is a minimum, but the expression for this potential will

[20] Amer. Naturalist, vol. 56, 1922, p. 385.

vary according as pressure and temperature, or volume and temperature, for example, are held constant.

In concluding this section it is desirable to call attention to a modification, in outward form, of which the analytical condition for equilibrium,

$$Q' = \text{minimum}, \quad \delta Q' = 0 \tag{14}$$

(see Chapter XII) is susceptible. Since certain parameters p_1, p_2, . . . are to be held constant in the application of this condition, the addition of a set of terms $P_1\,dp_1 + P_2\,dp_2 + \ldots$ to the expression $\delta Q'$ for a small virtual displacement will in nowise alter its value. We may, then replace the condition (14) by the fully equivalent one

$$0 = (d\Phi)_p = \frac{\partial Q'}{\partial X_1}\,dX_1 + \frac{\partial Q'}{\partial X_2}\,dX_2 + \ldots + P_1 dp_1 + P_2 dp_2 + \ldots \tag{15}$$

where the subscript p denotes that the parameters p_1, p_2, . . . , conjugate to the parameters P_1, P_2, ... are to be held constant in forming the expression (15). This statement of the condition (15) adds, of course, nothing new to the case. It is mentioned here only on account of its *formal* agreement[21] with the similar conditions for equilibrium which, as already pointed out, play an important rôle in thermodynamics. However, in the analogous equations of thermodynamics the expression $d\Phi$ is a complete differential. In the present instance we have no basis for the supposition that (15) is the true differential of a function $\Phi\,(X_1, X_2, \ldots P_1, P_2, \ldots)$ The question may, indeed be raised, whether by a suitable choice of parameters and variables it can be achieved that (15), in the case here under consideration, is such a complete differ-

---

[21] Compare, for example, Van Laar, Sechs Vorlesungen über das thermodynamische Potential, 1906, p. 43.

This formal agreement seems to extend also to another feature. The thermodynamic condition for stable equilibrium demands that the second differential $(d^2\Phi)_p$ shall be positive, and this in turn demands that $\dfrac{\partial p}{\partial v}$ shall be negative.

(See M. Planck, Thermodynamik, 1905, pp. 134, 190; Duhem, Traité d'Energétique, 1911, vol. 1, p. 466; A. Winkelmann, Handbuch der Physik, 1906, vol. 3, p. 590.) Similarly, in the general case, stability demands that if G, g are conjugate parameters of the type (1) of footnote 5, then $\dfrac{\partial g}{\partial G} < 0$.

ential. But this is a separate problem, on which we shall not here expend further effort. Only this shall be noted in passing: Whereas, in the thermodynamical treatment of physico-chemical phenomena a function Φ is given (essentially as the expression of the laws of thermodynamics), and whereas certain consequences are derived from this known function, the type of problems with which we are here concerned is of inverse nature. We are given certain data regarding the behavior of these systems, for example, the fact that their evolution follows more or less closely a system of equations of the type of the general equations (1) (Chapter VI) of the Kinetics of material transformation; and the problem may be raised, as to whether there exist functions Φ analogous to the functions known as thermodynamic potentials, in terms of which the behavior of the system can be concisely epitomized, after the manner of thermodynamics. If such a plan could be successfully carried out, the result would be a species of quasi-dynamics of evolving systems, in which certain parameters P played a rôle analogous to forces, without being in any sense identical with forces (or even with generalized forces); certain other conjugate parameters p would play a rôle analogous to displacements, and certain functions Φ would resemble in their relations to certain events in the system, the energy functions Φ (free energy, thermodynamic potentials) of thermodynamics.

That certain isolated portions of such a general system of quasi-dynamics have some degree of viability seems probable. Whether the general system is capable of development in a form possessing any considerable utility shall here be left an open question. For at this point we shall leave the path followed so far, and shall strike out in a new direction, with a view to sketching, not a system of quasi-dynamics or quasi-energetics, but the dynamics and energetics, in the strict sense, as ordinarily understood, of life-bearing systems in the course of evolution.

PART IV
DYNAMICS

CHAPTER XXIV

THE ENERGY TRANSFORMERS OF NATURE

Die Natur hat sich die Aufgabe gestellt das der Erde zuströmende Licht im Fluge zu erhaschen und die beweglichste aller Kräfte, in die starre Form verwandelt, aufzuspeichern. Zur Erreichung dieses Zweckes hat sie die Erdkruste mit Organismen überzogen,welche lebend das Sonnenlicht in sich aufnehmen und unter Verwendung dieser Kraft eine fortlaufende Summe chemischer Differenzen erzeugen. Diese Organismen sind die Pflanzen. Die Pflanzenwelt bildet ein Reservoir, in welchem die flüchtigen Sonnenstrahlen fixiert und zur Nutzniessung geschickt, niedergelegt werden.—*J. R. Mayer.*

We approach now the third and last stage in our enquiry, toward which all that has gone before may be said, in a way, to have been in the nature of preparation.

The fundamental equations of kinetics

$$\frac{dX_1}{dt} = F_i(X_1, X_2, \ldots ; P, Q) \tag{1}$$

may appear at first sight to contain no hint of dynamical, of energetic implications. These can be read into the equations only by calling to mind the physical nature of certain of the components whose masses X appear in the equations: These components—aggregates of living organisms—are, in their physical relations, *energy transformers.* The evolution which we have been considering, and shall continue in this last phase to consider, is, then, essentially the evolution of a system of energy transformers; the progressive redistribution of the matter of the system among these transformers. The dynamics which we must develop is the dynamics of a system of energy transformers, or *engines.*[1]

Fundamental Characteristics of Energy Transformers. We shall do well to begin by calling to mind some of the fundamental elements or characteristics of energy transformers or engines, and of the manner of their working. An engine, such as a steam engine, for example, receives energy from a *source* such as a coal fire. This energy is absorbed by a *working substance* (water or steam), which, in the proc-

---

[1] See also A. J. Lotka, Jl. Wash. Acad. Sci., 1924, p. 352.

ess, undergoes modification or change of state (in a general sense of the term); the working substance, at some stage in the operation of the engine, again gives out energy, of which *a part* in engines of human construction, commonly appears in a particular, selected form adapted to some end useful to and purposed by the maker or owner. Another fraction of the energy discharged by the working substance, is passed on to a *sink* or absorber of energy, which may be simply the surrounding air, or in the case of a naval engine it may be the sea water employed to cool the condensed steam before it returns to the boiler. This discharge of a portion of the energy from the source into a sink is practised, not designedly because any useful purpose is served thereby, but unavoidably because, in the case of all forms of heat engines, the second law of thermodynamics inexorably demands this payment of a tax to nature, as it were.

Cyclic Working; Output and Efficiency. A finite change of the working substance, performed just once, can yield only a finite amount of work. Hence an engine of this type, in order to operate continuously so as to furnish a steady supply of energy of indefinite amount, must of necessity work in a *cycle*, returning periodically to its initial state many times. For a given engine, working under given conditions, the total output W/t per unit of time is proportional to the quantity M (mass) of working substance and its frequency of circulation, n, per unit of time, through the cycle; thus

$$\frac{W}{t} = k\,Mn \qquad (2)$$

Regarding the variation in the output for different engines, and for operation under different conditions, two fundamental laws of the greatest theoretical and practical importance, the very corner-stones of the edifice of thermodynamics, inform us that

1. The *maximum* output of which a heat engine is capable *under ideal conditions* of working is *independent of the nature of the working substance,* and of the details of *mechanism* and construction of the engine.

2. This maximum output obtainable under ideal conditions of operation *depends solely upon the temperature of the source and that of the sink;* with a suitably chosen temperature scale the law of the maximum output W can be put in the extremely simple form

$$W = Q\,\frac{T_0 - T_1}{T_0} \qquad (3)$$

where Q is the energy drawn from the source, T_0 the (absolute) temperature of the source, and T_1 that of the sink. The ratio $\dfrac{W}{Q}$ which measures the fraction of the energy Q converted into work is spoken of as the *efficiency* of the transformer.

The actual performance of a heat engine always falls short—and usually far short—of the theoretical maximum (3) attainable under ideal conditions of *reversible* operation, whereas all real processes, as has been pointed out in an earlier chapter, are *irreversible*. The first service rendered by the laws of thermodynamics is thus a negative one, to save us from vain efforts to achieve the impossible. They tell us what we *cannot* do; they give us no guarantee as to what we *can* do, in this matter of engine efficiency. In other fields these same principles are, indeed, found competent to yield us information of most positive character, as the physicist and physical chemist knows from boundless wealth of example; the very fact that they hold independently of substance and form lends to their application a catholicity hardly equalled elsewhere in science, and at the same time gives into our hands an instrument of the most extreme economy of thought, since we are relieved, in such application, of the necessity of treating each particular case, with all its complication of detail, on its own merits, but can deal with it by the short cut of a general formula. Still, the austere virtue of this impartiality with respect to substance and form becomes something of a vice when information is sought regarding certain systems in which mechanism plays, not an incidental, but the leading rôle. Here thermodynamics may be found powerless to assist us greatly, and the need for new methods may be felt. The significance of this in our present concerns will be seen as the topic develops.

Composite and Coupled Transformers. The simplest type of transformer of the kind that here chiefly interests us would comprise one working substance fed from one source and discharging to one sink.

Two or more such transformers may, however, work in parallel from one source, thus forming in the aggregate one *composite transformer*. Or, two or more may be *coupled* in series or cascade, the sink of one functioning as the source for the next of the series. So, for example, W. L. R. Emmett has constructed a composite engine consisting of two separate engines, the first operating with mercury for its working substance, at a higher temperature, and the second operating with water at a lower temperature. It is to be observed that two such "coupled" transformers again constitute a transformer, a *compound* transformer, which may possess certain special virtues, from the standpoint of the engineer, or in other respects.

Accumulators. A special type of transformers is that in which the energy is transformed into a latent form, and is thus stored up for future use. A great variety of accumulators are in technical use. In the simplest case such an accumulator may consist of empounded water or a raised storage tank, ready upon the opening of a sluice or a valve to discharge its stored up energy. More closely akin to the systems in which we are here primarily interested is the lead accumulator or secondary battery, in which electrical energy is transformed into and stored as chemical energy, somewhat as the energy of sunlight is, in the leaves of plants, transformed into chemical energy and stored up in the form of starch.

This type of chemical storage is of very particular interest because of the remarkable phenomena to which it is competent to give rise through the circumstance that the substance in which the energy is stored in chemical form is itself the working substance of a transformer. For in that case, if a mass hM stores an amount of energy W, we have, according to (2) for a small interval of time dt

$$\frac{dW}{dt} = \frac{hdM}{dt} = k\, M\, n \qquad (4)$$

If the transformer functions at a constant rate (i.e., with a fixed number of cycles per unit of time) and if the coefficient k is independent of the size of the transformer, we have by integration of (4)

$$M = M_0 e^{\frac{k_n}{h}} \qquad (5)$$

The transformer under these conditions, *grows* according to the law of compound interest.[2]

For small ranges of size the assumption of a sensibly constant k is reasonable, and the law thus deduced may be expected to represent the facts tolerably well. For greater range we must regard k as a function of M and write

$$k = a + b\, M + c\, M^2 + \ldots \qquad (6)$$

[2] Compare L. J. Briggs, The Living Plant as a Physical System. Jour. Wash. Acad. Sc., 1917, vol. 7, p. 95.

so that (4) becomes

$$\frac{h\,dM}{M\,dt} = n\,(a + bM + \ldots) \tag{7}$$

In second approximation, therefore, (breaking off the bracketed series at the second term) we find for the law of growth of the transformer the Verhulst-Pearl law (see Chapter VII).

$$M = \frac{a/b}{\dfrac{m_0}{M_0}\,e^{-\frac{n}{h}\,a\,t} - 1} \tag{8}$$

where $m = M + a/b$ and the subscript zero denotes the value of the variable at the instant $t = 0$.

Anabions and Catabions. The living organism partakes of the functions both of an energy accumulator and of an energy dissipator. The former function is especially marked in plants and in the young growing organism. Biological terminology speaks of the process of energy accumulation by the growth (synthesis) of the working substance as anabolism, and of the liberation of the stored energy with conversion into other forms as catabolism. Organisms in which anabolic processes predominate are conveniently classed together as anabions (plants), those in which catabolic processes predominate, as catabions (animals). The line of division cannot be sharply drawn, a fact which was commented upon in some detail in the first chapter. But in the majority of cases organisms have a pronounced bias toward one or the other of the two forms, and no difficulty arises in classifying them.

We may form the conception of a *system of transformers* comprising, in the most general case, individual single transformers, aggregates of composite transformers, and coupled transformers; some or all of which may partake in greater or less degree of the nature of accumulators.

It is precisely such a system of transformers that is presented to us, on a vast scale, in nature, by the earth with its population of living organisms. Each individual organism is of the type of the simple transformer, though it does not operate with a single working substance, but with a complex variety of such substances, a fact which has certain important consequences.

Plant and Animal as Coupled Transformers. Coupled transformers are presented to us in profuse abundance, wherever one species feeds on another, so that the energy sink of the one is the energy source of the other.

A compound transformer of this kind which is of very special interest is that composed of a plant species and an animal species feeding upon the former. The special virtue of this combination is as follows. The animal (catabiotic) species alone could not exist at all, since animals cannot anabolise inorganic food. The plant species alone, on the other hand, would have a very slow working cycle, because the decomposition of dead plant matter, and its reconstitution into CO_2, completing the cycle of its transformations, is very slow in the absence of animals, or at any rate very much slower than when the plant is consumed by animals and oxidized in their bodies. Thus the compound transformer (plant and animal) is very much more effective than the plant alone. We shall have occasion to refer to this matter again.

It is, of course, conceivable that the anabolic and catabolic functions should, in their entirety of a complete cycle, be combined in one structure, one organism. Physically there is no reason why this should not be, and, in fact, nature has made some abortive attempts to develop the plant-animal type of organism; there are a limited number of plants that assimilate animal food, and there are a few animals, such as *Hydra viridis*, that assimilate carbon dioxide from the air by the aid of chlorophyll.[3] But these are exceptions, freaks of nature, so to speak. For some reason these mixed types have not gained for themselves a significant position in the scheme of nature. Selection, evolution, has altogether favored the compound type of transformer, splitting the anabolic and the catabolic functions, and assigning the major share of each to a separate organism.

The several individual organisms of one species form in the aggregate one large transformer built up of many units functioning in parallel.

---

[3] *Hydra viridis*, however, is probably not a single organism, but an organism of the animal type harboring in its body separate plant-like organisms with which it lives in symbiosis.

And lastly, the entire body of all these species of organisms, together with certain inorganic structures, constitute one great world-wide transformer. It is well to accustom the mind to think of this as one vast unit, one great empire.

The World Engine. The great world engine—in which each of us is a most insignificant little wheel—has its energy source, its firebox, so to speak in the sun,[4] ninety-eight million miles away from the working substance (the "boiler"). From the engineer's standpoint this would be an execrably bad design, if a high efficiency alone were the aim in view. For of the five hundred thousand million million million horsepower which the fiery orb radiates into space year in, year out, a ridiculously small fraction $\dfrac{1}{2,200,000,000}$ is intercepted by the earth. It would take more than two billion earths placed side by side to form a continuous shell around our sun at the earth's distance, and thus to receive the total output of solar heat. The other planets receive corresponding amounts. The remainder of the sun's disbursements sweeps past us into the depths of space, to unknown destiny.

Of the energy that reaches the earth, 35 per cent is reflected (principally from the clouds), and 65 per cent is absorbed. The surface of the solid globe receives on an average[5] not quite 2 gram-calories (1.94) per square centimeter, placed normal to the beam, per minute, or enough heat to melt a layer of ice 424 feet thick every year. Arrhenius[6] quotes Schroeder to the effect that about 0.12 per cent of this energy is absorbed by the green vegetation, the gate of entrance through which practically[7] all the energy taking part in the

[4] The recognition of this fact is credited by Herbert Spencer (First Principles, § 172, footnote) to Herschel (Outlines of Astronomy, 1833).

[5] C. G. Abbot, The Sun, 1911, p. 298. In the tropics, at noon, a plot of 250 acres receives energy at the rate of one million horsepower (W. W. Campbell, Science, 1920, vol. 52, p. 548).

[6] Jour. Franklin Inst., 1920, p. 118. Compare also G. Ciamician, Die Photochemie der Zukunft (Sammlung Chemischer Vorträge, 1922, p. 429). Assuming an area of one hundred twenty-eight million square kilometers as inhabited by plants, Ciamician computes that thirty-two billion tons of dry matter per annum is produced, the equivalent of 17 times the world's annual coal production.

[7] Certain bacteria whose metabolism is based on iron, sulphur or selenium derive their energy from other sources. They are thus independent of sun-

life cycle must pass. And of this last amount only 24 per cent falls to plants cultivated for human needs.[8] The forests take the major share, 67 per cent; 7 per cent falls on the grass steppes, and 2 per cent on desert plants. If these figures leave the mind somewhat confused with detail, it may assist the imagination to form an adequate picture of the life cycle in its totality if we reflect that the total energy thus coursing through the system every year is of the order of 22 times[6] the world's annual coal production. Conversely this statistical fact may serve to form for us a correct estimate of the really cosmic magnitude of human interference with the course of nature.

The organic circulation, the living part of the world engine, though to us of most direct interest, is quantitatively speaking only a small part of the whole. If the organic cycle gives occupation to an amount of energy of the order of 20 times the world's coal consumption,

---

light—a fact of the greatest significance in connection with the problem of the origin of terrestial life as we know it today. For green plants carry on their life business by the aid of chlorophyll, a substance representing a high degree of specialization, such as could not very well be supposed to exist in the most primitive life forms.

[8] H. A. Spoehr, Jour. Ind. and Eng. Chem., 1922, vol. 14, p. 1144. Regarding the efficiency of cultivated plants in recovering solar energy for the use of man, the calculations of H. A. Spoehr are of interest. On the basis of 1.5 gram calories per square centimeter per minute for the value of the solar radiation received at the earth's surface, he computes the daily energy income per square meter (six hours insolation) as 5400 kilogram calories. Figuring the heat of combustion of coal at 8000 kilogram calories, this gives the equivalent of 0.675 kilograms of coal per square meter, or 16.4 tons of coal per acre. For ninety days of insolation this represents the equivalent of 1476.63 tons of coal.

Spoehr then proceeds to obtain a figure for the efficiency of a wheat crop in the utilization of this energy. Assuming a large yield of 50 bushels or 17.619 hectoliters per acre, and considering this entirely as starch, we find an energy equivalent of 0.623 ton of coal. The efficiency here, then, is measured by the very low figure $\frac{0.623}{1476} = 0.0004 = 0.04$ per cent.

It should be noted, however, that not all the heat absorbed by the plant appears stored up in the body of the plant. A large amount is used up in the work of evaporation (transpiration). According to L. J. Briggs (Jour. Washington Acad., 1917, p. 92; Journal Agr. Research, 1914, pp. 1–63), the energy stored by the plant represents from 1 to 5 per cent of the energy dissipated during the growth of the plant. See also C. L. Holsberg, Jour. Ind. Eng. Chem., 1924, vol. 6, pp. 524–525: Progress in Chemistry and the Theory of Population.

the winds represent some 5000 times that amount of coal.[9]   Ocean
currents are another large item.   Some idea of the magnitude of the
energy here involved may be gathered from an estimate given by
L. J. Henderson according to which the gulf stream alone conveys[10]
two-hundred million tons of water per second through the straits of
Yukatan.   If this body of water were cooled to arctic temperature we
should have a transfer of energy at the rate of eight and a half billion horsepower.   Most important of all, in the inorganic cycle, is
the circulation of water by evaporation, precipitation, and river flow
(including waterfalls) back to the ocean.   Of the masses involved
a picture has been presented in Chapter XVI.   As to the energy
involved, Henderson estimates the horsepower of evaporation from
100 square kilometers of tropical ocean at over one-hundred million
horsepower.

C. P. Steinmetz[11] has calculated that if every raindrop falling in
the United States could be collected, and all the power recovered
which it could produce in its descent to the ocean, this would yield
about three-hundred million horsepower.   G. Ciamician[12] quotes an
estimate by Engler of the world's total water power as the equivalent of seventy billions of tons of coal.   According to C. G. Gilbert
and J. E. Pogue[13] the production of hydroelectricity in the United
States in 1910 was the equivalent of forty-million tons of coal,
whereas nearly ten times that amount went into the production of
steam and carboelectric power.   These authors further estimated
that the water power developed at the date indicated represented
about 10 per cent of that readily available, and 3 per cent of the total
that might be open to development under elaborate arrangements
for storage.[14]

[9] For a discussion of the Atmosphere considered as an engine see Sir Napier
Shaw's Rede Lecture, published in Nature, 1921, p. 653.   This author arrives
at the estimate that "the best you can expect from the steam-laden air of the
equatorial region working between the surface and the stratosphere, under
favorable conditions, is a brake-horsepower efficiency of 25 per cent."

[10] L. J. Henderson, The Fitness of the Environment, p. 182.

[11] Survey Graphic, 1922, vol. 1, p. 1035 (cited by H. A. Spoehr, Jour. Ind.
Eng. Chem., 1922, vol. 14, p. 1143).

[12] Die Photochemie der Zukunft; Samml. Techn. Vorträge, 1914, p. 431.

[13] Power, its significance and needs; Smithsonian Institution Bulletin 102,
Part 5.

[14] For a comprehensive survey of power development actual and potential
see F. G. Baum, U. S. A. Power Industry.   Also W. S. Murray, A Superpower
System for the Region between Boston and Washington.   United States
Geological Survey Professional Paper 123 of 1921.

Relation of Transformer Cycle to Circulation of the Elements.
The circulation of substance in the organic world and its inorganic
background, which was considered in an earlier chapter in its purely
material relations, now acquires a new significance. We recognize
in it now a typical characteristic of the great world engine which,
for continued operation, must of necessity work thus in cycles. The
picture presented to our minds is that of a gigantic overshot mill
wheel, receiving from above the stream of sunlight with its two
hundred twenty-seven million gross horsepower—though much of
this is spilt without effect—and discharging below its dissipated
energy in the form of heat at the general temperature level. The

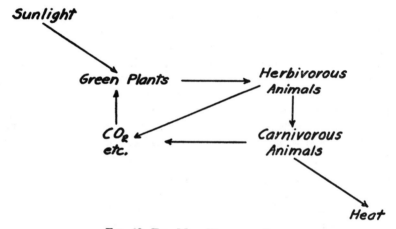

FIG. 68. THE MILL-WHEEL OF LIFE

main outstanding features of the wheel are represented diagrammatically in figure 68. But in detail the engine is infinitely
complex, and the main cycle contains within itself a maze of subsidiary cycles. And, since the parts of the engine are all interrelated,
it may happen that the output of the great wheel is limited, or at
least hampered, by the performance of one or more of the wheels
within the wheel. For it must be remembered that the output of
each transformer is determined both by its mass and by its rate of
revolution. Hence if the working substance, or any ingredient of the
working substance of any of the subsidiary transformers, reaches its
limits, a limit may at the same time be set for the performance of the
great transformer as a whole. Conversely, if any one of the subsidi-

ary transformers develops new activity, either by acquiring new resources of working substance, or by accelerating its rate of revolution, the output of the entire system may be reflexly stimulated. As to the significance of this for the evolution of the system as a whole more will be said later, in the discussion of certain phases of the evolution of the human species in particular; for it is hardly necessary to remark that the case of man presents features of so remarkable character that it calls for special consideration, quite aside from the pardonable excess of interest which we personally feel in the creature.

Evolution of the World Engine. The picture we must keep before us, then, is that of a great world engine or energy transformer composed of a multitude of subsidiary units, each separately, and all together as a whole, working in a cycle. It seems, in a way, a singularly futile engine, which, with a seriousness strangely out of keeping with the absurdity of the performance, carefully and thoroughly churns up all the energy gathered from the source. It spends all its work feeding itself and keeping itself in repair, so that no balance is left over for any imaginable residual purpose. Still, it accomplishes one very remarkable thing; it *improves* itself as it goes along, if we may employ this term to describe those progressive changes in its composition and construction which constitute the evolution of the system. For—the statement will bear reiteration and emphasis—this is the conception we must form of organic evolution: the evolution of the great world engine as a whole, not merely that of any single species of organisms considered separately. What is the trend of this development? Toward what end does the great transformer shape and reshape itself? A provisional answer to the question will be suggested in due course.* For a time we must now abandon our broad viewpoint, and turn from the consideration of the great transformer as a whole, to a discussion of certain of its subsidiary engines which present points of special interest and importance.

*See page 357.

CHAPTER XXV

RELATION OF THE TRANSFORMER TO AVAILABLE SOURCES

As an enterprise, mathematics is characterized by its aim, and its aim is to think rigorously whatever is rigorously thinkable or whatever may become rigorously thinkable in course of the approved striving and refining evolution of ideas.—*C. J. Keyser.*

Distributed and Localized Sources of Energy. In Carnot's classical analysis of the operation of a heat engine the source of energy is taken for granted as one of the fundamental data of the problem.

In nature sources of energy are not thus supplied unconditionally, and for our present purposes it becomes necessary to extend the analysis of transformer operation so as to take into its scope also some of the significant characteristics of the sources from which the engines of nature derive their supplies. And here a fundamental distinction is to be made between two kinds of sources, namely, (1) evenly, or at least continuously distributed sources, and (2) localized sources, heterogeneously distributed.

If the transformer draws its energy supply from a source uniformly distributed over a region R, at any point of which it can make contact with the source, then, evidently, within the region R the performance of the transformer is independent of its location. So, for example, plants derive their energy from sunlight falling upon them gratuitously, and draw their supplies of material partly from atmospheric carbon dioxide and oxygen diffusing to them by a spontaneous process, and partly from dissolved salts seeping to their roots automatically, that is to say, by a process essentially independent of any intervention on the part of the plant. And quite in accord with this general distribution of plant food, the typical plant is a sessile, passive organism.

If, on the contrary, the transformer draws its supply from discontinuous, heterogeneously distributed sources, then continued operation demands at least some degree of relative motion between the transformer and the sources, so that occasional collisions may occur between the transformer and a source.

Random and Aimed Collisions. Purely *random collisions*, such as those contemplated in the kinetic theory of gases, may suffice to bring an adequate supply to the transformer.[1] But evidently the output of the transformer will be enhanced if, instead of relying upon a precarious supply gleaned in fortuitous encounters, a suitable *correlation* is established between the motion of the transformer and the location of the sources. This may be accomplished in two ways, as follows:

1. There may be actual mechanical union[2] positively connecting transformer and source, so that there is a *functional relation* (in the mathematical sense) between the motion of the transformer and the topography of the source. A simple instance in point is a trolley car. Here there is a definite relation between the topography of the system (track), the reaction of the transformer upon it, and the distribution of the source. The car is not free to move except along the track and along the trolley wire.

2. Contact with the source may not be positively secured, but merely rendered more probably than in *purely random collisions*, by the occurrence of *more or less accurately aimed* collisions. Source and transformer are in this case mechanically independent, the motion of the source is *not* fully determined when the topography of the system is given; a certain *freedom* remains. There is, in this case, not functional relation, but only *correlation* between the motion of the transformer and the topography of the system: no specific motion is *determined*, only certain motions are rendered *more probable* than others.

Negative Correlation. It is to be noted, of course, that such correlation between the motion of a transformer and the location of features

---

[1] For an experimental investigation of the movements of lower organisms (Paramecium, Colpidium, Trachelomonas) see Przibram, Pflügers Archiv, 1913, vol. 153, pp. 401–405. The movements were found to follow the law deduced by Einstein and Smoluchowski for Brownian movement (which, of course is random), namely that the mean square of the displacements of a particle in any direction in equal intervals of time t is proportional to t. The order of magnitude of the movements of the organisms, however, and the influence of temperature, were quite different in the case of Brownian movement. (For an account of the Einstein-Smoluchowski law see, for example, C. Schaefer, Einführung in die theoretische Physik, 1921, vol. 2, p. 487.)

[2] Compare L. T. y Quevedo, Essai sur l'automatique, Revue Générale des Sciences, 1915, vol. 26, p. 601.

of its environment is competent to bring other benefits aside from a
a supply of energy and material (food).   All transformers are more or
less vulnerable.   Exposed to an environment varying from point to
point and from instant to instant, a transformer will in general sooner
or later meet with an injurious stress, that is to say, a stress that will
change its structure or constitution to a point where effective operation is impaired or altogether abolished.   If it is desirable, in the
interest of increased output, that collisions with suitable energy
sources be rendered *more probable* than in purely random motion, it is
evidently equally desirable, in the interest of continued operation of
the transformer, that collision with harmful features in the environment be rendered *less probable*.   In other words, in addition to
apparatus establishing a *positive correlation* between the motion of the
transformer and the location of sources, it is desirable that there be
also provided apparatus establishing *negative correlation* between
such motion and the location of injurious features of the environment.
Collisions should, as far as possible, be aimed *toward* sources, and
away from points of danger.   The fate, the success of the transformer,
will evidently depend both on the versatility of the aim, and on its
accuracy; on the *number and character of targets* picked out for aim,
and on the *closeness* with which the hits upon the target cluster around
the bull's eye.

The Correlating Apparatus.   It is on the general plan indicated in
the preceding paragraph that nature's mobile transformers, especially
the typical animal organisms, operate.   In the competition among
these, for food and for safety, the accuracy and the versatility of
aim characteristic of each species will evidently be most important
determinants of relative success or failure, and hence of the trend of
evolution.   The dynamics of evolution thus appears essentially as
the statistical dynamics of a system of energy transformers, each
having a characteristic vulnerability, a charasteristic versatility and
accuracy of aim.   It is here that the method of thermodynamics is
inadequate.   Its austere virtue of impartiality toward different
mechanisms becomes a vice when information is sought regarding
systems in which mechanism plays a leading rôle.   The mechanism,
or, to use a somewhat broader term free from mechanistic implications,
the *apparatus*, by which the correlation is established between motion
and environment, by which *behavior is adapted to circumstances*, is
here not an incidental detail to be lightly dismissed as of secondary

importance, but must occupy the very center of attention. To a somewhat detailed consideration of this apparatus we now proceed; in the interest of vivid, realistic presentation of the subject it will, however, be desirable to abandon from this point on the very general treatment and, to speak now specifically in terms of biological units, organisms, rather than in terms of the broader physical concept of energy transformers. It should be constantly borne in mind, however, that this change in attitude, or, it were better to say, in terminology, is chiefly a matter of convenience and effectiveness of presentation, and the fundamental physical principles involved, as set forth in the more general terms, should never be allowed to sink far below the surface of our immediate thought.

The Component Elements of the correlating Apparatus. The continued existence of the organism, toward which his actions are aimed, demands that he shall direct his energies, his activities in accordance with the state of his environment, of the external world, avoiding unfavorable conditions, and seeking out those favorable or necessary to his maintenance. This includes the locating and seizing of food.

But as a material, physical system, his actions are primarily determined by his own state. Hence, in order that his actions, determined *immediately* by the state of the organism himself, may be *mediately* determined by the state of the external world, apparatus must be provided whereby the state of the organism becomes in a certain suitable manner a function of the state of the external world. The external world is *depicted* in the organism by a certain apparatus, a set of organs and faculties, which we may appropriately term the *Depictors*.

The depictors include first the *Receptors* or Organs of Special Sense (eyes, ears, nose, etc.); and second the *Elaborators*, whose function is to combine and further elaborate the crude information furnished by the senses. The physical location and structure and mode of operation of the elaborators is much less obvious than that of the receptors. In fact, we ordinarily recognize them rather as faculties (Memory, Reason) than as organs.

Another set of organs and faculties, the *Adjustors*, determine the particular reactions, the behavior of the organism, in the light of the information brought in by the receptors and further elaborated by the elaborators. So the hungry bird, sighting a worm on the lawn, flies down to the spot from the tree on which it is perched, and secures its prey. The sight of the worm, together perhaps with the memory of earlier meals collected near the same spot, acts as a stimulus or *Drive* to responsive action. This last step, action, commonly involves the use of members, or motor organs, *Effectors*, such as wings, feet, hands, etc. In complicated cases, as in human behavior, the elaborators may also play an important rôle in the effector step of the process by which motion is correlated to environment, behavior adapted to circumstance. So, for example, the traveller, before setting out on a journey, plans his itinerary, perhaps months or years in advance.

Receptor-Effector Circuit Begins and Ends in Environment. It is a noteworthy fact that this process of correlating action to conditions is essentially cyclic in character: It has its origin in the external world, which becomes depicted in the organism, provokes a response, the terminal step of which is usually, if not always, a reaction upon the external world. The net result is, in a sense, that the external world has reacted upon itself. The organism has acted as an intermediary. There is something more than a mere surface significance in this fact. For it is true generally that animals function essentially as catalysers, as agents assisting in a change that is "trying" to take place on its own account. So the green grass is, in a sense, hungry for oxygen, namely in the sense that its oxidation is accompanied by a diminution of free energy. The animal consuming the grass and deriving from its oxidation the requisite energy for further activity has not initiated any revolutionary process, but has merely helped nature in its course, has merely rolled the ball downhill, so to speak. This is all that the animal organism is competent to do, and man is not exempt from this restriction: In all our doings, whether we will it or not, we are assisting in a fundamental natural process, we are obeying an inevitable law of energetics.

Correlating Apparatus Not Peculiar to Living Organisms. It must not be supposed that the typical elements of the correlating apparatus, the receptors, adjustors and effectors, are wholly peculiar to living organisms. They can be very clearly recognized also in certain mechanisms of human construction. In fact, owing to the circumstance that the operation of such man-made mechanism is fully known to us, that they harbor no mysterious "vital" principle or ill-understood element of consciousness, such purely mechanical contrivances furnish particularly apt illustrations of the principles involved in the operation of the correlating apparatus.   It is therefore well worth while to consider here a simple example of this kind.

Some time ago there appeared on the market an ingenious toy, primarily designed, no doubt, merely to amuse; but, in point of fact, highly instructive.   Its general appearance and simple mechanism are illustrated in figure 69.   The beetle "walks" on two toothed wheels, of which one is an idler, while the other is rotated by a spring whose gradual release is ensured by a simple escapement device. At its forward end reckoning in the direction of motion (at the "head") the toy is provided with a pair of antennae, of which one is a dummy, and rises clear of the table upon which the beetle is placed to exhibit its talents.   The other antenna is operative and is so bent downward as to glide along the table top, in contact with it.   A little

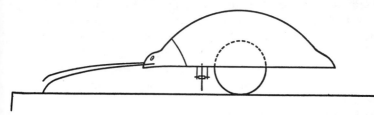

FIG. 69. MECHANICAL WALKING BEETLE, EXHIBITING THE SEVERAL CHARACTERISTIC ELEMENTS OF THE CORRELATING APPARATUS

in advance of the propelling wheel is another smaller toothed wheel, running idle, and disposed transversely to the direction of the driving wheel.   This transverse wheel clears the table without contact in the normal working position of the beetle.   The animal, if placed somewhere near the center of the table, makes a straight track, apparently intent upon reaching the edge and seeking destruction in a species of mechanical suicide.   But the moment the operative antenna clears the edge of the table, the body of the toy, till then held up by the contact of the antenna with the table surface, sinks down a fraction of an inch, and the transverse wheel now contacts with the table.   In consequence the toy rotates until the running wheel is parallel with the table edge, and the insect continues its peregrinations with the operative antenna hugging the side of the table top.

Clearly here the antenna is a receptor, which "apprises" the insect of certain features in its environment, which *depicts*, in a crude but sufficient manner, the environment *in* the toy. The law of depiction is here extremely simple; a depression in the external world (table top) is translated into a downward tilt in the angle of repose of the toy.

The adjustor, in this case, is the transverse wheel, about as simple an example of an adjustor as can well be imagined. It "construes" the information furnished by the receptor antenna, and modifies in accordance with this information the law of motion of the toy, in such manner as to preserve the beetle from a fall which might destroy that stability of form on which the continued operation, according to schedule, of the mechanism depends.

It would be easy to cite a number of other examples of devices constructed either as toys, scientific curiosities, or for actual technical use, which exhibit more or less prominently the typical correlating apparatus, with receptor, adjustor and effector. By far the most highly perfected of such automatic devices is the modern machine-switching apparatus for telephones, which eliminates the "operator" at the central offices. This device, which fulfills an amazing multiplicity of functions, will be found briefly described in non-technical language in the April number 1923 of The Bell System Technical Journal.

Perhaps more directly in line with our present interest here is a mechanical chess player that was designed some years ago by L. Torres y Quevedo;[3] this device successfully counters any move (with a limited number of pieces, merely as a matter of simplicity) that a living opponent may choose to make upon the board. The game of chess itself is so well conceived a conventionalization of the battle of life[4] that it is well worth the while to make a seeming digression to analyze the fundamental elements of this remarkable game. The bearing of this analysis upon certain problems of biological evolution will then become apparent.

[3] A description will be found in the Scientific American Supplement, November 6, 1915, p. 296.

[4] The aptness of this illustration has no doubt been remarked by many. I have recently noted the following pertinent references: F. L. Wells, Mental Adjustments, 1917, p. 6. Eddington, Time Space and Gravitation, 1920, p. 184; T. H. Huxley, A Liberal Education and Where to Find it. Collected Essays, 1894, vol. 3, p. 81. A bibliography of the mathematical treatment of chess will be found in W. W. R. Ball, Mathematical Recreations, 1911, Chapter VI, p. 109.

Chess as a Conventional Model of the Battlefield of Life. A game of chess is a succession of physical events. How is its course determined?

The elements that determine this course are as follows:

1. A topographic map, a chart of geometric constraints, the chess board.

2. Movable upon this chart, a number of movable points (chessmen), each the *center* of a *field of influence*, defined for each movable point in relation to the geometric constraints. So, for example, the field of influence of a pawn extends to the two squares diagonally in front of the pawn.

3. A law restricting the time-rate of advance of each moving point (moves alternate from white to black).

4. A law defining the influence upon each other of two points *in collision*, i.e., two points whose fields of influence have interpenetrated to a prescribed extent. An example of this is the rule that a chessman arriving upon a square occupied by a hostile piece, throws the latter off the board.

5. A law restricting the movements of the points when not in collision, i.e., when outside one another's field of influence. So, for example, a bishop may move only diagonally.

6. The elements enumerated so far place *restrictions* upon permissible changes (moves). These elements alone cannot, evidently, *determine* any occurrence of any kind: Absolute immobility, for example, or any random move that did not violate the rules of the game, would equally satisfy the conditions enumerated.

7. In addition to the elements, 1, 2, 3, 4, 5, there must therefore be in operation some positive principle (tropism) which not merely restricts possible occurrences, but which determines actual events. In chess this principle is furnished by the effort of each player to bring about checkmate. Each move is so *aimed* (with greater or less *accuracy* and breadth of view, *versatility*, according to the skill of the player) as ultimately to force a checkmate.

From the battlefield of chess we now turn our eyes on the scene of the great biological contest: Before us is a topographic map, over which move those organisms that are by nature gifted with motion. We may think of each such organism as a moving point, the *center* of a *field of influence*. As the chessplayer must accustom his mind's eye to see, radiating out from each chessman, its field of influence upon the board, so we, in envisaging the battleground of organic evolution, must see each organism carrying around with it, as if rigidly attached to its body, a field, or a target, of zones, of the following character.

A. Zones of Influence. In general the motion of the individual will be determined by laws too complicated to be readily analyzed, and therefore will be described as *random*. But there will upon occasion be a rather abrupt break away from such random movement, according as a certain feature of the environment lies without or within certain zones. For example, the movements of a fly wandering about on a window pane are, presumably, in all cases physically determinate. But in a homogeneous field (uniform illumination etc.), the motion will assume, on the whole, a random character. We may suppose that, in first approximation at any rate, the migrations of the individual will follow some such law as those developed, for example by Sir Ronald Ross,[5] by Pearson and Blakeman,[6] or by Brownlee[7] for random migration. But, bring some particle of food within the field of sensuous observation of the fly, and the law of motion instantly changes from random to more or less clearly directed.

We may, then, construct about each individual a sort of target of zones of influence. The ideal would be to draw this target on a quantitative plan, according as a stimulus of strength s exerts a directing influence d at a distance r. In practice there may be difficulty in constructing these zones, but we may at least conceive them as drawn.

We may say that a given organism is "in encounter" with a given point (e.g., a feature of the topographic chart) when that point falls within its field of influence. Similarly we may say that two organisms are in encounter when the one falls in the field of influence of the other. This encounter is mutual or one-sided according as each is within the other's field, or as only one is in the other's field, but not conversely, for example if A sees B, but B does not see A; or, to take an example

[5] Sir Ronald Ross, Prevention of Malaria, 1922, second edition, pp. 179, 700.

[6] K. Pearson and J. Blakeman, Drapers' Company Research Memoirs, III:XV, 1906.

[7] J. Brownlee, Proc. Roy. Soc. Edin., 1910–1911, vol. 31, pp. 262–289; of other references related to this subject the following have been noted: F. Y. Edgeworth, Entomological Statistics, Metron, 1920, vol. 1, p. 75; W. H. Cole, Science, 1922, vol. 55, p. 678; W. B. Hardy, Nature, December 30, 1922, p. 866 (Twelfth Report of the Development Commissions 1922).

from chess, a bishop may threaten a pawn, though the pawn does not threaten the bishop. Zones of influence may extend over millions of miles, as in the case of a traveller steering his course by the stars.

B. Zones of Mobility. We may stake out around each organism a target of zones indicating the distance which it is physically capable of travelling in 1, 2, . . . n units of time. These zones also we shall think of as attached to the organism and carried round with it in its wanderings through the landscape.

It is clear that the fate of the organism, and the history, the evolution of the system as a whole, will depend, first, on the character of the zones of influence and the zones of mobility; and second, on the nature of the correlation, the law of the *aimed* movements, established through these zones. We may seek to establish analytical expressions for this dependence.

Let q be a parameter defining the character or "pattern" of a target of zones of influence or of mobility of the organisms of species S. Thus, for example, q might be parameter, or one of a set of parameters, defining visual acuity, measured on some suitable scale, at a distance of 5, 10, 15, . . . feet, under standard conditions. Or, q might be a parameter defining the minimum time required for the organism to reach a point 5, 10, 15, . . . feet from his actual position, under standard conditions.[8]

Analytical Statement of Problem. We may now enquire:

1. What will be the effect upon the rate of growth of the species if the parameter q is increased by a (small) amount dq? If r is the fractional rate of increase of the species S, can we establish an expression for the partial derivative $\dfrac{\partial r}{\partial q}$?

A glance at the chess analogy will help to make clear the nature of the question thus raised. In chess we might ask: What would be the effect upon the course of the game if, other things equal, we were to modify in some stated particular the rules limiting the permitted moves of a given piece, for instance by allowing a pawn to move *two* squares, instead of the conventional *one?*

2. A second enquiry of peculiar interest relates, not to the character (pattern) of the zones of influence and mobility, but to the form of

---

[8] Isochrone charts of essentially this character, relating to travelling facilities, were, according to Darmstaedter, first suggested by K. Richter in 1833 and actually prepared by Sir Francis Galton in 1881 (L. Darmstaedter, Handbuch zur Geschichte der Naturwissenschaften und der Technik, 1908, p. 792).

relation established, through these zones, between the action of the organism and his environment.   For it is hardly necessary for us to be reminded that two individuals or species with the same visual acuity, for example, may react in very different manner on seeing the same thing.

Here again the chess analogy is helpful.   The corresponding enquiry with regard to chess is: What would be the effect upon the course of the game, if, with unchanged rules as to the moves of the pieces, a given change were made in the method, or the ability, of one of the players?

To deal with these problems it is desirable to introduce two concepts, that of the *Behavior Schedule*, and that of *Specific Productivity* in a given activity.

THE BEHAVIOR SCHEDULE

It has been remarked[9] that "a living organism is both cause and effect of itself."   We may say in somewhat more detailed statement, that the organism goes through a certain routine of motions or activities which are rendered possible by its structure, and which, in turn, are a necessary condition for the continued existence of that structure. These activities in general involve the expenditure of certain quantities of free energy, and a part of the energy so expended necessarily is spent in collecting (*earning*) a "replacement" amount equal to the total expenditure, to balance the account, to cover the *cost of living*. While this phenomenon is, in a general way, characteristic of all mobile forms of life, the particular method followed in this cyclic activity of gathering and spending free energy varies in the most multiform manner from one species or type of organism to another.

Each type of organism may thus be said to possess a characteristic *Behavior Schedule*, which may be defined in terms of certain coefficients as follows: Of its total expenditure E per unit of time, a representative individual of the population will spend, on an average a fraction λ_j in a particular activity A_j, which may be defined as the maintaining of a parameter U_j at the value u_j.   So, for example,[10] a human being may expend on an average, per day,

[9] Kant, Kritik of Judgment.   Transl. Bernard, London, 1892, p. 274.
[10] The figures in this example are chosen arbitrarily, although an effort has been made to make them reasonably realistic.   In view of the wide variations in standards and cost of living in different countries, different social

number of calories

180	external work (services sold) in maintaining his daily food supply at..........................	3,000 cal.
2,500	internal work (physiological work) in maintaining his body temperature at................	98°F.
130	external work (services sold) in maintaining his house rent at, daily..........................	$2.00
60	external work (services sold) in maintaining his daily supply of clothing at....................	$0.75
30	external work (services sold) in maintaining his daily supply of sundries at....................	$0.25
100	external work (services sold) in maintaining the rate of increase of the population at....	1 per cent per annum

3,000 calories—total expenditure and total earnings

(*Note:* 1 calorie = 3086 foot pounds.)

SPECIFIC PRODUCTIVITY

Consider some particular activity A_j which results in maintaining a parameter U_j (e.g., food capture per head per unit of time) at the value u_j, then we will define P_j, the Specific Productivity of energy E_j spent in activity A_j by

$$P_j = \frac{u_j - c_j}{E_j} \qquad (c_j \text{ a constant}) \qquad (1)$$

and we note that

$$\frac{\partial u_j}{\partial P_j} = E_j \qquad (2)$$

---

strata, and at different epochs, close figuring, in such an example as this, would be out of place. Numerical data pertinent to this example will be found scattered widely in various sources, of which the following may here be mentioned: J. Amar, Le Moteur Humain, 1914, p. 254; R. Hutchison, Food and Dietetics, 1902, p. 37:46; J. LeFèvre, La Chaleur Animale, 1911; F. H. Streightoff, The Standard of Living, 1911.

EFFECT OF CHANGE IN ZONE PATTERN
(Intra-Species Evolution)

We are now prepared to consider the analytical representation of the influence of changes in the pattern of the zones of influence and the zones of mobility, on the one hand, and, on the other, of a change in the behavior schedule, on the proportional rate of increase r of the species of organisms under discussion.

This proportional rate of increase, $r = \dfrac{dX}{Xdt}$, is in general a function of the parameters U (food capture, shelter, etc.), so that we may write

$$r = r(u_1, u_2, \ldots u_j, \ldots) \tag{3}$$

and

$$\frac{\partial r}{\partial P_j} = \frac{\partial r}{\partial u_j}\frac{\partial u_j}{\partial P_j} \tag{4}$$

$$= \frac{\partial r}{\partial u_j} E_j \tag{5}$$

Now the specific productivity P_j in activity A_j itself depends upon the character of the zone pattern. For, the more perfectly the individual is apprised of the relevant features of its environment (i.e., the more perfectly developed its zones of influence), the better, other things, equal, will it be able to direct its activities to the ends defined by the parameters $U;$ and a similar remark evidently applies to the zones of mobility. If, then, q is a parameter defining the character of these zones, we may write

$$P_j = P_j(q) \tag{6}$$

and

$$\frac{\partial r}{\partial q} = \frac{\partial r}{\partial P_j}\frac{\partial P_j}{\partial q} \tag{7}$$

$$= \frac{\partial r}{\partial u_j}\frac{\partial P_j}{\partial q} E_j \tag{8}$$

or, more generally, since a change in q may affect not only a single productivity P_j, but also others, $P_1, P_2, \ldots P_n$

$$\frac{\partial r}{\partial q} = \sum_{j=1}^{j=n} \frac{\partial r}{\partial u_j}\frac{\partial P_j}{\partial q} E_j \tag{9}$$

the summation being extended over all the activities A_1, A_2, . . . A_j, . . . A_n in so far as they are affected by the parameter q. (It is immaterial whether those not so affected are included in the summation or not, since they will contribute a zero term.)

It lends a certain interest to the relation (9) if we observe that such partial derivatives as $\dfrac{\partial r}{\partial q}$, $\dfrac{\partial r}{\partial u_j}$ possess a concrete signification, as follows:

Consider two small increments Δq_1 and Δq_2 in two parameters q_1 and q_2. (To make matters concrete, suppose q_1 measures visual acuity, q_2 auditory acuity.) If Δq_1 and Δq_2 are such that

$$\frac{\partial r}{\partial q_1}\Delta q_1 - \frac{\partial r}{\partial q_2}\Delta q_2 = 0 \tag{10}$$

i.e., such that

$$\frac{\Delta q_1}{\Delta q_2} = \frac{\partial r}{\partial q_2}\Big/\frac{\partial r}{\partial q_1} \tag{11}$$

then it will be *indifferent* for the rate of the increase of the species whether visual acuity is increased by Δq_1 or auditory acuity by Δq_2. We might say, in this sense, that the increments Δq_1 and Δq_2 are, in this event, *equivalent*, or that that they have the same total value (in exchange against each other) for the species. Moreover, from (10) it is evident, on this same understanding, that the partial derivative $\dfrac{\partial r}{\partial q_1}$ measures the value (in exchange) *per unit*,[11] to the species, of the parameters q_1; and $\dfrac{\partial r}{\partial q_2}$ similarly measures the value (in exchange) per unit of the parameters q_2. We may symbolize these facts by writing

$$\frac{\partial r}{\partial q} = v_q \tag{12}$$

$$\frac{\partial r}{\partial u_j} = v_{u_j} \tag{13}$$

The relation (9) then appears in the form

$$v_q = \sum_{j=1}^{j=n} v_{u_j}\frac{\partial P_j}{\partial q_j}E_j \tag{14}$$

---

[11] An arbitrary proportionality factor enters, which is conveniently made unity by suitable choice of units.

Certain steps in the development set forth above are reminiscent of the hedonistic calculus of Jevons and his school of economists. One is thus naturally led to look for a relation between *value* (in exchange) as here defined, and *economic value in exchange*, as conceived by those authors. It should be expressly noted, however, that the reasoning here followed, and the conclusions reached, are quite independent of **any** economic theory. As for the relation of the present reflections to economic theory, this will become apparent in the paragraphs that follow.

EFFECT OF CHANGE IN BEHAVIOR SCHEDULE

We may note, first of all, that

$$\frac{\partial r_j}{\partial E_j} = \frac{\partial r}{\partial u_j}\frac{\partial u_j}{\partial E_j} = \frac{\partial r}{\partial u_j}\,p_j \tag{15}$$

where $p_j = \dfrac{\partial u_j}{\partial E_j}$ defines what we may term the *marginal* productivity of energy expended upon the parameter U_j. This *marginal* productivity p_j will, in general, differ from the total productivity P_j defined by equation (1).

It is, however, desirable, to express the relation between r and the behavior schedule in another way, with the following considerations in mind.

Rigid or Automaton Type and Elastic Type of Behavior Schedule. The apparatus by which the coefficients λ defining the behavior pattern are determined varies widely in different species of organisms. At one extreme we may suppose that we have an organism with a rigid, inelastic behavior schedule, the coefficients λ being determined explicitly, once for all, by the properties of the individual. The extreme case of this kind is to be found, presumably, in plants, where, for example, the amount of energy expended in anabolism to replace wear and tear (e.g., annual leaf-fall) may be taken as a comparatively simple function of the leaf area. Many of the lowest forms of animals, actuated by simple *tropisms*, no doubt also approximate closely to such a rigid behavior schedule, what might be termed the *automaton type* of behavior schedule.

But in the higher animals, and most particularly in man, we have an elastic behavior-schedule. Here the λ's are not fixed in simple **explicit** manner by the physical character of the organism. **We** encounter here the phenomenon which we experience in ourselves subjectively as *free choice* between alternative courses of action, alternative values of the λ's open to us to choose from.

This cannot mean, of course, that the λ's are wholly arbitrary, or physically indeterminate. *Some* action is and must be taken. But the natural principle which operates in the determination of the λ's, of the behavior schedule, is not immediately obvious.

The avenue of approach which seems to give most promise of lending us an insight into the relations here involved, is the following:

The elastic type of behavior schedule, the *free-choice* schedule, as distinguished from the *automaton* type, is essentially a characteristic of the more highly organized among the mobile (animal) organisms. This fact is so prominently displayed to us in our own selves, that the adaptive superiority of the elastic type over the automaton type is commonly (and perhaps in a measure unjustly) taken for granted. If this assumption of such superiority be true, then the principle which operates in determining the coefficients λ's must be that they tend, on the whole, to be adjusted, in the operation of free choice, toward values favorable to the growth of the species. In the ideal case of perfect adaptation the λ's would, according to this view, be such as make r, the proportional rate of increase of the species, a maximum. Let us see what this would imply.

In reacting upon its environment to influence the parameter U_j, the organism itself necessarily undergoes some modification, since it gives up energy E_j, (subjectively this modification is commonly felt as *fatigue*). In other words, if the state of the individual is defined by the values of certain (internal) parameters $f_1, f_2 \ldots$, then the expenditure of an element of energy δE_j by the individual, if not accompanied by other effects, is accompanied by a change $\delta f_1, \delta f_2 \ldots$ in the parameters f. At the same time the (external) parameter U_j is modified by δu_j.

The effect of these modifications upon r is given by

$$\delta r = \left\{ \frac{\partial r}{\partial u_j} \frac{\partial u_j}{\partial E_j} + \frac{\partial r}{\partial f} \frac{\partial f}{\partial E_j} \right\} \delta E_j \tag{16}$$

where, for brevity, the contracted notation has been employed

$$\frac{\partial r}{\partial f} \frac{\partial f}{\partial E_j} = \sum_{K=1, 2, \ldots} \frac{\partial r}{\partial f_k} \frac{\partial f_k}{\partial E_j} \tag{17}$$

If r is to be a maximum, (δr) must vanish for any arbitrary small value of δE_j, so that we must have for every subscript j, according to (16)

$$\frac{\partial r}{\partial u_j}\frac{\partial u_j}{\partial E_j} + \frac{\partial r}{\partial f}\frac{\partial f}{\partial E_j} = 0 \tag{18}$$

or, adopting the notation of (12), (13), (15)

$$v_{u_j}p_j + v_f p_f = 0 \tag{19}$$

Relation between Ideal and Actual Organism. We have thus far considered an ideal type of organism of the free choice type of behavior schedule, constructed on the principle that the λ's shall be so chosen as to make the proportional rate of increase r a maximum.

It remains to consider the relation between this ideal type of organism and the actual organism. The actual organism is not consciously guided by any consideration of the effect of his actions upon the rate of increase of his species. At least the instances in which such considerations are operative are so exceptional that we may well leave them out of account. What guides a human being, for example, in the selection of his activities, are his tastes, his desires, his pleasures and pains, actual or prospective. This is true, at least, of some of his actions, those which are embraced in his free-choice type of behavior schedule. That the human behavior schedule[12] also contains an element of the non-elastic (automaton) type may be admitted in deference to those who have leveled their destructive criticism at the hedonistic account of human behavior. We may, however, restrict our discussion here to that portion or phase of conduct which is determined by hedonistic influences. In this case, then, we are dealing with an organism which seeks to make, not r, but Ω, its total pleasure ("ophelimity" in Pareto's terminology) a maximum. Argument precisely similar to that developed above here leads to the condition.

$$\frac{\partial \Omega}{\partial u_j}\frac{\partial u_j}{\partial E_j} + \frac{\partial \Omega}{\partial f}\frac{\partial f}{\partial E_j} = 0 \tag{20}$$

---

[12] In a modern civilized community we cannot very well speak of one typical behavior schedule of the individual, owing to the division of labor, with specialization of individuals in different pursuits. This matter will be found discussed more particularly, in Chapter XXVIII dealing with the *adjustors*.

It is immediately seen that (18) and (20) will lead to the same adjustment of the activities of the individual if, and only if the marginal ophelimities $\dfrac{\partial \Omega}{\partial u_j}$ are proportional to the corresponding derivatives $\dfrac{\partial r}{\partial u_j}$ i.e. if

$$\frac{\partial \Omega}{\partial u_j} = k \frac{\partial r}{\partial u_j} \tag{21}$$

We see then, that an organism actuated by *pleasure* and *pain* will so distribute its activities as to make r a maximum, if, and only if, its marginal ophelimities are proportional to the corresponding derivatives $\dfrac{\partial r}{\partial u_j}$.

Effect of Small Departure from Perfect Adjustment. If we look upon the sense of pleasure and pain as an adjunct serving the express purpose of directing the activities of the organism towards ends beneficial to the growth of the species, then a species for which condition (21) were satisfied would represent perfect adaptation in this respect.

This leads us to a somewhat different setting of our problem regarding the influence of a change in the behavior pattern upon the rate of increase of the species.   Instead of enquiring after $\dfrac{\partial r}{\partial E_j}$, we may seek information regarding the influence, upon r, of a change in the tastes or desires of the species as defined by the derivatives $\dfrac{\partial \Omega}{\partial u_j}$.   An answer can be given at any rate in the neighborhood of the "perfect" adjustment of tastes defined by (21), i.e., for a species whose behavior schedule does not depart materially from that defined by (18). Consider a species for which the ideal (perfect) adjustment is given by

$$v_{u_j} p_j + v_f p_f = 0 \tag{22}$$

Suppose that this species *actually* adjusts its activities according to the plan (23) departing slightly (by an "error of valuation" $\delta\epsilon$) from the perfect adjustment, namely

$$(v_{u_j} + \delta\epsilon) p_j + v_f p_f = 0 \tag{23}$$

Then it can readily be shown[13] that

$$\frac{\delta r}{\delta \epsilon_j} = - v_{u_j} p_j \bigg/ \frac{\partial}{\partial u_j} (v_{u_j} p_j + v_f p_f) \qquad (24)$$

which is the required analytical expression for the influence of a small "error of valuation" upon the rate of increase of the species.

The utility which such formulae as here developed may possess must be sought, not so much in their application to numerical examples—data for this are now and may long remain unavailable—as in the light they throw, quantitatively, upon the biological foundations of economics, in the relations which they reveal between certain biological and certain economic quantities. It must be remembered that the mathematical method is concerned, not only, and indeed not primarily, with the calculation of numbers, but also, and more particularly, with establishment of relations between magnitudes.[14]

Relation of Economic Value to Physical Energy. The behavior schedule has been quantitatively defined in terms of energy. This, if not the only possible definition, is at any rate a convenient one, and has also the advantage of emphasizing the important relation of the organism to the energy sources of his environment. His correlating apparatus is primarily an energy capturing device—its other functions are undoubtedly secondary. Evidence of this is manifold. The close association of the principal sense organs, eyes, ears, nose, taste buds, tactile papillae of the finger tips, with the anterior (head) end of the body, the *mouth* end, all point the same lesson,[15] which is further confirmed by the absence of any well developed sense organs in plants.[16] Exceptions here do indeed prove the rule, for sensitive plants, with a well-defined correlating apparatus, are just those which have departed so far from norm as to consume flesh food. And contrariwise, we ourselves are "blind" toward the one food that is omnipresent and which we consume by

[13] A. J. Lotka, Jour. Washington Acad. Sci., 1915, vol. 5, p. 397.

[14] Compare A. Cournot, Researches into the Mathematical Theory of Wealth, English translation by Irving Fisher, 1897, p. 3.

[15] Herbert Spencer, Principles of Biology, vol. 2, p. 166; E. H. Starling, Science, 1909, p. 394; A. J. Lotka, Annalen der Naturphilosophie, 1910, p. 67.

[16] For a resumé of "plant psychology," see C. H. Farr, Atlantic Monthly, December, 1922; also Sir Frederick Keeble, The Plant Commonwealth and Its Mode of Government, Nature, 1924, vol. 144, pp. 13, 55.

an almost unconscious, vegetative process, namely oxygen. If we seek an insight into the "psychology of plants," it may be well to begin by imagining what our mental state would be if, in all our food quest, we remained as passive and indifferent as in the function of breathing.

The life contest, then is primarily a competition for available energy, as has been pointed out by Boltzmann.[17] Energy in this sense and for this reason *has* value for the organism—which is a very different thing from saying (as some have said or implied) that economic value *is* a form of energy. It is true that different kinds of energy are in a certain sense interconvertible into each other at fairly definite rates by exchange upon the market, in a human population. But the conversion factors here involved are of a totally different character from those that enter into the analytical expression of the law of conservation of energy.

This must be immediately apparent from the fact alone that the "mechanical equivalents" of the several forms of energy are absolute constants, whereas the economic conversion factors are somewhat variable, though they have often a species of approximate constancy, a fact which calls for explanation.

Economic Conversion Factors of Energy. A simple example may help to clarify the view; the case of the automatic vending machine, the penny-in-the-slot chocolate dispenser, for instance.

The salient facts here are:

1. A definite amount of money brings in exchange a definite amount of commodity (and of energy).

2. The physical process is a typical case of "trigger action," in which the ratio of energy set free to energy applied is subject to no restricting general law whatever (e.g., a touch of the finger upon a switch may set off tons of dynamite).

3. In contrast with the case of thermodynamic conversion factors, the proportionality factor is here determined by the particular mechanism employed.

Reflection shows that all transformation of money or of economic assets of any kind into energy by exchange upon the market is of

---

[17] Der zweite Hauptsatz der mechanischen Wärmetheorie, 1886 (Gerold, Vienna), p. 210; Populäre Schriften, No. 3, Leipsic, 1905; Nernst, Theoretische Chemie, 1913, p. 819; Burns and Paton, Biophysics, 1921, p. 8; H. F. Osborn, The Origin and Evolution of Life, 1918, p. XV.

this character. It is always a case of trigger action. Somewhere there is a store of available energy, which can be tapped with an expenditure of greater or less effort. The payment of the price sets in motion the requisite machinery for the release of that energy (or for its transfer of ownership, the release being delayed at the discretion of the buyer).

In view of the entire absence of any general law regulating the ratio of energy released to energy applied in such cases of trigger action, we may ask the question, how does it come about that economic conversion factors, economic ratios-in-exchange of different forms of energy, display any regularity whatever? The answer is not far to seek. The approximate constancy of the economic conversion factors is traceable to the approximate constancy in type of the mechanism involved, namely the human organism and its social aggregations. Just as one particular slot machine will always deliver a certain package of chocolate, so a certain social organization under similar conditions will render (approximately) the same amount of selected form of energy in return for a stated sum of money. As to the circumstances that quantitatively determine these economic conversion factors, for a discussion of these the reader must be referred to the literature;[18] only this may be remarked here, that the conception advanced by Ostwald,[19] for example, that the determining feature is the (physical) *availability* of the particular form of energy, is inadequate.

Collective Effect of Individual Struggle for Energy Capture. Our reflections so far have been directed to the selfish efforts of each organism and species to divert to itself as much as possible of the stream of available energy. But if we recall once more the admonition of Bunge—Nature must be considered as a whole if she is to be understood in detail—we shall be led to enquire: What must be the

---

[18] A. J. Lotka, Proc. Natl. Acad. Sci., 1921, vol. 7, p. 192.

[19] W. Ostwald, Die Energie, 1908, p. 164. Of other literature more or less pertinent to the subject the following may be mentioned: G. Helm, Die Lehre von der Energie, Leipsic, 1887, pp. 72 et seq. W. Ostwald, Energetische Grundlagen der Kulturwissenschaften, Leipsic, 1909, p. 155. Die Philosophie der Werte, Leipsic, 1913, pp. 260, 314–317, 326, 328; Budde., Energie und Recht, Leipsic, 1902, p. 56; Winiarski, Essai sur la Mécanique Sociale, Revue Philosophique, 1900, vol. 49, p. 113; J. Davidson, Qu. Jour. Economics, August, 1919, p. 717.

effect, upon the world-as-a-whole, of the general scrimmage for available energy?

It has already been pointed out that the operation of the correlating apparatus is of the nature of a cycle beginning and terminating in the external world; that the grazing cow is able to subsist because the grass is "hungry for oxygen," that animals are essentially catalysers, oiling the machinery, as it were and assisting energy in its downhill path to levels of lower availability (higher entropy). If we had only the animal kingdom to consider we should in the first instance be disposed to conclude that the cosmic effect of the scrimmage for available energy would be to increase the total energy flux, the rate of degradation of the energy received from the sun. But plants work in the opposite direction. And even among animals, greater efficiency in utilizing energy, a better husbanding of resources, and hence a less rapid drain upon them, must work to the advantage of a species talented in that direction.[20] There are thus two opposing tendencies in operation, and it is difficult to see how any general principle can be applied to determine just where the balance will be struck.

The Law of Evolutiou Adumbrated as a Law of Maximum Energy Flux. This at least seems probable, that so long as there is an abundant surplus of available energy running "to waste" over the sides of the mill wheel, so to speak, so long will a marked advantage be gained by any species that may develop talents to utilize this "lost portion of the stream." Such a species will therefore, other things equal, tend to grow in extent (numbers) and this growth will further increase the flux of energy through the system. It is to be observed that in this argument the principle of the survival of the fittest yields us information beyond that attainable by the reasoning of thermodynamics.[21]

As to the other aspect of the matter, the problem of economy in husbanding resources will not rise to its full importance until the available resources are more completely tapped than they are today. Every indication is that man will learn to utilize some of the sunlight that now goes to waste. The general effect will be to increase the rate

[20] Compare J. Johnstone, The Mechanism of Life, 1921, p. 220.

[21] This fact has been recognized independently by the writer and also by H. Guilleminot. For details see A. J. Lotka, Proc. Natl. Acad. Sci., 1922, p. 153.

of energy flux through the system of organic nature, with a parallel increase in the total mass of the great world transformer, of its rate of circulation, or both.[22]

One is tempted to see in this one of those maximum laws which are so commonly found to be apt expressions of the course of nature.[23] But historical recollections here bid us to exercise caution; a prematurely enunciated maximum principle is liable to share the fate of Thomsen and Berthelot's chemical "principle of maximum work."

STATISTICAL MECHANICS OF SYSTEMS OF ORGANISMS

Let us call to mind once more the picture of the life conflict viewed as the interplay of organisms moving over a topographic chart and suffering a succession of collisions with each other and with features of their environment.

We might seek to develop, for such a system, a discipline of statistical mechanics similar to that which the physicist has developed to deal with the kinetic theory of gases and allied problems.

No attempt will be made here to carry out this project in any degree of completeness, or to carry it to such ultimate conclusions as it may be competent to furnish. But it may not be out of place to indicate at least a few points, in addition to the pertinent matter contained in the preceding paragraph, that can be offered as first steps toward the development of such a discipline.

Mean Free Path. In the elementary kinetic theory of gases it is shown that the mean free path l of a molecule in a gas is given by[24]

$$l = \frac{1}{N\pi s^2} \tag{25}$$

---

[22] For a more detailed discussion of this point see A. J. Lotka, Proc. Natl. Acad. Sci., 1922, p. 147.

[23] Compare J. Larmor, Proc. London Math. Soc., 1883–1884, vol. 15, p. 159; Petzoldt, Maxima and Minima und Ökonomie.

[24] See, for example, Winkelmann, Handbuch der Physik, 1906, vol. 3, p. 696. This elementary result is based on the simplifying assumption that the velocity of all the moving molecules is the same. Taking into account the velocities ranging according to the Maxwellian law, it is found that $l = \frac{1}{\sqrt{2}\,N\,\pi\,s^2}$. But for our purposes it is quite sufficient to accept the simple elementary method and its result.

where N is the number of molecule per unit volume, and s their diameter. This, of course, relates to motion in three dimensions.

We may apply similar methods to the case of two species, N_1 individuals of S_1 and N_2 individuals of S_2, operating on a square mile, say, of ground. If the field of influence of S_1 is a circular field of diameter s it is easily shown that (according to the elementary theory) the mean free path for the individuals of S_1 is, expressed in miles,

$$\underline{l} = \frac{1}{N_2 s} \tag{26}$$

Frequency of Collisions and of Capture. If v is the average velocity of the individuals of S_1, the frequency collision will be, approximately at any rate,

$$F = v N_1 N_2 s \tag{27}$$

In general not all collisions, but only a certain fraction c, will result in capture. The total captures per unit of time, per square mile, will then be

$$C = c v N_1 N_2 s \tag{28}$$

It may be noted in passing that the expression thus found represents, in certain cases at any rate, the term $k\, N_1 N_2$ which appears in equation (38) of Chapter VIII, where it was introduced without analyzing its precise physical significance.

Influence of Size of Organism. It is interesting to observe the influence of size of the predatory organism on the frequency of capture. Suppose, leaving all other factors the same, we halve the size of the predatory organisms, so that the new value of N_1, which we may designate by a prime, is given by

$$N_1' = 2N_1 \tag{29}$$

If the velocity of the smaller organisms is unchanged, we shall have for the new frequency of capture

$$F' = 2N_1 N_2 c v s \tag{30}$$

More appropriate, perhaps, is the supposition that the new velocity v' is related to the old v in the proportion of the linear dimensions, i.e., as $\sqrt[3]{\dfrac{N'}{N}} = \sqrt[3]{2} = 1.26$ We should then have

$$F' = \frac{2}{1.26} N_1 N_2 cvs \qquad (31)$$

$$= 1.6 \, N_1 N_2 cvs \qquad (32)$$

$$= 1.6 \, F \qquad (33)$$

There is then, other things equal, an advantage for predatory species in small size. In nature, presumably, there is a tendency to strike a compromise between the advantage thus gained, and certain disadvantages, such as relative defencelessness, incurred by decreased stature.

Curves of Pursuit. The coefficient c which occurs in (28) is open to further discussion and analysis. A collision is characterized by the fact that through its duration the *law of motion* differs essentially and discontinuously from the law of motion between collisions. The coefficient c evidently depends on the law of motion *during* collision. During collision the two individuals follow a course of the type known as a *curve of pursuit*. For a discussion of these curves so far as they have been studied, the reader must be referred to the pertinent literature.[25] The mathematical theory of problems in pursuit and conflict generally has hitherto been developed principally, if not exclusively, in connection with warfare. In any effort to deal with the more general theory of conflict between biological species it may be well to have an eye open to the methods followed in the treatment of problems of military and naval tactics. Here, however, this mere hint must suffice.

Random Motion under a Bias. Various problems relating to the motion of a point following in part a random course, but at the same time controlled by some kind of directing influence, have been dealt with by L. Bachelier in his *Calcul des Probabilités*, 1912, to which the reader may be referred. Chapter XX, on *Probabilités Cinématiques*, may be found suggestive in connection with the type of motion presented by living organisms, a motion that can be regarded as containing both a systematically directed and also a random element.

Use of Models. Another point shall be passed over here with a mere suggestion. The mathematical treatment of the statistical mechanics of the kind of systems here taken in view may appear to threaten formidable difficulties. It is to be hoped that this will not

---

[25] See, for example, Boole, Differential Equations fourth edition, p. 251.

altogether prevent its attack, even if at first sweeping simplifications must be made in the fundamental assumptions. But the writer wishes to draw particular attention to one method that in the past has not been used to any considerable extent, and which may be found serviceable where ordinary analytical methods become forbidding. The method to which I refer is a special form of the graphic method, namely the method of *working models*. It is well worth considering whether interesting light may not be thrown on various problems of biological conflict, by the use of models designed to imitate the biological warfare somewhat after the manner in which the war game imitates the armed conflict of nations.

CHAPTER XXVI

THE CORRELATING APPARATUS

Let us now consider the character of the material Nature whose necessary results have been made available . . . . for a final cause.—Aristotle.

In preceding pages we have dealt with the correlating apparatus, and its functions, in the gross, without paying more than passing attention to the details of its constitution and operation. It is desirable now to fill in some of these omitted details; we shall consider in turn the depictors, elaborators, effectors and adjustors, with especial attention to the case of the human species. For it goes without saying that a particular interest attaches to the study of the correlating apparatus in man, if only because in no other creature has it developed such singular excrescences as that which prompts, for example, the writing of this book and furnishes the means for the accomplishment of the task. Man thus stands out, if not as a superior being, at any rate as a highly peculiar creature. One might perhaps dispute the propriety of the study so unhesitatingly advocated by Pope; but one cannot truthfully deny the fundamental fact of man's inordinate interest in himself. Moreover, there are certain very important phenomena that play a prominent rôle in the operation of the correlating apparatus, phenomena for the study of which our chief source, indeed our only altogether indisputable source of data, lies in our own self: that group of phenomena briefly summarized under the term *consciousness*. Inevitably therefore, a study of the correlating apparatus, if carried out in any detail, will center largely about the manifestation of this apparatus in the human species.

In dealing with the several elements of the correlating apparatus it will be convenient to depart somewhat from what might appear the most natural order. Receptors and effectors, though functionally separated at the two extreme ends of the operative cycle, are in certain respects rather closely related in practice. Similarly there is in certain respects an approach between the elaborators and the adjustors. We shall, accordingly, consider the several elements in the order Receptors, Effectors, Elaborators, Adjustors.

THE RECEPTORS

The receptors, as has already been noted, are one of the two classes of organs or faculties concerned with the depiction of the environment in the organism (the other class being the elaborators). A typical receptor is the eye, which, in the most literal sense, depicts the external world upon the retina. The law of depiction, in this case, is given by the principles of geometrical optics, and is most easily expressed in terms of two systems or reference frames of coördinates, the one fixed with regard to suitably chosen features in the external world, the other fixed with regard to the eye that forms the image. So, for example, the impression my eye received at noon today was determined by the fact that it was located at the N.W. corner of Monument Square and was pointed upward at an angle of about 45 degrees, and turned in the E. S.E. direction. The tip of the Washington Monument, whose coördinates in the "external world" system are x, y z, say, was thus depicted upon my retina[1] by a point with the coördinates x', y', z'. This appearance in the analytical, expression of the depicting process, of two coördinate reference frames, or at least something equivalent, is very characteristic and should be particularly noted. We shall have occasion to refer to this matter again.

But the picture formed by the eye, typical as it is of the process of depiction, is nevertheless essentially incomplete. We know our own world picture as something much more expansive, much more intimate and profuse in detail. When I view a landscape I have not merely in my eye a dead photograph of the rolling hills and placid valleys, in their garb of green, and stirring with life. These things I *see;* but at the same time I *hear* the bells of the grazing herd, and all those familiar noises that belong to the *tout ensemble* of the rustic scene; while the fragrance of the sun-scorched woods, or perhaps the perfume of flowers, enters to fill out another aspect of the picture. So all our receptors or sense organs are, in a larger sense, depicting organs, each supplying its special share toward that composite world picture into which their several contributions are united and further

---

[1] Strictly speaking this is an inverted statement of the facts. We are directly cognizant of sense impressions x' y' z', as our prime data, and we infer, or hypothecate, as secondary data, corresponding coördinates x, y, z, of an external world. See Chapter XXXIV, footnote 2. But for our present purpose the more usual (naïve) viewpoint will serve.

developed by certain special faculties, the *Elaborators*, notably the Memory and Imagination.

Artificial Receptors. A detailed discussion of the natural receptors with which our body is supplied by the physiological processes of embryological development and growth is unnecessary here, since these things are fully discussed in special works devoted to these subjects, such as for example, Ladd and Woodworth's Elements of Physiological Psychology (Scribner's, 1915). But a special development of the receptors in man, which has had, and is destined still to have, an altogether superlative importance in the evolution of the world is passed over in total silence in most works of the character cited, and calls for discussion here in some proportion to the importance of this phase of the subject: the artificial aids and adjuncts to our senses which the ingenuity of man has pressed into his service. With prophetic eye Robert Hooke in 1665 foresaw—no doubt very imperfectly—what these aids were destined to accomplish for the human race.

The next care to be taken, in respect to the senses, is a supplying of their infirmities with instruments, and, as it were, the adding of artificial organs to the natural; this . . . . has been of late years accomplished with prodigious benefit to all sorts of useful knowledge. . . . . It seems not improbable, but that by these helps the subtility of the composition of bodies, the structure of their parts, the various texture of their matter, the instruments and manner of their inward motions, and all the other possible appearances of things, may come to be more fully discovered. . . . .

That the artificial adjuncts to our correlation apparatus are subject to a process of evolution by selection, by trial and error, was clearly recognized by David Hume,[2] who in this, as in other important points, anticipated the conceptions of Darwin and Spencer. The last mentioned was the first to realize fully and to point out clearly the rôle of man-made contrivances, as artificial sense organs on the one hand, and as artificial members (effectors) on the other.[3] As we

---

[2] Dialogues concerning Natural Religion, 1757, Edition of 1907, pp. 189–190. Hume's reflections relate particularly to the artificial effectors (as represented by a ship, for example), but the underlying principle is, of course, the same.

[3] Compare Herbert Spencer, Principle of Psychology, Chapter VII, Section 164; Emerson, The Conduct of Life, Everyman's Library Edition, pp. 159–190 (original edition, 1860); Wiener, Die Erweiterung unserer Sinne, Leipzig 1900; Lehmann, Die Kinematographie, Leipzig, 1911, p. 1.

look back today upon the progress in recent centuries, it is plain beyond all possible misunderstanding that the ushering in of the era of the man-made adjuncts to his natural body has given not only a new direction to the process of evolution, but has speeded up its progress to an extent without the remotest parallel in the history of our globe. How long it may have taken man to develop his organ of sight by the slow processes of physiological evolution we are quite unable to say, but this is certain, that the time is reckoned in many millions of years. Contrast with this the following brief historical record: The use of spectacles was introduced about 1350.[4] The invention of the microscope is credited to the Dutch optician Janssen, 1590. A modern microscope is capable of a magnification of several thousand diameters. (This, however, does not indicate its "separating" power, which in point of fact, is only about 200 times greater than that of the naked eye.) Particles too small to be formed into a distinct image by the microscope can still be detected by the ultra microscope, invented by Zsigmondy in 1903. By the method of X-ray photography developed chiefly by Laue 1912 and Bragg 1915, direct optical evidence of the arrangements of atoms in a crystal is obtained, and the distance between the layers, of the order of $\frac{1}{100,000,000}$ of an inch, is measured. This represents, in effect, a million-fold improvement on the separating power of the eye. The method of C. T. R. Wilson[5] 1912 renders visible to the eye the track of an electron, whose diameter is of the order of one ten-million-millionth of an inch. The power of the natural vision is, in such case as this, virtually multiplied by two hundred billion. The step from the use of a crude pair of spectacles in 1300 to this was taken in the space of about six centuries—and much of the progress is condensed within a space of less than three decades. The evolution of man's artifical sense organs has proceeded at a pace so utterly out of scale with that of his natural equipment that the aid of diagrammatic representation quite forsakes us here. Any attempt to plot such progress as this on a single scale in rectangular coördinates could

[4] Darmstaedter in his Handbuch der Gechichte der Naturwissenschaftem states that the Emperor Nero in A.D. 63 employed a cut emerald to view the gladiator contests. Roger Bacon in A.D. 1250 recommended the use of lenses for persons of weak sight. The chronicle of St. Catherine's Convent at Pisa mentions Alessandro de Soina as maker of spectacles.

[5] Proc. Roy. Soc. Ser. A., vol. 87 (1912), p. 277.

merely result in two limbs of a curve, the first essentially coinciding with the time axis, the second rising abruptly, at an angle indistinguishable from a right angle.[6]

The historical sketch thus drawn represents but a diminutive fragment of the total development of man's artificial correlating apparatus. It is out of the question to cover here in any exhaustive manner even the aids to vision alone. We must pass by with a mere mention the astronomical telescope, which opens the pupils of our eyes one hundred inches wide;[7] or that fantastic application of the stereoscope to astronomical objects, which enables us to see the universe as it would appear to a gigantic being with his eyes many millions of miles apart. As for a general survey of the entire field of our artificial sense organs, to give this would amount to nothing less than the writing of a work, in several volumes, on general observational methodology. For our purpose here these hints must suffice.

THE EFFECTORS

The natural effectors, like the natural receptors, have received their full share of attention, and it is not proposed to add here to the existing literature[8] on this special phase of the subject. As to the artificial aids to the effectors, these are plainly evident on every hand, and do indeed give a stamp altogether its own to this unprecedented industrial era in which we live. Gilbert and Pogue in their memoir on Power[9] estimate that the use of power derived from coal and other extraneous sources (i.e., not from the human body) gives to each man, woman and child the service equivalent of 30 servants. But in point of fact this figure, based merely on the total horsepower developed, gives an altogether inadequate picture of the real facts. Machinery has not only increased our energy output, it has immensely multiplied the speed of production. One extreme

[6] Compare also H. Heath Bawden, The Evolution of Behavior, Psychol. Rev., 1919, p. 247.

[7] Or more than double this, with the aid of Michelson's interference device.

[8] The following may here be mentioned: J. Amar, Le Moteur Humain, 1914; A. Keith, Engines of the Human Body, 1920; O. Fisher (Teubner), 1906 Grundlagen für eine Mechanik der lebenden Körper; C. Bell, Animal Mechanics, 1838 (Library of Useful Knowledge); W. M. Feldmann, Biomathematics, Lippincott 1923; L. L. Burlingame, General Biology, (Jonathan Cape) 1923.

[9] Smithsonian Institution Bulletin, 102, Part 5.

example of this is seen in the printing plant. A modern newspaper press, with a crew of 6 to 10 men, can turn out 80,000 complete 16-page papers per hour, all folded, counted and delivered ready for the carrier boys. It may be left to the reader to make some kind of estimate of the time that would be required to write the same matter out in longhand, to say nothing of the folding and counting.

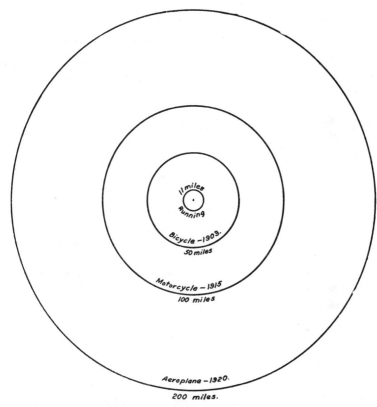

FIG. 70. THE EVOLUTION OF MAN'S MEANS OF TRANSPORTATION

Distance travelled in one hour by different means of conveyance

Artificial Effectors; Industrial Evolution. In the development of our artificial effectors, as with the receptors, the progress of evolution has been a rocket-like ascent. To take a simple and very moderate example, the evolution of means of personal transportation is exhibited diagrammatically in figure 70, which, is in essence a target of zones of operation of the kind referred to in Chapter XXV. The figures on which the diagram are based, some of which may very well have been superseded, are the following:

TABLE 33

Distance travelled in one hour by different modes of conveyance

MEANS OF TRANSPORTATION	MILES		YEAR
Man walking................................	8	G. E. Larner	1905
Man running................................	11	J. Bouin	1913
Man on bicycle............................	50	H. Caldwell	1903
Man on motorcycle........................	100	O. Walker	1915
Man on aeroplane.........................	200	About	1920

It has already been noted that the evolution of man's artificial aids to his effectors, by a process of "survival of the fittest" was recognized as early as 1757 by David Hume. We can now add, from the modern quantitative viewpoint, that this resemblance between the development of our inorganic accessories and that of organic populations extends also, in a number of instances, to the growth curves. So, for example, figure 71 exhibits the curve of growth of American Railways (United States).[10] It will be recognized as the typical S-shaped Verhulst-Pearl curve of growth.

Singular Effects of Industrial Evolution. Aside from its obvious result of greatly enhancing the effectiveness of the correlating apparatus, the modern development of its artificial aids has had certain other less obvious and in some respects rather singular effects. For the artificial portion of our correlating apparatus differs in several important respects from our native endowment. My microscope does not die with my body, but passes on to my heirs. There is thus a certain permanence about many portions at least of the artificial apparatus. And for that very reason the development of this artificial equipment of human society has a cumulative force that is unparalleled in ordinary organic evolution. This cumulative effect is most of all marked in the artificial aids to our elaborators.

[10] Figures for 1840 Sci. Am. Reference Book, 1914, p. 235; 1850 to 1910; World Almanac, 1921, p. 277; figure for 1918, Statistical Abstracts, 1920, p. 814. Compare also R. Pearl, The Population Problem, Geogr. Rev., October, 1922, p. 638.

The most singular feature of the artificial extension of our natural body is that they are shared in common by a number of individuals. When the sick man consults the physician, who, we will say, makes a microscopic examination, for example, the patient is virtually hiring a pair of high-power eyes.   When you drop a nickel into the telephone box, you are hiring the use of an ear to listen to your friend's voice five or ten miles distant.   When the workingman accepts a wage of forty dollars for his weekly labor, he is in fact paying to his em-

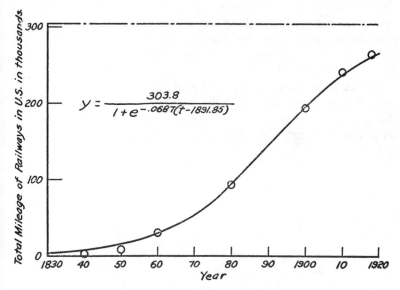

$$y = \frac{303.8}{1 + e^{-.0687(t-1891.85)}}$$

FIG. 71. GROWTH OF AMERICAN RAILWAYS

ployers an undetermined amount for the privilege of using his machines as artificial members to manufacture marketable wares.[11]

The modern development of artificial aids to our organs and faculties has exerted two opposing influences.

On the one hand it has in a most real way bound men together into one body: so very real and material is the bond that modern society might aptly be described as one huge multiple Siamese Twin.

On the other hand, since the control over certain portions of this common body is unevenly distributed among the separate individ-

[11] In certain branches of industry (e.g., shoemaking) a rental is actually paid by the worker for the use of machines.

uals, certain of them may be said in a measure to own parts of the bodies of others, holding them in a species of refined slavery; and though neither of the two parties concerned may be clearly conscious of the fact, it is often resented in a more or less vague way by the one less favored. Herein lies one source of much of the social unrest that has accompanied the development of modern industrialism. The more optimistic among us may entertain a hope that in time the unifying influence of our ever growing common body may outweigh the disruptive forces that ever and again manifest themselves too plainly for our comfort. That a species of "slavery," that is to say of ownership of one person's body by another or by others, should prevail, is in the last analysis an absolutely unavoidable situation, once we recognize that no sharp lines are drawn to separate the individual from his fellow; willy-nilly we must accept the fact. We may, however, seek to control the distribution of this ownership in the way most advantageous to the general welfare. That is the purpose of our property laws, such as they are and such as they will be.

CHAPTER XXVII

EXTENSION OF THE SENSUOUS WORLD PICTURE

> . . . . bodily eyes
> Were utterly forgotten, and what I saw
> Appeared like something in myself, a dream,
> A prospect of the mind."
>
> —*Wordsworth.*

The Elaborators. While the sense organs (receptors) are the prime agents in the formation of our world picture, they are not the sole agents that contribute. The further elaboration of this picture is largely the work of our mental faculties: *memory*, which stores impressions and makes our picture a chronological album or file rather than a single snapshot: and *imagination*,[1] which fills in those features of the landscape that are hidden from view by intervening obstacles. This process of filling in hidden features may be either arbitrary, as in the demonistic interpretation of nature current among savages and surviving among us in many superstitions, in the play of the child, and in the fancy of the poet; or, the process of filling in may be more or less rigorously directed by certain rules which long experience has taught us to be productive of a *realistic* picture, a picture which, when comparison with actuality becomes possible, is found to be "in accord with facts;" one that may safely be made a basis for *zweckmässig* action.[2] The realistic type of thinking, the kind which "works," has perhaps been evolved by a process of survival of the fittest from the other kind (termed autistic thinking).[3] The body of rules which realistic thinking follows constitutes the science of *logic*. The constructive exercise of the imagination within the limits prescribed by logic is what we call the process of *reasoning*. *When*

---

[1] It should be noted in passing that the word imagination itself means image-formation or depiction.

[2] It is deserving of emphasis that the function of imagination is not merely the conception of mythical creations, but also, and quite particularly, the presentation, to the mind, of realities. Hence imagination plays an important rôle in the exact Sciences.

[3] See F. L. Wells, Mental Adjustments, 1917, p. 46.

its premises are suitably chosen, for instance, on the basis of sense perceptions, the product is a contribution to a realistic world picture.

The Scientific World Picture: Coördinate Systems. The last refinement in world depiction is the scientific world picture. In the exact sciences this assumes the numerical form. So, for example, the position of a particular object in space is identified, in the simplest case (namely, if the object is sufficiently described as a *point*) by the statement of three numbers, the space coördinates of that point. The motion of the point is then described or represented (pictured) by a set of equations

$$x = f_1(t)$$
$$y = f_2(t)$$
$$z = f_3(t)$$

where x, y, z are the coördinates of the moving point at instant t, this last being also identified by means of a number.

Now an infinite number of equally appropriate pictures of this kind can be given for the motion of the point, for the coördinates x, y, z can be chosen in an infinite number of ways. They may be rectangular coördinates, or polar coördinates; their reference frames may be fixed on the earth, or on the sun, or in any other suitable manner. But each choice of a system of coördinates will furnish its own particular set of functions f; each picture will in this respect differ from every other such picture. Not a little of the success of the scientific investigator depends on his judgment in choosing a suitable system of coördinates, such as will furnish the simplest and most *convenient* picture, the most convenient functions f. So, for example, the motion of the planets is most simply described with reference to a frame of coördinates fixed to the sun, and not, for example, one fixed to the earth. The discovery of a particularly convenient reference frame, though in a sense it adds nothing to our knowledge of concrete facts, may nevertheless constitute one of the major events in the progress of human knowledge. For, such discoveries "make the Universe anew within the minds of men."[4]

The Ego as a Coördinate Reference Frame. It is a matter of very particular interest that the first rudiments of this numerical world picture, in terms of coördinates, is to be discerned in one of

W. C. Curtis, Science and Human Affairs, 1922, p. 186.

the most fundamental traits of the human mind, one of the most elementary, irresistible, naïve intuitions to which we are all subject, namely, the distinction between a self and an external world. If we wished to express mathematically the relations between the appearance upon the ground glass screen of a photographic camera, and the "external world" about the camera moving through that world, we should undoubtedly find that the simplest expression would be obtained in terms of a reference frame fixedly attached to the more solid features of the external world, and a second reference frame fixedly attached to the camera.

So we find it most convenient to express the infinite variety of sense perceptions (the totality of our world-picture) and the relations between them in terms of a *self* and an *external world*. This naïve intuitional view may be taken to be the rough unanalyzed raw material out of which, by a process of attenuation and abstraction, the scientific method has finally peeled the kernel of the two systems of coördinates—the one in which the external world is described, and the second, privately owned by the individual as it were, in which his world picture is recorded. The *self* thus appears as something of the nature of a (somewhat blurred) reference frame of coördinates, or rather, a set of several such frames, for the individual is quite accustomed to a multiple entry system of bookkeeping, in which the same object is entered both as *seen* and as *felt*, for example.[5]

The Ego Immaterial. This conception of the *self* as something of the nature of a system of coördinate reference frames will be found rather helpful in several connections. So, for example, it instantly makes clear why we cannot conceive of the self as something material.

[5] It is no doubt this double entry system that is largely responsible for our construct of an *external world* compounded of what are at bottom nothing more than complexes of sensations. As E. B. Holt remarks, "even two reflexes acting within one organism bring it about that the organism's behavior is no longer describable in terms of the immediate sensory stimulus, but as a function of objects and situations in the environment" (The Freudian Wish, 1916, p. 76). Those complexes of sensations which we refer or ascribe to *objects* are characterized by a greater or less degree of permanence. It is this permanence of association of certain sensations that induces us to postulate an object as their carrier. Such relative permanence lends a peculiar interest to the sensation complex, so that it has truly been said that the aim of science is the search for the *invariants* of Nature (E. W. Brown, Scientific Monthly, 1921, p. 408).

When I say that *I* (the *ego*) was at Grand Central Station yesterday at noon, it is true that from the nature of things a certain object which I speak of as *my* body, i.e., the body of the ego, was there at the time stated. But this is merely an implication, it is not a simple identification of the ego with the body, otherwise the phrase *my* body would be pointless. Once I become accustomed to think of the ego as something of the nature of a coördinate reference frame, the matter is perfectly clear. The thing that counts, in the depiction of the world in *me*, is the position of my *reference frame* relative to the external world. To say that *I* was at the station yesterday at noon is to say that this reference frame was thus situated. The body attached to this reference frame is in that sense *my* body. And clearly, the ego so defined is something immaterial.

Interpenetration of Egos. Then again, it is a notorious fact that the boundaries between the self and the external world cannot be clearly drawn.[6] The objective significance of this has already been noted, in the discussion of our artificial receptors and effectors, which are largely "shared" by a number of persons. The conception of the self indicated above makes it immediately clear that any attempt to establish boundaries between the self and the external world, or, for the matter of that, between two selves, is not only useless but meaningless. Coördinate reference frames have no boundaries, and freely interpenetrate each other, being merely immaterial aids to fix our ideas. So the overlapping of many egos in fields common to them, their essential unity with one another and with the universe, ceases to appear as a strange thought entertained by peculiarly minded people, and becomes an obvious truth.

[6] Compare F. B. Sumner, Scientific Monthly, 1922, vol. 14, p. 233. "The organism and the environment interpenetrate one another through and through—the distinction between them is only a matter of convenience." Also C. J. Keyser, Mathematical Philosophy, "How blind our familiar assumptions make us! Among the animals, man, at least, has long been wont to regard himself as a being quite apart from and not as part of the cosmos round about him. From this he has detached himself in thought, he has estranged and objectified the world, and lost the sense that he is of it. And this age-long habit and point of view, which has fashioned his life and controlled his thought, lending its characteristic mark and color to his whole philosophy and art and learning, is still maintained, partly because of its convenience, no doubt, and partly by force of inertia and sheer conservatism, in the very teeth of the strongest probabilities of biological science. Probably no other single hypothesis has less to recommend it, and yet no other so completely dominates the human mind."

Where is Mind?[7]   The question which has sometimes been raised, as to location of the mind, is also seen in a better light.   The thing that counts, in the affairs of the individual, is the relative position of the several reference frames, his own and that of the external world.   Where the adjustors, even their concrete, material apparatus, are located, is inconsequential.   We may be in doubt whether the expression "the location of the mind" has any meaning; but there can be no doubt that such location is of no practical consequence.   If it can in any sense be said that mind perceives the world of physical phenomena, this at least is certain, that it does so exclusively through the channels of our sense organs.   The mind looks into the physical world through the pupils of our eyes as the small boy watches the ball game through a knothole in the fence; the position of the knothole determines how much he shall see of the game, and in what perspective.   And the mind plays upon the physical events in our world as the organist plays upon the pipes of a modern organ, from a keyboard whose location is immaterial.   The question "Where is the mind?" or "Where is the ego?" might, if we rightly understood all the pertinent facts, appear as absurd as the tourist's request to be shown the equator.[7]   These terms are merely symbols of reference by the aid of which we describe relations between things.[8]

And quite in accord with this, we see in death not so much even as the dissolution of a system of coördinates, but merely the loss of their pragmatic significance:

[7] Compare Bertrand Russell, The Analysis of Mind, 1921, pp. 141–142. "The subject appears to be a logical fiction, like mathematical points and instants.   It is introduced, not because observation reveals it, but because it is linguistically convenient, and apparently demanded by grammar.   Nominal entities of this sort may or may not exist, but there is no good ground for assuming that they do.

"If we are to avoid a perfectly gratuitous assumption we must dispense with the subject as one of the actual ingredients of the world."

[8] From this point of view one is scarcely disposed to agree altogether with the proposition of Sir C. S. Sherrington in his Providential Address before the British Association at Hull (1922): "The *how* of the mind's connection with its bodily place seems still utterly enigma."   Nature, 1922, vol. 110, p. 351.   For a presentation of a point of view somewhat opposed to the one here set forth, the reader may be referred to an article *The Group Mind and the General Will* by J. Laird, in the Monist, 1923, p. 453.

And then so slight, so delicate is death
That there is but the end of a leaf's fall,
A moment of no consequence at all.
—*Mark Swann.*

Fundamental Premises and Implicit Assumptions. It has been noted in passing that the practical adequacy (Zweckmässigkeit) of the world picture formed by the aid of the elaborators depends on the judicious choice of the premises upon which the further elaboration is based. This, of course, is a very important condition. In so far as the premises are direct data of observation, the condition resolves itself into a demand for care and accuracy in taking observation, and for judgment in weighing evidence, especially where the data are presented in statistical form, with perhaps a considerable margin of doubt attached to each individual report.

But there are other less obvious cases, in which a scrutiny of the fundamental assumptions is needful and presents no little difficulty. For some of these premises relate, not to observational data but to conceptual structures peculiar to the world picture into which these data are fitted. Such premises are the fundamental postulates and axioms of geometry. By a stroke of genial intuition the founder of Euclidian geometry set down among his fundamental premises the parallel axiom, which states, in effect, that through a given point one and only one straight line can be drawn parallel to a given straight line. The true character of this fundamental premise remained hidden from the understanding of geometricians for many centuries. So difficult is it sometimes for us to become clearly aware of the nature of fundamental assumptions underlying our reasoning. Not till the end of the eighteenth century (Gauss 1792) was it realized that the parallel axiom, so far from being a "necessary truth," is essentially of the nature of an arbitrary assumption, and is only one of several alternatives each of which can claim equal legitimacy, each of which leads to a separate system of geometry. The Euclidian system was, until recently, the one in terms of which the world picture of the physicist found most convenient description. But in recent years, observations of electrons moving with velocities approaching that of light, and a number of other phenomena harmoniously comprehended in Einstein's theory of relatively, have given us a new world picture that finds its most convenient representation in terms of non-Euclidian geometries.

Difficulty of Shaking off Preconceived Premises. The examination, and, where need be, revision of our fundamental premises is a task of a wholly different order from that of rearing upon these premises a structure of logical argumentation. It is a task that often demands the efforts of giant intellects, of men of altogether unusual independence of thought. Most of us are held back by our preconceived, intuitive judgments, which, blindly entertained, blind us also against the recognition of possible alternatives. "The main reason for the painfully slow progress of the human race is to be found in the inability of the great mass of people to establish correctly the premises of an argument."[9] Nor is it only the great mass of the people, the average minds, that suffer from this ineptitude. Of Dr. Johnson, MacAuley remarks

How it chanced that one who reasoned on his premises so ably should assume his premises so foolishly is one of the great mysteries of human nature. The same inconsistency may be observed in the schoolmen of the middle ages. These writers show so much acuteness and force of mind that the modern reader is perpetually at a loss to comprehend how such minds came by such data.

As a matter of fact our innate perversity in this matter, our inveterate conservatism in all that concerns some of those "implicit and unrecognized assumptions out of which sophistry is bred," is not due to negative influences, to sloth of mind, alone. There is a strong positive misguiding influence at work also: The *wish* is father to the thought.[10]

The fact is, we are confronted here with a species of aberration of our adjustors; an aberration which our race must outgrow if it is to come into its full inheritance under the sway of evolution. For, as Simpson remarks, "the stabilization of our institutions rests ultimately upon our ability to know and to test assumptions,

[9] Elliott, Am. Math. Monthly, 1922, p. 331.
[10] There is, fortunately, a natural corrective for our inclination to allow likes and dislikes to influence our reason. This corrective is found in the instinct of *curiosity*, the faculty that impels men to seek the truth, even if it be unpalatable. In fact, a certain type of mind seems to take a particular satisfaction in digging up such otherwise displeasing revelations; the cynic and even the muckraker thus has his useful function. It is probably safe to say, too, that curiosity—a desire to know life in all its phases, to "experience reality"—is fundamentally the motive that impels some individuals to taste of the less savory phases of life.

and upon a willingness to revise them without partizanship, or bitterness, or distress."[11]

One direction in which we may be called upon to make such a revision is our conception of the self or ego, along the lines already indicated. The old intuitive conception of the self, which narrows it down and fences it off rigorously from the rest of the world, may have to give place to a broader conception. This may require the breaking through of inhibitions that obstruct our view and prevent us from gaining a full and lively realization of our essential unity with the universe; it may involve in some degree a retracing of our steps in past evolution; a retrenchment of our overdeveloped self-consciousness, to make room for a more comprehensive world-consciousness.

THE COMMUNICATORS

Aside from the ordinary receptors and elaborators, there is another avenue, a highly specialized type of receptors, by which the world picture acquires further detail and extension, namely by communication from one individual to another. How far the faculty of such communication may be developed in species other than our own is today an open question; nor is this of much consequence for us here, as we are concerned with principles rather than with concrete examples, and a single indubitable instance, such as we have in ourselves, suffices for the establishment and exemplification of the principle.

Orthogenesis in Human Evolution. In the human species the communication of information from one to another takes place chiefly through speech, tradition and carved, written or printed records. The incalculable significance of these aids to the individual's elaboration of his world-picture needs no emphasis. In a recent number of *Nature* there appeared Professor Bohr's address on the structure of the atom, delivered on the occasion of the award to him of the Nobel prize for 1922. In this historical survey of the development of his theory he mentions nearly fifty names of investigators who directly or indirectly contributed to this part of our world-picture. A person intelligently reading this lecture, making the picture part of his own mental stock-in-trade, is thus virtually

[11] Simpson, Am. Math. Monthly, 1922, p. 331.

endowed with fifty pairs of eyes and hands, and has the benefit of the workings of fifty brains, for the most part master brains of the first rank, for the list includes such names as, Faraday, Maxwell, J. J. Thomson, Rutherford, Hertz, Lorentz, Planck, Einstein, to mention only a few. It is this thought-transmitting propensity of the human species, more than any other, that gives it a superlative lead over all the other creatures of the globe.[12] Man is the only animal who in any considerable measure bequeaths to his descendants the accumulated wisdom of past generations. Evolution in this case proceeds not merely by the slow process of selection, but is immensely hastened by the cumulative and continuous growth of a body of knowledge exempt from those laws of mortality which set a term to the life of the individual. Such evolution by a process not directly dependent upon (although subject to) selection is what biologists have termed *orthogenesis*—the direct genesis of a trait or species by the pursuit of an inherent trend or bias, irrespective of selective influences. Such orthogenesis (of the functional, not the physiological kind noted in Chapter XXII) is exhibited not only in the cumulative effect of tradition and printed records, but even more strikingly in the basic process itself by which the scientific world picture is developed. This development has not been wholly an evolution by selection, by survival of the fittest, at least not if we take the word survival in its literal sense. On the contrary, this is perhaps the clearest example extant of evolution by orthogenesis, by the unfolding of an inherent trend independently of any selecting influences. Our Galileos, our Newtons, our Thomsons, our Einsteins, have not been singled out by a process of lethal selection from among others less fit to survive. The process by which viable, pragmatically competent systems of thought (or world-depiction) are evolved is quite other than this. The Copernican system has survived over the Ptolemaic, not because the originators and the supporters of the former were better adapted to life under the then existing conditions— rather the reverse was true. It is not even a mere principle of economy of thought that gave victory to the Copernican system. The decisive factor

[12] The importance of the accumulation of human knowledge through tradition, permanent records, and lasting technical installations has been emphasized by A. Korzibski (Manhood of Humanity, Dutton, 1921) to whose central thesis—the existence of a fundamental hiatus between man and the rest of creation—I cannot, however, subscribe.

was that the comparative simplicity of the Copernican system eased the further advance of knowledge, which had been very effectively checked by the intricacies of the epicycles. It is not so much that the human mind has a bias for simplicity—though that may be true —as that, with its finite limitations, the mind progresses faster and farther as soon as a simpler system is substituted in place of a more complicated, even when both systems are otherwise competent truly to represent facts.

Orthogenesis does not, of course, *suspend* selection. Of two species, that one will most survive, whose orthogenesis, if any, leads it in a favorable direction. Presumably, destructive orthogenesis may occur, as well as constructive. Indeed, it has been suggested that some of the extinct monster species were thus drawn to their doom by an orthogenesis, controlled perhaps by endocrine glands, that swelled their dimensions beyond all bounds of propriety. What is most significant is that orthogenesis, whether constructive or destructive, must accelerate the pace of evolution. No more telling demonstration of this could be asked than the prodigious advance made by man in recent centuries and decades, advances traceable directly to the orthogenetic character of the evolution of his mental furniture. The provocative agent in this orthogenesis is *curiosity*, the faculty that anticipates needs, that solves problems before they become burning issues; that inspires research in pure science, and throws in for good measure practical applications, as gifts that are often only too truly gratuitous. And coupled with this curiosity, a native impulse that induces men to impart their findings to others.

Meanwhile orthogenesis continues.[13] Man has travelled far, from the crude intuitive recognition of the ego and the non-ego, the first dim realization of a depiction of one system of coördinates upon another; to our latest conception of the part played by coördinate reference frames in our intercourse with nature. The most modern world-picture, as drawn for us by Einstein and his followers, seems to outstrip, for the time being, not only our needs, but our immediate opportunities for practical application. But that is the virtue of orthogenesis.

[13] For a somewhat detailed presentation of the case of orthogenesis in man see the author's article *Biassed Evolution* in Harper's Magazine, May, 1924.

CHAPTER XXVIII

THE ADJUSTORS

Was wir Willen nennen ist nichts anderes als die Gesammtheit der teilweise bewussten und mit Voraussicht des Erfolges verbundenen Bedingungen einer Bewegung. . . . . In der bewussten Willenshandlung fallen Ursache und Zweck Zusammen.—*E. Mach.*

From the nature of things the adjustors are more recondite, both in their material substance and in their operation, than either the receptors or the effectors. It has already been remarked that the location of the adjustors is inconsequential; partly for this reason, and partly because their concrete material apparatus does not need to be external (as must be that of the receptors and effectors), we have at most a very imperfect consciousness of the location of the adjustors. It is chiefly from hearsay that the man in the street associates the brain with mental processes.

It is, then, not greatly surprising, that the functioning of the adjustors should be shrouded in a good deal of mystery, which even introspection into our own experience does not by any means dispel. If unsatisfied curiosity is the *fons et origo* of human interest, such interest should certainly not be lacking in this phase of our present enquiry.

Mechanistic and Teleological Interpretation of Adjustors. We have seen, from the example of a simple toy, that typical and fully competent adjustors can very well be provided in and by purely mechanical structures. In the toy beetle *anticipatory* correlation between the reaction of the beetle and untoward variations of the environment is established as follows: The beetle is progressing along the straight line AB, (see fig. 72). Its law of motion is that of uniform progression along this straight line. Suppose a scale of centimeters is laid along AB. Successively higher scale divisions along A B are reached at successively later intervals. In fact, this scale, with the beetle moving along it (at constant velocity, we may suppose, to simplify the argument) constitutes a clock. If at the time $t = 0$ the driving wheel of the beetle is at the zero mark, scale divisions to the left correspond to and represent past instants, and those to the right represent future instants. Suppose the antenna is 5 divisions long, and that the table edge is at division mark 15. If for any reason the adjustor apparatus failed to function, at time $t = 15$ the driving wheel of the beetle *would* pass the table edge and fall over. When the adjustor apparatus *is* functioning, five time units in anticipation of the threatened catastrophe the antenna "senses" the danger, and the creature turns aside into the path of safety. Note that this anticipatory reaction depends upon the *correspondence* between *points forward* upon the line of advance, and *future instants* of time. A supposititious future, a *future that may be*, is depicted, instant by instant, by successive points in the line of advance of the beetle on the *supposition that its law of motion*

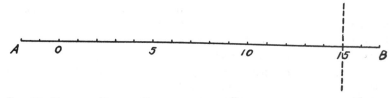

FIG. 72. HOW THE FUTURE ENTERS INTO THE DETERMINATION OF THE MOTION OF THE WALKING MECHANICAL BEETLE, THUS IMITATING PURPOSIVE ACTION (TELEOLOGY).

continues unchanged. The behavior of the beetle is determined in terms of this depiction of a supposititious future.[1]

[1] This conception of a *future that may be* is found both in A. N. Whitehead, Principles of Natural Knowledge, and also in E. Mach's Analyse der Empfindungen (1903, p. 78). The expression seems to raise a question as to just what meaning may justly be ascribed to it in a determinate universe. One admissible meaning is indicated in the text above: The future that *may be* is that computed by extrapolation according to a law of motion that in fact does not hold up to the instant under consideration. Another construction that suggests itself is that the future that *may be* is one compatible with certain differential equations, but not necessarily with the integration constants.

The toy beetle shows very clearly how a future that *may be* can, seemingly, influence the course of events. It is interesting to note that there is another circumstance which also is competent to explain the apparent influence of this fictitious future upon the present course of events. Mach points out, with especial reference to the seemingly miraculous foresight displayed by certain

The depiction in this case is plainly mechanical or geometric. We, as living, conscious organisms, in certain circumstances exhibit a precisely analogous behavior; our action is determined by a picture (psychic in this case) of the future that we seek to avoid or to attain.[2] "In human purpose the result to be attained is first pictured in consciousness, and the thinker then proceeds by a series of acts to fulfill his preconceived aim." The law of "preconceiving" is precisely the same in both cases, at any rate in the simple case in which the reaction is one of avoidance of an unfavorable condition. An image of the future of the system is constructed *on the supposition that the mechanism or organism does not interfere*. This is the future that *may* be. Interference, financed from the fund of free energy, then takes place accordingly, thus modifying the course of events and determining the future that *will* be.

Little doubt enters our mind in construing the course of events in these two cases. We are directly conscious of our own volition (whatever its precise physical significance may be.) We hesitate not at all in describing our action as purposive, as directed to and determined by an end, by a *final cause*. As to the tin beetle, we have dissected him and fully understand his mechanism. We would think it foolish, with our peep behind the scenes, to impute to him volition or purpose; we describe his action as mechanical, as fully determined by an *efficient* cause.

The Doubtful Cases. But what shall we do when confronted with a case that falls into neither of these categories? An amoeba, for example? We cannot enter the amoeba in spirit and become parties to its conscious experience; we do not even know whether it has any such experience. On the other hand its mechanism is not completely known to us. To class it among purposive, teleological beings so long as we are ignorant of its working, and to be prepared

---

instinctive actions, that the life process is essentially periodic in character, repeated over and over in successive generations, and that it may not be so much the future of individual A that influences its action, as the past of its progenitors A', A'', . . . who were placed in similar circumstances on earlier occasions. "Es ist dann nicht eine *mögliche* Zukunft die wirken *könnte*, sondern eine unzählige Mal dagewesene Vergangenheit, die gewiss *gewirkt hat*."

[2] H. C. Warren, Journal of Philos. Psych. and Sci. Method, 1916, vol. 13, p. 5.

to reclassify it among "purely mechanical" structures[3] as soon as we come to understand its physical operation, seems hardly a very commendable way to marshal our mental stock-in-trade. There is here involved something of those mysteries to which reference has

---

[3] "Die Vitalisten begehen nun den Fehler, die Zielstrebigheit dort zu leugnen, wo ihre Ursache durch physikalische Gesetze erklärbar ist, da sie eben diese Zielstrebigkeit als mit den physikalischen Gesetzen nicht zusammenhängend betrachten." (C. Doelter, Aus dem Grenzgebiete des Organischen und Anorganischen, 1906, p. 13.) It is a singular fact possessing a certain psychological interest, that as soon as we understand the *modus operandi* of a teleological mechanism we are disposed to reject its interpretation in terms of "final causes." Why this preference for the mechanistic view? There is another closely analogous case. So long as we remain in ignorance of the precise working of our nervous system in the phenomenon of memory, we are forced to contemplate this faculty as being perhaps wholly psychic in character. To quote Bertrand Russell (Analysis of Mind, 1921, p. 92), "I am inclined to . . . . hold that past experience only affects present behavior through modifications of physiological structure. But the evidence seems so far from conclusive that I do not think we ought to reject entirely the possibility that mnemic causation may be the ultimate explanation of mnemic phenomena." Here also we feel that just as soon as a physical basis of memory were made manifest, we should discard the hypothesis of a purely psychic *mneme*. A certain light is perhaps thrown on this curious psychological bias when we consider the matter from the point of view of the equations of motion of a mechanical system. We noted in Chapter IV (pp. 47, 48) that conceivably the equations representing the course of events might contain a lag or a lead, that is to say, the motion at time t might, for example, depend explicitly upon the condition of the system at time $(t - a)$ or perhaps at time $(t + b)$, or both. We also noted in passing that something of this sort seems actually to be the case in systems comprising living organisms, since the reaction of these upon their environment is a function of their previous history through the intervention of memory, and a function of the future through the intervention of volition. But we also noted particularly that the appearance of a lag or lead in the equations might be spurious. So for example the rate of incidence of new malaria cases today may be expressed as a function of the number of persons bitten by infected mosquitoes nine days ago (period of incubation). But this is merely a short way of describing the state of these persons today, so that the equation could also be written without the lag term. Why do we, in mechanical systems, give preference to an equation free from a lag term, whenever such can be framed? The first thought that suggests itself, perhaps, is that we do this from a bias for simplicity. But this is probably not the true explanation. More likely we make this selection because there is something arbitrary about the lag term. It does not give a unique representation of the process. The differential equation free from a lag or lead, on the contrary, is more free from arbitrary features, and is presumably in some sense unique.

been made. The mystery may be in part of our own making. The difficulty in answering a question sometimes arises from the fact that the question has been badly put. Certainly no harm can come from an effort to make a survey of some of the relevant facts and their relations. To such a survey we shall proceed forthwith. Here it may be well to summarize briefly three cardinal points in our observations so far:

1. Mechanisms teleological in their operation can be constructed, which we would not in any ordinary sense of the word describe as conscious.

2. The active types of teleological mechanisms in nature (animals) impress us as being in some sense conscious, though in the case of the lower rungs on the scale we feel very doubtful as to just what meaning to assign to this statement.

3. In our own selves we *feel* that consciousness (volition) plays a dominant rôle in the teleological operation of our bodies, and, in particular, in the operation of the adjustors.

Adaptive Adjustment of Tastes. In all that has been said so far the individualistic character of tastes has been emphasized. A man's likes and dislikes are essentially his own personal affair. As Pareto[4] remarks, if a man dislikes spinach, it is useless trying to prove to him, as one would demonstrate a proposition in geometry, that spinach tastes good. Judgments of this kind are typically not of that class in which "universal assent" can be attained, the class with which the worker in physical science is mainly concerned.[5]

Now this does *not* mean, as might perhaps at first sight appear, that tastes of different individuals are wholly random collections of likes and dislikes, dealt out purely haphazard, like the cards from a well shuffled pack. However erratic human desires may appear in detail, in the gross they display a species of uniformity, of law, of constancy; a fact recognized long ago by Adam Smith, who "considered a science of economics possible because of a few outstanding traits of man which guaranteed self-preservation, while also promoting the welfare of society at large." [6] The same constancy in the

---

[4] Manuel d'Économie Politique, 1909, p. 62.

[5] Compare N. Campbell, The Elements of Physics, J. W. N. Sullivan, Aspects of Science, 1923, p. 30.

[6] O. F. Boucke, Am. Ec. Review, 1922, p. 599.

average performance (symptomatic of desires) of men was again noted by Quetelet, and more particularly by Herbert Spencer,[7] who was presumably the first to recognize the full significance, in the evolution of the race, of that "adjustment of feelings to actions" which has made "pains . . . . the correlatives of actions injurious to the organism, and pleasures . . . . the correlatives of actions conducive to its welfare." This, as Spencer points out, is the inevitable outcome of natural selection, since "there must ever have been, other things equal, the most numerous and long-continued survivals among those races in which these adjustments of feelings to actions were the best, tending ever to bring about *perfect adjustment.*"

Genuine Utility for Social Service. And what is the "perfect adjustment?" A hint of the quantitative method of approach to this question has been given in Chapter XXV. The argument there set forth suggests something of the nature of an absolute standard of value, to which actual standards established in the community must approach, however imperfectly. Without attempting any quantitative definition, or, indeed, any definition at all, such an absolute standard has been directly or implicitly mooted by many. Irving Fisher[8] thus speaks of a *genuine utility for social service*, a concept which is evidently intended to be purified from the caprice of the individual. The question is, remarks T. N. Carver,[9] "not what men are actually like, but what men fit best into the cosmos. What are the earmarks of a good man, that is, of a man who adds strength to the community or nation? It is not enough if we study the variations of human institutions, habits, morals, etc. We want to know what institutions, habits and moral systems work well, what kind of a nation or social organization fits into the cosmos and grows strong under the conditions of the Universe. Similarly, as to individual motives, it is not simply a question as to what motives actually govern human behavior, though it is important that we should know that. It is of equal importance that we know what motives or combinations of motives work well." Just as man has

---

[7] Herbert Spencer, Principles of Psychology, section 124; Data of Ethics. section 34.

[8] Irving Fisher, Am. Econ. Review, June, 1918, vol. 8.

[9] T. N. Carver, Qu. Jour. Econ., November, 1918, p. 197.

learned, in the progress of ages, to *think logically*, to think in accord with reality, so he must yet learn to *will rightly*, that is, in harmony with Nature's scheme. We have here a thought that seems fundamental for a natural system of ethics. I will not follow it up further at this point, but shall take occasion to return to it in the closing chapter.

CHAPTER XXIX

CONSCIOUSNESS

Vous connaissez, n'est-ce pas, cette jolie griserie de l'âme? On ne pense pas, on ne rêve pas non plus. Tout votre être vous échappe, s'envole, s'éparpille. On est la mouette qui plonge, la poussière d'écume qui flotte au soleil entre deux vagues, la fumée blanche de ce paquetbot qui s'éloigne, ce petit corailleur a voile rouge, cette perle d'eau, ce flocon de brume, tout excepté soi même.
—*Alphonse Daudet.*

Intimately involved, both in the process of world depiction, and in the operation of the adjustors, as we know them in ourselves, is the phenomenon of *consciousness*. In preceding pages this has been taken for granted. But our study would be incomplete indeed if we did not give some separate consideration to a phenomenon that is of so superlative importance in the shaping of the world's events.

Consciousness is a natural phenomenon which we know directly in ourselves, and whose existence we infer in others from their behavior in view of its greater or less resemblance, in *type*, to ours.

Relation of Consciousness to Physical Conditions. What mainly interests us here, regarding this phenomenon, is its *relation* to *physical processes* and structures.

These relations are presented to us in two aspects, and we may accordingly distinguish them as (1) conditional, and (2) operative relations; that is to say, first relations between consciousness and the physical conditions necessary for its manifestation; and second, relations between consciousness and physical events that seem to be dependent upon consciousness for their occurrence, in the operation of the correlating apparatus. The enquiry into these latter relations must cover (*a*) the function of consciousness in directing the course of events, and (*b*) the origin of conscious mechanism or apparatus which so directs that course; the reasons that can be assigned, if any, why organic evolution should have seized upon consciousness as a tool to secure adaptive (zweckmässig) behavior in the organism.

CONDITIONAL RELATIONS

It is frequently pointed out with critical emphasis that mechanistic attempts to *explain* consciousness are philosophically unsound.

Such strictures are based upon a misconception of the function of science, mechanistic or other. Science does not *explain* anything, consciousness occupies in *this* respect a position in no wise peculiar. Science does not *explain* electricity, for example. Science is less pretentious. All that falls within its mission is to observe phenomena and to describe them and the *relations between them.* It is true that in loose parlance such statements are commonly made as: The inertia of matter is *explained* by the electron theory. But all this means is that certain *relations* have been *established* between the properties of an electric charge, and those of a mass of gross "matter;" that the laws of motion of matter can be *comprehended* in the laws of motion of an electron. If *explanation* means the making *comprehensible* in this sense, then this is explanation. But who should say that the attempt to *establish relations* between consciousness and other phenomena is philosophically unsound? One would be disposed to retaliate by questioning the soundness of his philosophy.

Quite on the contrary, the study of the relations between consciousness and other phenomena is not only legitimate, but altogether alluring and full of promise.

Here, however, a difficulty confronts us at the outset. Strictly speaking, the only consciousness I can ever know (unless altogether revolutionary developments in our sources of knowledge should follow) is my own. This seems to impose most serious restrictions upon the investigations.

A Fundamental Hypothesis Admitted. However, there is general assent that, in this study, we shall admit the fundamental hypothesis that the consciousness of my fellowmen exists and is sufficiently like my own to constitute a proper subject for study as a type phenomenon. We even go farther, and quite willingly admit the propriety of investigations regarding the consciousness of dogs, cats, apes, mice, sparrows, and so forth, as manifested by their behavior. All this is well enough, until some one begins to ask impertinent questions. Just where are we to stop in hypothecating consciousness? And what do you mean by saying that Jones's consciousness is *like* Smith's? or *like* that of a dog? or of an amoeba? These questions are embarrassing. But so long as we deal with restricted material and restricted enquiries regarding the relations between consciousness and other phenomena, we find in practice we can ignore these fine points. And then certain basic propositions find at least provisional acceptance. The first of these we may enunciate as follows:

Consciousness is Closely Bound Up with Life Processes and Structures. The statement hardly requires exemplification. Starve a man, and he becomes unconscious. The same may happen after a blow on the head, and so on.

Unfortunately, however, our proposition is not so proof against criticism as it appears. For it is admitted that we observe consciousness only by its manifestations similar to those which we know directly in ourselves. The inference that consciousness is absent in non-living matter reminds one somewhat of the assumption commonly made by ignorant persons that insects or similar voiceless creatures feel no pain. Since non-living matter lacks the familiar means of manifesting any consciousness which it might possess, it is evidently not permissible to base, upon the absence of such familiar manifestation, any conclusion as to the absence of consciousness. We are really arguing in a circle: First we agree to postulate consciousness where certain manifestations are observed. Then we turn around and say that the presense of these manifestations is characteristic of consciousness, and their absence of its absence.

The truth is, all we can state with any degree of confidence is that, if non-living matter possesses any kind of consciousness, this must be of a character so radically different from our own as wholly to transcend our powers of imagination. This may appear at first sight a rather pointless observation. But it must be remembered that the statement holds true with almost equal force with regard to *living* matter, in the case of such elementary forms as *amoeba,* for example. The importance of such reflections as this is that it draws our attention to the significance of *forms* or *modes* of consciousness. The general scheme of nature is more readily understood if we contemplate the several material objects as gifted with graded modes of consciousness, than if we suppose them sharply divided into conscious and unconscious. It is true that this point of view commits us to admit the existence of modes of consciousness utterly inaccessible to human experience. But this admission is not as damaging as it may appear, for, in a restricted measure at least, we are forced to make it in any case as soon as we hypothecate consciousness in a dog or a flea, for example.

Allowing, however, for these finer distinctions, the statement may stand that consciousness of the character familiar to us in ourselves, or of a character approaching to this, is closely bound up with life processes, in the way indicated.

Consciousness Dependent on Metabolism. The Personal Element.
This suggests that the continued conscious state of matter requires
constant *excitation* by the metabolic processes, somewhat as the continued maintenance of a magnetic field in the neighborhood of a
conductor requires constant excitation by the passage of a current.
And since metabolism is essentially a state of chemical flux, or chemical reaction *in progress*, one is led to suspect that the conscious state
may be in some way correlated to that transitional state through
which matter must pass on its way from one stable molecular combination to another[1]—a state regarding which our knowledge today is
extremely fragmentary. Almost the only direct evidence we have of
matter actually in that state is the observation by Sir J. J. Thomson
and by F. W. Aston of such molecular débris as CH_3 and the like, by
a method capable of detecting these fugaceous aggregations of atoms
even though their life period be only a few millionths of a second.
Meanwhile it must be borne in mind that in the case of the highly
complex and bulky molecules characteristic of organic matter, the
"intermediate" state between two compounds may be something
more lasting. It is even conceivable that "open" molecules may, in
this realm of chemistry, be the more stable configuration; the molecules may perhaps be more or less in a state of oscillation, in a species
of tautomerism, between two "closed" compounds. This would,
in a way, harmonize with the continuity of consciousness, as known
to us, if consciousness be indeed typically associated with the "open"
state of molecules. On the other hand it may give us at least some
distant idea of the meaning of consciousness as applied to so-called
non-living inorganic matter. Such consciousness as may here occur
would be, it seems, of the nature of flashes of almost infinitesimally
short duration. If this conception appears fantastic, it must be borne
in mind that brevity of time is altogether a relative concept; by geological standards human life itself is merely a flash of lightning in the
eternal darkness; and though to most of us the altogether impersonal
species of consciousness which seems to be here implied must appear
inconceivable, those who have observantly come through the experience of syncope may not find the thought so unreasonable.

Pendant la syncope, dit un auteur qui a pu étudieur sur lui même ce phénomène, c'est le néant psychique absolu, l'absence de toute conscience, puis on

---

[1] Compare Schönbein, Jl. f. prakt. Chemie, vol. 40, p. 152.

commence à avoir un sentiment vague, illimité, infini, un sentiment d'existence générale sans ancune délimitation, sans la moindre trace de distinction
entre le moi et le non moi; on est alors une partie organique de la nature ayant
conscience du fait de son existence, mais n'en ayant aucune du fait de son
unité organique; on a, en deux mots, une conscience impersonelle. . . .
On a des sensations stupides, si je puis m'exprimer ainsi, c'est à dire, des
sensations qui, justement parcequ'elles restent isolées, ne peuvent pas être
connues, mais seulement senties.[2]

In an entirely normal state, too, certain persons seem to have
realized the experience of a species of impersonal consciousness. An
example of this is to be seen in the quotation from Daudet's *Lettres de
mon Moulin* that has been placed at the head of this chapter.[3] Thus
the phenomenon of the *ego* is neither as fundamental nor as simple
as it may appear to the naïve observer. The occurrence of primitive
consciousness of a kind, which does not recognize an ego, is not only
possible, for ought we know, but should be regarded as decidedly
probable. It may indeed, be argued with much plausibility (as we
have already had occasion to note) that the *ego* is a mere artifice, an
aid to thought (just as a frame of rectangular coördinates is a mere
figment, convenient for the purpose of defining the position and configuration of geometrical structures), but has no objective existence,
and forms no indispensable element of the more general phenomenon
of consciousness.

The separation of "chemical" processes from other physical processes is almost certainly merely a matter of convenience. If, then
we tentatively associate consciousness with certain states of chemical
strain in molecules, we are forced to contemplate the possible extension
of our conception to matter under physical strain generally. Space
does not permit us to follow up in detail the implications of such a
point of view. It must suffice to indicate that it leads us to question

[2] Herzen, Le cerveau et l'activité cérébrale, 1887, p. 236; quoted by Janet,
L'automatisme psychologique, 1889, p. 43.

[3] A very similar thought is expressed by Theodor Dreiser in *Proteus* (American Mercury, 1924, vol. 1, p. 9):

> "And I am the birds flying in the air over the river,
>
> . . . .
> The sun, the shade,
> The warmth, the grass,
> And myself
> And not myself
> Dreaming in the grass."

whether a much frowned upon species of anthropomorphism may not, after all, be in some sense legitimate. When we say that a soap bubble, for example, *tends* to contract under surface tension, or perhaps when we use even less guarded language and say that it is *trying* to contract, our terms are commonly thought reprehensible as being more picturesque than scientific. Yet we ought to be prepared for the conception that the straining of the bubble to contract may not be so fundamentally different a thing from the straining of an amoeba to engulf a food particle, or the straining of a Newton to assimilate a new conception or to solve a problem in philosophy. The two phenomena may be far separated, indeed, upon the scale of evolution, yet they may be two rungs upon the same scale.

CHAPTER XXX

THE FUNCTION OF CONSCIOUSNESS

In the last chapter we have considered some of the reflections that suggest themselves in connection with the first fundamental proposition, namely that consciousness, as we know it in ourselves, is closely bound up with life processes and structures.

A second basic proposition regarding consciousness, which will find at least provisional acceptance, is that consciousness, as known to ourselves, is of variable content, and that its *content is a function*[1] *of our past and present bodily states*. The form of the functional relation[2] is in part known, but only in part. It is, of course, by virtue of this functional relation that consciousness plays a part in the receptor-adjustor-effector apparatus.

This leads us to the second aspect of the relation between consciousness and physical structures and events, namely, the function which consciousness fulfills in the organism, and the problem as to how it has come about that living organisms have appropriated to themselves, in the course of evolution, the property of consciousness, or, to be more precise, of that particular type of consciousness which is characteristic of them.

OPERATIVE RELATIONS

One function of consciousness in the operation of the receptor-adjustor-effector apparatus has already been considered, namely the part which it plays in elaborating further the crude data for the world-picture supplied by the special senses.

But consciousness plays an equally fundamental rôle in the operation of the adjustors. It is quite evident that no amount of cold, intellectual information, pure and simple, can in itself ever

---

[1] In the mathematical sense.

[2] For a discussion of the metaphysical aspect of this functional relation the reader must be referred to the special literature. Attention is particularly directed to a paper by L. T. Troland in the Jour. Washington Academy, 1922, vol. 12, p. 141. See also H. C. Warren, Jour. Phil. Psych. and Sci. Method, pp. 20-21, footnote.

determine an action. If I am standing at a street crossing, and my senses inform me that, should I start to walk across at this moment, I should be killed by a passing car, this information in itself can have no effect one way or the other upon my action. In addition to the cold knowledge, there must be something of the nature of *motive*, which gives me an interest, on the one hand in the act of crossing (as for example to reach the restaurant across the street and satisfy my hunger), and on the other in avoiding collision with with the street car (the anticipatory image in my mind, of the suffering which this would cause).

In the lower organisms motivation appears to us almost wholly mechanical and fatalistic. The tropisms of a moth apparently draw it toward a light with the same mechanical inevitableness as the gears of the toy beetle constrain it to follow the table edge. The opposite extreme, the highest refinement and complexity in motivation, we observe in our own selves.

In human purpose the result to be attained is first pictured in consciousness, and the thinker then proceeds by a series of acts to fulfill his preconceived aim. . . . . The typical purposive experience consists in a thought of some future occurrence followed by a series of actions which culminate in the very situation which the original idea represented.[3]

But what determines "the result to be attained," which is thus pictured in the consciousness? The matter has been well expressed by Veblen in a passage which at the same time brings out clearly the relation of the purely intellectual functions of consciousness to the emotional (motivating) functions:

The ends of life, the purposes to be achieved, are assigned by man's instinctive proclivities; but the ways and means of accomplishing those things which the instinctive proclivities make worth while are a matter of intelligence. . . . . Men take thought, but the human spirit, that is to say, the racial endowment of instinctive proclivities, decides what they shall take thought of, and how, and to what effect.

---

[3] H. C. Warren, Jour. Phil. Psych. and Scientific Method, 1916, vol. 13, p. 5. Compare also F. L. Wells, Mental Adjustments, 1917, p. 11. "The free imagination of wished-for things results well for the mind through painting in more glowing colors the excellence of what is wished for, and firing the ambition to strive for it more intensely." For a rather different viewpoint see B. Russell, Analysis of Mind, 1921, pp. 75–76.

Dynamic Psychology; Instinctive Drives to Action. Thus, in our analysis of the operation of the correlating apparatus, we are led to a consideration of the fundamental instincts that furnish the driving power behind the activities of the organism. The study of these instincts has been organized into a definite branch— Dynamic Psychology— of which we can here note only a few of the outstanding features. We are treading upon ground not altogether cleared, at this date, from controversial entanglements.

Certain psychologists, notably Freud and his followers, have taken the view that the really fundamental drives for action can be reduced to a very few, such as hunger, the sex call, and the gregarious instinct.[4] From these the less elementary motives are, according to this school, *derived* by a process of "sublimation." In contrast with this R. S. Woodworth regards as separate and independent sources of action those drives which are operative in the course of creative activities:

The various creative proclivities which (Freud) refers to the redirected energy of the sex instinct as their sole driving force, have in Professor Woodworth's opinion driving forces of their own. Of sublimation he holds that when an intellectual interest, say, is made to supplant a sex impulse, the latter is not drawn into service, but resisted.[5]

Individual Traits. Instinct of Workmanship and Self-Expression. We may well leave it to the psychologists to settle their

---

[4] McDougall in his *Introduction to Social Psychology*, lists twelve "simple instincts" as follows:

INSTINCT	CORRESPONDING AFFECT	INSTINCT	CORRESPONDING AFFECT
Flight....................	Fear	Parenthood............	Tenderness
Pugnacity................	Anger	Reproduction..........	Sex
Repulsion................	Disgust	Feeding.	(Appetite)
Curiosity................	Wonder	Gregariousness........	
Self-assertion............		Acquisition............	
Self-abasement..........		Construction..........	

Such lists as this seem rather arbitrary, and in some degree dependent on the whim of their author. Compare for example F. W. Taussig, Inventors and Money-Makers, 1915, p. 7; Irving Fisher, The Survey, March, 1919, p. 937.

[5] M. F. Washburn reviewing Woodworth's *Dynamic Psychology*, 1918, in Science, 1918, vol. 48, p. 373.

difference of opinion in this field. For our purposes it is enough to know that these drives to action are operative, that some ends to men are "instinctively worth while." And if we ask: What are those ends that are instinctively worth while,—we find that a mere list of primitive instincts is at most only a very inadequate answer to our question. In their broad fundamental instincts men are, indeed, essentially alike. But that adjustment of the relative intensity of their several instinctive proclivities, which finds its material expression in the behavior-schedule, in the coefficients λ (Chapter XXV) is capable of infinite variation. What is "worth while" is after all a matter of *taste*, and *de gustibus non est disputandum*—"people of radically different temperaments cannot come to any understanding by intellectual means,"[6] their vain efforts to do so lead only to mutual repugnance, for "differences of taste produce greater exasperation than differences on points of Science."[7] This divergence of tastes among men, responsible as we must no doubt hold it for many bitter feuds between individuals and between nations, is not without its useful aspect. In the present state of the human race, with its divisions of labor and its specialization, there is room for all sorts and conditions of men, and this statement applies not only as regards their abilities, but also, and perhaps more particularly, as regards the channels into which each seeks by preference to divert the stream of his energies, the sphere in which he most willingly applies his abilities. Much could be said in support of the proposition that differences in temperament, rather than differences in intellectual endowment, determine the place that each man is fitted to occupy in the social scheme. For, as Young has said, "With the talents of an angel, a man may be a fool." It is not enough to *be able*, there must be a strong impulse *to do*. "Not only to know, but according to thy knowledge to do, is thy vocation," says Fichte. A study of motivation in exceptional men, men of genius, is both instructive and inspiring. The dominat-

---

[6] Rosa Mayreder, quoted in the The Lancet 1913, p. 1006. Compare also William James, On a Certain Blindness in Human Beings.

[7] MacAuley, Critical Essays, p. 501. The contrast has been drawn particularly between introverts and extroverts "who find it so difficult to understand each other, and so easy to despise." Compare also Nature, July 21, 1923, p. 88: "In actual life the want of *rapport* between these types is a matter of daily observation."

ing drive in the life of such a man is undoubtedly the imperative impulse to translate into outward expression, into concrete reality, that inward image which, as Warren very aptly observes, is the first essential element in human purposive action.   Creative minds have borne their own eloquent testimony:

As the sculptor must dream the statue prisoned in the marble, as the artist must dream the picture to come from the brilliant unmeaning of his palette . . . . , so he who writes must have a vision of his finished work[8] . . .

An attribute which may be taken for granted in every artist is passionate intensity of vision.   Unless vision is passionately intense, the artist will not be moved to transmit it, ...[9]

Lowell, consulted by a young author as to the royal road to good style, advises him that the first requirement is to have something that "will not stay unsaid."   The same intentness upon outward expression of the inner vision speaks in the words of Carlyle:

A certain inarticulate self-consciousness dwells dimly in us, which only our works can render articulate and decisively discernible.   Our works are the mirror wherein the spirit first sees its natural lineaments.   Hence, too, the fallacy of that impossible precept, Know thyself; till it can be translated into this partially possible one: Know what thou canst work at.

Blessed is the man who has found his work: let him ask no other blessedness. Know thy work, and do it; and work at it like Hercules.

This imperative impulse to materialize a mental conception is by no means the monopoly of the artist.   In this bantering style Arnold Bennett says of the amateur inventors "They have glimpsed perfection; they have the gleam of perfection in their souls."   This is the goad that drives them on to unrelenting effort: the vision of their finished work.

The race of contrivers and inventors does obey an inborn and irresistible impulse.   Schemes and experiments begin in childhood and persist as long as life and strength hold.   It matters not whether a fortune is made or pecuniary distress is chronic: there is increasing interest in new dodges, unceasing trial of new devices. . . . .   And it would seem that no satisfaction from pecuniary success or worldly recognition equals the absorbed interest of trial, experiment, novel problems, happy solutions.[10]

---

[8] M. R. S. Andrews in *The Perfect Tribute*, 1907, p. 6.

[9] Arnold Bennett.

[10] Taussig, Inventors and Money-Makers, 1915, p. 21; see also A. J. Lotka, Independent, July 12, 1919, p. 54.

Influence of Special Attitudes. There is undoubtedy a relation between the intensity of development of the instinct of workmanship and the natural endowment, the talents of the individual. The two things do not run altogether parallel, unfortunately, as evidenced by the well-known *crank* type of individual, who has something of the enthusiasm of genius, but lacks judgment in directing his energies into worth while channels. There are too, men lacking the impulse to put to competent use great natural gifts that they possess. But the general rule holds that: "Special aptitudes clamor for the opportunity of asserting themselves. The tasks which are their fit occasion of self-expression are the supreme joy of the man of genius, who will suffer every earthly privation rather than brook the thwarting of his talents."[11]

It might be supposed that such exceptional development of the instinct of workmanship and self-expression as speaks in the words cited can play but a subordinate rôle in a world peopled for the most part with "ordinary" individuals. But this is a misconception on several counts. How effective may be the inspiration which we can all draw from the testimony of our betters is perhaps an open question. But it must be remembered that in the shaping of the world's events men of genius play a part proportionate to their greatness. It has been remarked that the world's history could be written as a series of biographies of great men. The general average of excellence in a community is upheld and advanced by the exceptional few, the leaders in thought and deed.

But perhaps our chief interest in the manifestation of the instinct of workmanship and self-expression in its superlative measure, as we see it in the life and works of men of genius, lies in the fact that, after all, these men were human, even as we are; and that the trait which in them is developed to this high degree, is shared in some measure also by the rest of mankind. Here the instinct may not rise to such pitch as to be clearly felt and recognized by the individual; he may be only dimly conscious of a vague unsatisfied want when he fails to find a normal outlet for it. Psychiatrists and economists tell us that the individual thus thwarted is apt to ascribe his vague feeling of discomfort to any but the true cause, and that social unrest in our present industrial system is due in no small

[11] H. T. Moore, The Sense of Pain and Pleasure.

measure to the want of an adequate outlet for the instinct of workmanship and self-expression. "A human being whose instincts are balked becomes an enemy of society," for "primitive instincts can be guided but not suppressed. If they become pent up the danger of unrestrained outbreak is great."[12] And referring to the same matter Taussig remarks:

> It is obvious that the sum of human happiness would be greater if . . . . all commonly took direct satisfaction in the activities of earning a living. . . . The satisfaction of instinct conduces *pro tanto* to happiness, the balking of it to unhappiness. . . . . Among those instincts to which it seems possible to give wide scope, without danger of satiation or remorse, is that of *contrivance* (workmanship). And yet the modern organization of industry smothers it in a great and probably growing proportion of men.

If it is indeed true that the proportion of men so cramped in their creative efforts is growing, we have here a most regrettable condition, for the words of Emerson remain true:

> In every variety of human employment . . . . there are among the numbers that do their task perfunctorily, as we say, or just to pass, as badly as they dare—there are the working men on whom the burden of the busines falls—those who love the work and love to see it rightly done, who finish their task for its own sake; *and the state and the world is happy that has most of such finishers.*

The Industrial and the Social Problem. The instinct of workmanship thus gives rise to a twofold problem in human affairs. On the one hand, considering the modern human community in the gross, so far as the development of social conditions are or can be brought under intelligent control, it is evidently desirable to provide for the healthy satisfaction of this eminently desirable trait of human character: "We have here too valuable and creative a tendency to allow it to be longer neglected, thwarted and dissipated."[13]

On the other hand each individual, if life is to bring him a good share of that satisfaction which it potentially holds for him, must order his affairs (so far as circumstance permit) with his eyes open to the demand of this instinct of workmanship. Failure to do this may rob him of his just heritage; he may find, too late, that he has sold his birthright for a mess of pottage, that, in the words of Arnold

[12] Irving Fisher.
[13] Ordway Tead.

Bennett, "his existence is a vast and poisonous regret." But even if he is spared this extreme, it holds true in any case that "better self-understanding means better self-control, and a wiser ordering of one's actions along the normal paths of happiness."[14]

[14] F. L. Wells, Mental Adjustments, 1917, p. vii.

CHAPTER XXXI

THE ORIGIN OF CONSCIOUSNESS IN LIVING ORGANISMS

Die eigenartigen Züge der Organismen sind als provisorische Leitfäden auf-zufassen.—*E. Mach.*

We have had occasion to note that "behavior" very similar, in certain characteristics, to that of living organisms can be secured in a purely mechanical structure, such as that of the toy beetle.

This raises the question why nature should have resorted to consciousness as a means for bringing about those reactions so characteristic of the living organism. The most obvious answer that suggests itself is that, for some reason beyond our present ken, the conscious organism is simpler than any purely mechanical structure that could be built to perform even approximately the same diversity of tasks with the same degree of effectiveness. But certain difficulties arise if we accept (as is commonly done) the plausible hypothesis that to every state of consciousness there corresponds a definite state of the material structure of the conscious organism.

The Problem of Psycho-physical Parallelism. There is first of all the classical problem of psycho-physical parallelism. If the events in the physical world are wholly determinate, and if every conscious experience is in turn determined point by point by the physical substratum of the organism, what can be the utility of consciousness? For on this supposition my *willing* to perform a certain act is a mere incidental accompaniment of the physical circumstances that inevitably must bring about the object of my act. To quote H. C. Warren:[1]

In denying directive selection to forethought we reduce consciousness to the rôle of an epiphenomenon. If purposive thought is not effective in producing mental or muscular activity, of what value is consciousness in the universe? Is it anything more than a spectator of the physical changes which constitute real activity and form the basis of history?

---

[1] Jour. Phil. Psych. and Sci. Method, 1916, v. 13, p. 20.

Professor Warren finds the answer to this question in the "double-aspect" theory of consciousness.[2]

The objection (stated in the preceding paragraph) may hold against the traditional parallelistic world-view, but it loses force if we adopt the double-aspect standpoint. According to this interpretation our thoughts and purposes are only our way of experiencing what an independent observer might perceive as physiological activity. One set of occurrences is as "real" as the other.

So, for example, my feeling of "hunger," would appear to a suitably equipped outside observer as a contraction of my stomach, the presence in it of an accumulation of certain digestive fluids; a particular disposition of the molecules of certain nerves and certain portions of the brain, etc.

Physical Analogies. Such dual aspect of a phenomenon is known to us also outside of the particular case of consciousness. So, for example, the magnetic force (intensity) at a certain point is one aspect of the same phenomenon which could also be described by a statement of the position of the molecules of the permanent magnet, say, to which the field is due. The "problem" of psycho-physical parallelism is probably due to an inadequate statement of the case. It is probably, in this sense, of the nature of a pseudo-problem. To say that a necessary condition for the writing of these words is the *willing* of the author to write them, and to say that a necessary condition for the writing of them is a certain state and configuration of the material of his brain, these two statements are probably merely two ways of saying the same thing. A state of consciousness can be *described* either in terms of its "contents," or in terms of the disposition of the molecules, etc. of the brain, just as a magnetic field might be described either in terms of an intensity chart or in terms of the position of a number of magnets.

But, evidently, the double-aspect conception of consciousness helps us not at all to recognize, in the intervention of consciousness, any plausible reason for simplification of mechanisms to be gained by this means. For fruitful suggestions we must look elsewhere, and it is in

[2] For a discussion of this theory, originated independently by a number of authors (Fechner, 1863; Clifford, 1878; Bourrat, 1883; Prince, 1885; Strong, 1903; Heymans, 1905) see Tolman, Jour. Washington Acad. Sci., 1922, vol. 12, p. 153.

this difficulty that the theory of consciousness sketched in Chapter XXIX gives promise of assistance. For on the one hand the appearance upon the field of action of molecules in the "opened-up" state furnishes a whole range of states of matter that do not play a significant rôle in the operation of ordinary mechanism. With this extra material the conscious mechanisms may conceivably accomplish what the mechanic, working with matter in its ordinary states, is powerless to do without complications of structure altogether prohibitive. Again, our conception of the physics of conscious matter reveals to our view an interplay of forces, to effect purposive adjustment, *within the molecule;* whereas the mechanic, in his constructions, must bring contending forces to bear and to produce their resultants through separate material members, gross masses. Here, then, may be found the opportunity for that economy of parts which is characteristic of living, conscious mechanisms.[3]

In some such manner as this it seems possible to account with reasonable plausibility at least for the fact that in the evolution of the animal type of organism, the type equipped with a correlating apparatus, consciousness has been seized upon as an effective means to secure adaptive behavior.

Origin of Consciousness. One question remains as yet unanswered. Whence did the organisms derive this consciousness? Where and how did consciousness come into being: In a living organism? Then was the living organism unconscious prior to the event? Or else, did consciousness arise outside the organism? Then consciousness would not be tied inseparably to life.

The answer to these questions has already been foreshadowed. It is not consciousness that has been evolved—an elementary flash of consciousness may be a native property of matter—but a particular kind of integrated consciousness, a consciousness spun into a continuous thread by a faculty of memory, a consciousness embroidered as upon a canvas, whose function is to hold in place and in their proper relation the components of the picture. This background, this reference frame, in the state of development in which we observe it in ourselves, is the *ego*, to whom all experiences are referred. The material organs to which this integrating function is entrusted is the nervous system, including the brain.

---

[3] For a somewhat detailed discussion of this and related phases of the subject the author's article *The Intervention of Consciousness in Mechanics* may be consulted. See Science Progress, 1924, p. 407.

The nervous system is that bodily system, the special office of which, from its earliest appearance onward throughout evolutionary history, has been more and more to weld together the body's component parts into one consolidated mechanism reacting as a unity to the world about it. More than any other system it has constructed out of a collection of organs an individual of unified act and experience. *It represents the acme of integration of the animal organism.* . . . . As such it has spelt biological success to its possessor.[4]

---

[4] Sir C. S. Sherrington, Presidential Address at British Association Meeting, 1922. Nature, 1922, vol. 110, p. 350. Compare also A. G. Tansley, The New Psychology, 1916, p. 20, referring to Holt, The Freudian Wish, 1916, pp. 76–94. Tansley summarizes Holt's view in the words: "Professor Holt very clearly expounds the view that mind is merely the 'integration' of the organism's motor responses to stimuli. Professor Holt's position is that 'even two reflexes acting within one organism bring it about that the organism's behavior is no longer describable in terms of the immediate sensory stimulus, but as a function of objects and situations in the environment.' The secret of the connection of mind, and brain remains as dark as ever. Professor Holt does, indeed, admit that mind is a 'synthetic novelty'—'the advent of specific response . . . . is the birth of awareness and therefore of psychology itself.' But even if the integration of 'reflex responses' to become 'specific response' (i.e. response to an object or situation rather than to a mere stimulus) is rightly described as 'awareness,' and this is by no means self-evident, we are not thereby in the least degree helped to understand awareness or cognition in terms of anything else. *We are still absolutely bound to interpret mind in terms of our own mind—the only mind of which we have direct knowledge, though we may learn much about the conditions of its evolution."*

"The behavior of an organism adapted to its surroundings is related rather to the objects and situations of those surroundings than to physical and chemical stimuli as such, and this takes place by integration (i.e., the putting together to make a new whole) of simple motor responses to form complex ones. Thus the specific responses of an organism may be regarded as 'functions' (in the mathematical sense) of the objects and situations of its environment, and the history of the evolution of response to environment, i.e., of behavior, and of mind itself, is the history of successive integrations of these 'functions' to more and more complex purposes."

CHAPTER XXXII

ENERGY RELATIONS OF CONSCIOUSNESS

Die Physik wird in der Biologie viel mehr leisten wenn sie erst noch durch die letztere gewachsen sein wird.—E. Mach.

To the naïve observer, at any rate, consciousness appears to exert a directive action upon the course of events. If we regard the physical world as a determinate system, the events in which are completely determined by the physical laws to which matter and energy are subject, a question thus arises: Where, in such a scheme as this, is there any opportunity for the agency of consciousness to bring its influence to bear? Several alternative answers to this question seem compatible with our limited knowledge.

First Alternative: Possible Inaccuracy of Laws of Dynamics. First, the laws of physics as known to us may be an inaccurate representation of facts. Indeed, we know that they must be thus inaccurate, for we are far from having completely solved the problem of the Universe. It is therefore possible that something omitted from our formulation of dynamics and energetics is the origin of our perplexity. That such an eventuality as this cannot be wholly ignored is demonstrated, for example, by certain features of the Bohr theory of the atom. "The quantum conditions determining the permissible Bohr orbits can be explained physically only by attributing to the electrons a knowledge of the future."[1] This is a case in which the equations of motion contain a term with a *lead*, not a spurious lead that can be eliminated by suitable substitutes, but a real, essential lead that must of necessity appear in the equations. Let there be no misunderstanding. It is not intended to suggest that there is a direct relation between this circumstance and consciousness. The example is cited merely to show that the conceptions of classical dynamics are far from exhausting the types of conceptions, in such matters, that we must be prepared to contemplate. At the same time it is only fair to observe that it seems hardly logical for a being composed of electrons to affect great surprise at the fact

[1] C. G. Darwin, Nature, 1923, vol. 111, p. 771, vol. 112, p. 279.

ṫhat these electrons display certain properties reminiscent of consciousness.

Second Alternative: Singular Orbits with Indeterminate Motion. But, in point of fact, without going so far afield, we can see in the domain of classical dynamics opportunity for the entrance of consciousness as a directive agent upon the field of physical events. For there are certain cases in which the course of these events is not fully determinate in classical dynamics. Every case of unstable equilibrium is an instance in point. What do we know regarding the future fate of a cone set up and exactly balanced on its point? Any infinitesimally small force applied to it at any time will decide its fall in one direction or another. The history of such a system as this depends on *infinitesimals*, that is to say, on data of an order of magnitude that must escape the observation of our senses. To state the matter in more general terms, the orbits of a system moving in accordance with the laws of classical dynamics are of two kinds. *Stable* orbits are characterized by the fact that a small change in the conditions of the systems will bring about a small change in the orbit. Such is the orbit of a ball rolling down an inclined plane, after being started at an angle θ with a velocity v. If we slightly change the angle θ or the velocity v, or both, the orbit also will be but slightly changed.

But there are other, unstable orbits, such as that of a ball rolling along the ridge of a straight *watershed*. Such orbits correspond to singular integrals, or contain singular points. Here, if the angle of the initial velocity deviates ever so little from the orientation of the ridge, the ball will proceed along an orbit totally different from that following the ridge—it will descend into one or other of the valleys on the two sides of the ridge.

Here again, infinitesimal interference will produce finite, and, it may be, very fundamental changes in the result.

This, essentially, is the nature of the conception suggested years ago by Clerk Maxwell,[2] and independently, it seems, by J. Boussinesq.[3] It is to be noted that such unstable equilibria and

[2] Life of Clerk Maxwell, by Lewis Campbell and William Garnett, 1882, p. 434. L. J. Henderson, The Order of Nature, 1917, p. 213; J. W. N. Sullivan, Aspects of Science, 1923, p. 156.

[3] Cours de Physique Mathématique; Conciliation du véritable déterminisme méchanique avec l'existence de la vie, etc. Originally published 1878, republished 1922, Gauthier-Villars, Paris.

orbits as exemplified by the cone precariously balanced on its point
and by the ball performing its tight-rope trick along the ridge of a
watershed are typical of systems disposing of a fund of "available"
energy. Such a fund of free energy, in turn, is typical of living
organisms. To quote again Clerk Maxwell:

In all such cases there is one common circumstance,—the system has a
quantity of potential energy, which is being transformed into motion, but
which cannot begin to be so transformed until the system has reached a certain
configuration, to attain which requires an expenditure of work which in certain cases may be infinitesimally small, and in general bears no definite proportion to the energy developed in consequence thereof. . . . . . Every
existence above a certain rank has its singular points, the higher the rank,
the more of them. At these points influences too small to be taken into account
by a finite being may produce results of the greatest importance. All great
results produced by human endeavor depend on taking advantage of these
singular states when they occur.[4]

In the course of this our mortal life we more or less frequently find ourselves on a physical or moral watershed, where an imperceptible deviation
is sufficient to determine into which of two valleys we shall descend.[5]

This conception makes the interference of consciousness (will)
in physical events an *exceptional* occurrence:

It appears that in our own nature there are more singular points—where
prediction, except from absolutely perfect data, and guided by omniscience of
contingency, becomes impossible—than there are in any lower organization.
But singular points are by their very nature isolated and form no appreciable
fraction of the continuous course of our existence.[6]

**Third Alternative: Possible Influence of Factors Eliminated
from Equations of Dynamics.** As to the last quotation, perhaps,
one feels disposed to hesitate in adopting the standpoint suggested
by the great physicist. For it seems that even the most trivial
voluntary action involves the interference of consciousness in the
course of physical events, and of such more or less trivial voluntary
acts our waking consciousness is filled to the brim. A certain
interest may therefore attach to an alternative point of view which
has been developed by the writer elsewhere, and which is based on
the following consideration:

[4] Clerk Maxwell, loc. cit., p. 443.
[5] Clerk Maxwell, loc. cit., p. 441.
[6] Clerk Maxwell, loc. cit., p. 444.

A quantity which does not appear in the working equation describing the laws of action of a physical system may nevertheless play a significant rôle in the world's events. So, for example, a mathematical theory of wealth, covering at any rate certain aspects of economics, can be built up in terms of prices and sales alone, without pushing the analysis of fundamentals beyond this point; that is to say, without examining the human emotions and motives that, presumably, find their numerical expression in prices. On such basis as this, for example, Cournot founded his admirable "Researches into the Mathematical Theory of Wealth."

But to most of us it will appear quite evident that such a treatment as this is necessarily a very incomplete presentation of the actual events, however exactly it may represent the *resultant* effects observed. For it wholly ignores our desires and purposes, which to us appear very real and important constituents of the course of nature.

This example should open our eyes to the possibility, with which we must be prepared to reckon, that the equations of dynamics, however perfectly they may picture the course of certain physical events, may fail entirely to reveal or to give expression to underlying agency that may, in fact, be of fundamental significance. The interference of consciousness in mechanics may be very real, and yet the course of events may *appear* fully determined by the laws of dynamics.[7]

Energetics of Aimed Collisions. Aimed collisions imply a correlation between a present state or event and a future occurrence or eventuality (a future that will be or a future that may be). Psychologically this correlation is apprehended as purposive forethought. Physically it implies the disposal of a fund of free energy, since the energy for bringing about (or for avoiding) a future encounter cannot itself be derived from that encounter. There is thus of necessity a fundamental connection between purposive action and the disposal of a fund of free energy. Purposive behavior can and does occur only in material structures disposing of such a fund.

---

[7] For a more detailed presentation of this viewpoint the reader must be referred to the author's article *The Intervention of Consciousness in Mechanics*, Science Progress, January, 1924.

CHAPTER XXXIII

REVIEW OF THE CORRELATING APPARATUS

Man is the arch machine, of which all these shifts drawn from himself are toy models.—*Emerson.*

Some of the outstanding features of our reflections and observations in the chapters immediately preceding are summarized in tables 34 and 35, which at the same time bring out a number of other significant facts.

Table 34 sets forth systematically the main facts regarding the receptors and effectors, as exhibited particularly in the case of man. (A few entries shown in parentheses relate to species other than man, in cases in which man lacks the feature to be exemplified).

In this tabulation *Depictors* or *Informants* are shown as divided up into Receptors, Elaborators, Relators, and Communicators. The Receptors are further subdivided into Internal Ceptors, Contact Ceptors and Distance Ceptors. These terms hardly require explanation, especially in view of the other entries on the table, which will serve to elucidate them. In every case represented, the name of the corresponding faculty, the *native* or *natural* organs, and the *artificial* organ or organs are shown. The list of the latter is far from exhaustive.

The imagination, the faculty by the aid of which we hold before our mind's eye the material upon which we operate in the process of thinking, is shown divided into autistic and realistic imagination. The term autistic thinking has been introduced by psychologists to denote that type of thought in which the fancy is given free reins, unchecked by any demand for *correspondence* with reality; the thought of the savage, the child, the dreamer, the poet.[1] Realistic thinking, on the contrary, is constrained by the laws of *Logic*, which assure a due *correspondence* between the products of cogitation and the features of the external world to which they relate.

---

[1] "Les poètes se consolent, comme les enfants, avec des images." Anatole France , Le Jardin d'Épicure.

TABLE 34

Category	Group	Subgroup	Faculty		Organ — Native	Organ — Artificial
Depictors or Informants	Receptors	Internal ceptors	Pain		Nerves	Anesthetics, analgesics
			Inner sense		Viscera, etc.	X-rays, endoscope, etc.
			Muscular sense		Muscles, joints, etc.	Weighing balance
			Orientation		Semicircular canals	Plumb line, spirit level, gyroscope, compass
		Contact ceptors	Touch		Skin	Sclerometer
			Heat and cold		Skin	Thermometer, thermopile, etc.
			Taste		Taste buds	Chemical analysis
		Distance ceptors	Smell		Nose	Chemical analysis
			Hearing		Ears	Microphone
			Sight		Eyes	Microscope, telescope, spectroscope, interferometer, polarimeter, photographic camera, moving pictures, etc., photometer, photoelectric cell
			(Electricity).		(Muscular spasm).	Electrometer, galvanometer, etc.
			(Magnetism)			Compass, magnetometer
	Elaborators		Memory		Brain, nervous system	Records: carved, written, printed, photographic, phonographic
			Imagination	Autistic	Brain	Kaleidoscope
				Semi-realistic	Brain	Rhyming dictionaries
				Realistic	Brain	Mathematical tables, slide rules, calculating machines, statistical machines, equation machines, harmonic analysers, tide predictors, etc.
	Relators		Time sense (Sense of Rhythm)		Brain	Clock, metronome, chronometer, calendar, growth rings in trees, geological strata, radioactive minerals.
			Spatial sense		Brain	Graduated scales, verniers, calipers, gages, micrometers, comparators, interferometer, goniometer, transit, sextant, planimeter, intergraph, graduated vessels, dilatometer, hydrometer, drafting instruments
	Communicators	Receivers	Understanding		Ear / Eye	Telephone receiver, phonograph / Reading matter
		Transmitters	Speech (language)		Vocal apparatus	Telephone transmitter, grammophone
					"Gestural apparatus" facial expression (mien, sign language, etc.)	Writing, printing, mail, telegraph
Epictors or Transformants	Effectors	Internal	Anabolism	Reproduction	Ova, sperm / Genital organs	Artificial fertilization / Incubators, obstetric instruments
				Growth	All tissues, trophic / Glands and nerve centers	Chemical manufacturing plant
				Repair	All tissues, trophic nerves	
			Catabolism	Alimentation	Alimentary tract	Kitchen (cooking), canning industries
				Digestion	Respiratory system	Forced draft, carburetors, power plants: coal, oil, gas, water, electricity, etc.
					Circulatory system	Steam boilers, feedwater injectors, etc.
				Energization	Excretory system	Waste and garbage disposal plants, sewerage
			Temperature regulation		Skin, hair, (fur) / Neuro-chemical control / (Luminescence organs)	Clothing, buildings, cities / Heating, ventilation / Illumination
			Defense, internal		Antibodies / Phagocytes	Vaccines, antitoxic sera, antiseptics, disinfectants applied to body
		External	Defense, external / Offense, depredation		Hands, teeth, (claws) (electric organs)	Drugs, therapeutic agents, sanitation, disinfectants / Weapons, fisheries, game preserves, agriculture (plant industry, animal husbandry, dairying) fertilizer industries, quarrying, mining (fuel, ores, etc.)
			Equilibration		Neuro-muscular control by semicircular canals	Gyroscope (torpedoes, etc.)
			Production		Hands, etc.	Tools, machines, engines, mechanical manufacturing plant
			Locomotion		Legs, (wings), (fins)	Roads, wheeled vehicles, bicycle, motor-cycle, automobile, railways, ships, airships, aeroplanes

The item "semi-realistic imagination" calls for special notice. It was suggested primarily by the case of the so-called realistic novel. Such a novel is realistic as to the *types* presented, though the *specific instances may* have no counterpart in reality. Such semi-realistic thinking plays an important part in Science. Every physical formula is, in a sense, an instance of this type of thinking. When I say that the area of a rectangular surface measuring 2 by 4 feet is 8 square feet, this does not imply that any such rectangle exists in reality. It may exist or not, the statement has a certain quality of truth independent of the reality of such a rectangle; the statement relates to a type rather than to a specific instance.

The terms "Sense of Time" and "Spatial Sense" are self-explanatory. They are suggested without prejudice as to their metaphysical significance. We must accept it as a *fact* that we distinguish experience as having a definite *sequence* in time, and that we are able, unaided by artificial adjuncts, to gage with very fair accuracy equality of time intervals within certain somewhat narrow limits. Similar remarks apply to the entry Spatial Sense. Such entries are needed to make the table complete. If the reader, on metaphysical or other grounds dislikes these terms, others may be substituted at his discretion.

The item *Communicators* calls for little comment. These are, in a sense, receptors and effectors set apart for or employed in a particular, and a highly important use.

Just as the Depictors or Informants throw a picture of the external world upon or into the organism, so the *Epictors* or *Transformants* translate into material reality the plans conceived, the pictures formed in the mind. The Brooklyn Bridge, for example, is a material representation or picture of the plans that once were in the designer's mind.

These transformants include once again the elaborators, relators and communicators, for these fulfill a double function; the transformants further include the *Internal* and the *External Effectors*, whose nature and significance is apparent from the table.

If time had permitted, the writer would much have liked to give to this table a quantitative cast by adding columns showing persons employed, production, consumption, imports, exports, and capitals invested in the arts and industries corresponding to the several items shown in the table, adding, in other words, a quantitative description of the behavior schedule of human society. The table would thus give a coherent, biologically founded, picture of the life activities of the Body Politic. The behavior of this body as a whole, no less than that of its constituent organisms, is conditioned by its anatomical constitution and its biological needs. The substitution of artificial for natural organs in nowise alters this fact.

The adjustors could not very conveniently be accommodated in the scheme of table 34. They have been separately systematized in table 35.

The adjustors are here shown divided into two groups. The *Internal Adjustors* are those that control the distribution of effort in different pursuits in one organism, *within* the organism, so to speak. The *External Adjustors*, on the other hand, control the distribution of effort *among* the several organisms or groups of organisms comprised in one species.

Internal Adjustors. The internal adjustors operate through the faculty of *choice* (wish, will, etc.). Such choice may be made without any conscious reference to any objective principle, purely according to the dictates of instinctive impulse or tastes. No attempt is made to enumerate such instincts in any degree of completeness. They are shown classified according to the principal beneficiary into *egoistic* and *altruistic* instincts. The agent is not always conscious of the relation of his actions to the beneficiary. Thus, for example, the scientific investigator, working under the stress of the instincts of curiosity, workmanship, and self-expression, may have little or no thought of conferring a benefit on society. Such benefit nevertheless follows.

The choice may not be made simply in response to instinctive impulse. It may be more or less consciously guided by "principles," such as may be given either empirically, on the word of an accepted authority, the Church for example; or as worked out systematically by the agent himself (philosophy of conduct, ethics).

These two types of choice may be respectively termed *instinctive* and *reflective*, or, in analogy with the terms employed with regard to thought, the instinctive may also be classed as *autistic*, the reflective as *realistic*, since the former seeks no basis outside the individual himself, the latter tends to seek an objective basis. The discipline of *Ethics* here appears as a *regulator of conduct* in close analogy to the manner in which logic functions as a *regulator of thought*.

Man's correlating apparatus—the adjustors

ADJUSTORS		FACULTY	INSTRUMENT			BENEFICIARY
Internal	Choice	Autistic (instinctive)	Instincts	Egoistic	{ Hunger, Self-preservation, Primitive sex instinct, Curiosity }	} Self
		Realistic (reflective)		Altruistic	{ Secondary sex instinct: Conjugal, Filio-parental, Familial; Social: Herd, Workmanship, Self-expression or communication, Missionary, Intolerance }	Mate, Offspring, parent, Relatives } Society
			Ethics, philosophy of conduct			
External	Functional specialization		Physiological constitution	Sex { Male, Female, Abortive (workers, soldiers, etc.) }		
			Economic constraint (barter, market, money)	Classified gainful occupations		

This analogy is brought out with the greatest clarity in the following quotations, which should be read in parallel:

Logic: C. J. Keyser, Mathematical Philosophy, 1922, p. 136.

"Logic is the muse of thought. When I violate it I am erratic; if I hate it, I am licentious or dissolute; if I love it, I am free—the highest blessing the austere muse can give."

Compare also the saying of Seneca: "Si tibi vis omnia subjicere, te subjice rationi."

Ethics: Clerk Maxwell

". . . . an abandonment of wilfulness without extinction of will, but rather by means of a great development of will, whereby, instead of being consciously free and really in subjection to unknown laws, it becomes consciously acting by law, and really free from the interference of unknown laws."

In the development of ethics, as in that of logic, the influence of natural selection must be to favor those habits of thought and action which are conducive to the welfare of the species. And just as we have reached the point where at least the rudiments of logic are unassailably fixed in the healthy adult mind, so we may expect that socially sound principles of conduct will in time be more and more accepted as inevitable truths, their converse as "unthinkable," at least to the naïve mind. Indeed, in very appreciable measure this is the case even now. Theft, for example, is to the normal person utterly unthinkable. The philosophic mind will of course, still, at all times, be able to conceive of unethical conduct as a possible alternative, just as today the philosopher can, as a sort of *tour de force*, of mental gymnastics, overcome his native faith in an external world, and assume temporarily the rôle of the solipsist.

External Adjustors. The external adjustors, those that govern the distribution of effort among the several individuals of the species, present several points of much interest. Their operation is, of course, essentially restricted to species living in organized communities, such as the bee, the ant, and, quite particularly, man.

Nature has developed two entirely distinct methods of adjusting the distribution of activities among the several members of such a social group. The individual may be born into the world or nurtured to adolescence with a definitely specialized endowment of anatomical equipment and physiological and psychological faculties and predilections. So the queen bee is fitted for her very particular part, the drone for his, and the working bee for its task. Each is capable only of playing the part assigned, and presumably each is perfectly content, wholly innocent of the joys and sorrows characteristic of the other's calling. In our own human species this condition is nearly approached as regards the special tasks of sex, at least in their primary forms.

The second method adopted by nature is really a very singular, and one feels tempted to say, a highly ingenious one. Here the individual may have little or no natural disposition to specialize, in a blind obedience to the call of social expediency. Nature, as it were, gives the reins into his hands, and only demands the right to impose a tax on all his profits. Smith and Jones get together, Smith offers Jones a pound of bread, and Jones accepts it in return for six ounces of beef. Each is satisfied. Each has driven a purely selfish bargain, without the least thought of the good of the community. But the community has already collected its tax—the exchange, on the whole, is to its benefit.

Now this method has its advantages and disadvantages. One feels an unpleasant suspicion that 'if Smith and Jones, instead of driving a mutually selfish bargain, instead of working in a measure against each other, could be brought to combine their forces in the definite purpose of serving the community, the latter would collect, not only a residual tax, but a more complete benefit. In the simple example of the loaf and the steak this is hardly apparent, but there can be little doubt that in human affairs much is lost by internal friction, by men pulling this way and that, instead of pulling together.

The other disadvantage is that this method of division of labor frequently must fail to satisfy those working instincts which man still possesses, useless as they may appear in the circumstances. Now unsatisfied instincts are painful things.

But this method, in spite of such disadvantages as it may have, has established itself very firmly among us. It must possess fundamental advantages. And it is not difficult to point out where these enter into the scheme of things. The tasks of the beehive, the anthill, are comparatively simple and few. Two, three, perhaps four sets of instincts serve the required ends. But to quote Veblen,[2] "the higher the degree of intelligence and the larger the available body of knowledge current in any given community, ... the

[2] T. Veblen, The Instinct of Workmanship, 1914, p. 6.

more complicated will be the apparatus of expedients and resources employed to compass those ends that are instinctively worth while." So, in our own community, the list of different *gainful occupations* takes up over ten closely printed pages of the Statistical Abstracts of the United States. A behavior schedule of such complexity as this can hardly be taken care of by an assortment of as many *instinctive proclivities*. What is happening today is that the instinct of workmanship, so far as it plays a part in the working day of mankind, is sufficiently broad and plastic to adapt itself, with reasonable success, to a variety of tasks. Misfits there are, and some degree of heartache in consequence. But perfect adaptation is found in no department of life, neither can we expect it here.

CHAPTER XXXIV

CONCLUSION—RETROSPECT AND PROSPECT

Espérons dans ces êtres inconcevables qui sortiront de l'homme, comme l'homme est sorti de la brute.—*Anatole France.*

The Life Struggle in the Modern Community. It is not wholly from partiality, nor from self-complacency alone, that we are led to view the evolution of man, and especially of modern man, with a peculiar interest. An impartial judge, if such could be produced, would doubtless concede to the human species, as it stands today, an unique and predominant position in the scheme of Nature. For, civilized man has achieved the distinction of practically clearing the board of all foes of a stature in any way comparable with his own. This has resulted for him in a very special form of the struggle for existence. With the conflict against other species relegated to the background, man's combat with his own kind has been forced to the center of the stage. Increasing population pressure and continued success in the control of disease can only add to this effect, which is furthermore enhanced, while the struggle is at the same time forced into a very particular mold, by the industrial régime which has bonded the body politic into one organic whole. Under this régime we enter the battle of life *en bloc*. The activities of any one single individual are as a rule wholly incompetent to keep him or anyone else alive. The product of a day's work of a stenographer, for example, is a pile of papers covered with black marks. Taken out of its setting this is an entirely useless product, totally unfit to support the life of the producer. And much the same is true of the work of the bookkeeper, the draftsman, even the skilled engineer or chemist. The race as a whole, indeed, still contends with external opposing forces. But the individual, in a large proportion of cases, is conscious only of competition with his fellows. This competition takes the form of an intricate system of bargains to purchase the least intolerable form of dependence that the individual can secure, or to achieve such approach to independence as may be had. Whoever fails entirely in this struggle is Nature's convicted delinquent, the unfit, unable to draw to himself the needful share of the necessities of life, out of the general fund from which the body politic as a whole is supplied.

A new and characteristic form of the struggle for existence thus arises, the trend and presumptive outcome of which is for us a matter of evident interest.

Organization of Motive Lags behind Industrial Organization. While the human species, as a mechanical going concern, has become organized into a social whole, the motivation that keeps it going has not undergone the same thoroughgoing organization, but continues to be in great measure individualistic in type. Social ends are achieved through appeal to individualistic instincts. Our present industrial system operates by way of the *mutually selfish bargain,* in which each party to the transaction seeks his own advantage, regardless of the gain or loss to society as a whole. The system works tolerably well, beyond reasonable expectation perhaps; at least so it seems to those accustomed to the system. The competitive element which it introduces is not without salutary action. But, making proper allowance for this, one is left to ponder whether there may not, in due course, be evolved a superior system, that shall secure the interests of the community more directly, and with less loss by *internal friction* in the social machinery. There are certain difficulties in the way of achieving this in man by those instinctive methods which operate effectively in insect societies, as has already been pointed out. Human activities are too multifarious to permit of simple adjustment by a stereotyped set of instinctive proclivities that predestine each infant at birth for his own particular sphere of activity through life. Nevertheless, we are not left wholly without encouragement that the future evolution of our race may proceed in a direction that shall ultimately ease the conflict between man and man, and between man and the world at large.

Philosophy as a Necessary Part of Scientific Enquiry. We have already had occasion to refer to the importance of attaining a clear realization of the nature of our fundamental assumptions. The scientific investigator has, in the past, not given to this phase, the philosophic phase, of human enquiry, the attention which it sooner or later must demand as a necessary condition of unimpeded progress. For if we define philosophy as *the critical examination of the funda-*

mental data of experience,[1] it is seen that philosophy is not something apart from science, but must form an integral and essential part of every science. No science can be said to have reached the adult stage until critical examination of its fundamental concepts has at least begun.

Classification of the Sciences in Relation to Self and External World. Of all fundamental assumptions in our thinking there is probably none so basic, so all pervading, as that of the division of the universe (that is to say, of the totality of experience) into an *ego* and a *non-ego*, a *self* and an *external world*, a *knower* and the *known*, an *observer* and a *thing observed*, a *subject* and an *object*, *mind* and *matter*;—all of these pairs of terms are, as commonly employed, more or less close synonyms.

Both unsophisticated thought and scientific thought accepts this division as axiomatic, and the physical sciences propose to study the external world, while psychology proposes to study mind, or the ego.

Philosophy does not accept this division as axiomatic, but proposes, among other things, to inquire into the nature and significance of the distinction. The philosopher asks: What is ego, and what is non-ego? Where is the line drawn, and how do I come by this distinction? *Thus philosophy studies the relations between the ego and the non-ego.*[2] According to the point of view that has been here

---

[1] This definition contains an implicit assumption, namely, that there *are* fundamental data of experience. This is not necessarily true. It may be that, no matter how far the analysis be carried, the data arrived at as the most fundamental can always be resolved by further analysis into others more fundamental. Thus the characteristic feature of philosophic enquiry, which distinguishes it from scientific enquiry, is perhaps rather one of *direction* than one of result. While science builds up from axiomatic data, philosophy works from these axiomatic data downward in the opposite direction. This is the view proposed by Bertrand Russell in his work *Our Knowledge of the External World.*

[2] This statement evidently holds true quite independently of the *reality* or *objective existence* of the ego and the non-ego or external world. Disputes as to such objective existence seem rather pointless. The fundamental data of our experience are sense impressions. When certain relations obtain between certain sense impressions, we ascribe the latter to an external object. Thus, if I see a cat, and proceed to go through certain movements which I speak of as stroking the cat, I may presently have the sensation of soft fur against my hand, and a purring noise at my ear. In that case I say that the cat is *real*. Or, going through the same motions, I may feel the impact of my hand against

presented the ego is not a concrete thing, but is of the nature of a system of reference, in relation to which experience is described, somewhat as the geographical location of a city is defined in terms of longitude and latitude.   Just as longitude may be reckoned from the meridian of Paris or from that of Greenwich or from any other convenient datum circle, so experience is describable with reference to a number of different egos.

The relation between the ego and the external object is brought out with great clarity by Bertrand Russell in his Analysis of Mind (1921, p. 100), after this manner: Sets of photographs of the stars might be made, first by taking all kinds of views, in different directions, from one point in space.   The collection thus brought together would give the appearance of different stars in a certain place, or, as we may say, would be a catalogue of the world of stars as it appears from a certain *center of perspective*.   But another collection might be made by photographing the same star from all kinds of different points in space.   This collection would give us all the ap-

---

a hard surface, etc.   In that case I say that the supposed cat is merely the *image*, in a mirror, of a cat.   Fundamentally the so-called *real* cat is merely a convenient hypothetical construct, convenient because it greatly simplifies language and thought.   It would be possible to express in terms of sense impressions alone everything that is ordinarily expressed in terms of an external world.   For that very reason it is quite impossible to *prove* that this external world has a real or objective existence, or, for the matter of that, that it has not.   That the external world is a hypothetical construct is not ordinarily realised, because that construct is formed by an instinctive and unconscious process, so far as ordinary experience is concerned.   In extraordinary circumstances, that call for the exercise of intense conscious reflection, the hypothetical nature of the construct is immediately apparent, as for example in the case of the Bohr atom, or the Einstein space-time continuum.   But at bottom the *real* cat is just as hypothetical as the *theoretical* Bohr atom, although perhaps less subject to revision as to its precise description.

If we continue to employ the terms external world, object, etc., this must not be taken to imply that we are oblivious of the hypothetical character of these constructs, but only that we resort to the usual expedient, for the sake of grammatical simplicity.   No harm will result from this use of the conventional terminology so long as we bear in mind its character, and do not allow ourselves to be drawn into the discussion of pseudo-problems arising out of that terminology and not out of the fundamental facts.   Thus, for instance, to enquire whether *mind* has an objective existence is a question based on a misconception, not only of the term mind, but of the general character of all the data of our knowledge.

pearances of a certain star in different places, or, as we may say, they would be a catalogue of the different aspects of one object.[3]

The essential difference between the ego and the non-ego is, in this sense, merely a difference in the system of filing, so to speak, a collection of data. Arranged as a collection of observations from one perspective, they are the experiences of an ego. Arranged as a collection of aspects of the world from different perspectives, they are, in their totality, the appearances of the external world.

This double system of filing or cataloguing our experiences is responsible for certain of the divisions of science. This is indicated diagrammatically in the chart table 36, which exhibits, for example, the position of the Physical Sciences, in the general scheme of human enquiries, as the study of the external world, or of that set of data which by common consent we ascribe to an external world; certain other data we associate more particularly with the self, whom we regard as equipped with a body, and gifted with consciousness. This twofold aspect of the self gives rise to a corresponding twofold development of the science of living beings. Biology, with its branches, studies more particularly the body of the organism, while Psychology busies itself with the phenomena of consciousness, as such. The relation of consciousness to the prevailing state of the body is perhaps to be regarded as *par excellence* the sphere of study of Psychophysics.

With regard to the present and past the Self is a *Knower*. With regard to the future he is a *Willer*. That is to say, he has *direct* cognizance of certain past and present events through sensation and memory; he has *direct* cognizance of certain future events through his will.[4] In accordance with this twofold aspect of the Self, psychol-

[3] Compare also the *ontograms* and *phanograms* of K. Gerhards, Naturwissen-schaften, 1922, pp. 423–430, 446–452.

[4] Indirectly, i.e., by inference, he may have other knowledge regarding past, present and future. But as to *direct* knowledge the statement made above applies. It is very commonly overlooked that we have knowledge of the future through our will. This oversight is partly due to the fact that we *sense* this kind of future in a particular way, unlike our sensing of the past and present. It is partly also due to the masking of this kind of knowledge of the future through uncertainties surrounding the actual realization of our intentions. Upon reflection it will be found not unnatural that there should be an appearance of fundamental distinction between our knowledge of the past through memory, and our knowledge of the future through will. For, if for

ogy may be regarded as divided into two main branches, dealing respectively with the Self as a Knower and with the Self as a Willer. Some of the principal subdivisions of these two main branches are indicated on the chart. Thus the first branch comprises first of all the study of the avenues by which we enter into possession of knowledge, i.e., the study of the special senses, including both the natural senses, and their artificial auxiliaries; furthermore the general theory of knowledge (Epistemology, Erkenntnisstheorie, Scientific Methodology); and the sciences of thought, both autistic and realistic or logical.

The second major branch is shown as divided into Dynamic Psychology or Psychology of Motivation (including, for example, the study of instincts); Esthetics and the Theory of Value ; and Ethics.

brevity we may be allowed to speak in the customary terms of unsophisticated speech, we are, through *memory*, cognizant of the past state of the external world, in so far as there are *effects* (engrams) in our bodies of those past states; whereas, conversely, we are, through *will* cognizant of the future state of the external world, in so far as there are *causes* in us of those future states. This consciousness of causes within us of certain future (external) states, is just what we *call* will. Will is our subjective realization of what to an objective observer would appear as (physical) causes of the events "willed." Bertrand Russell's provisional definition of memory as "that way of knowing about the past, which has no analogue in our knowledge of the future," seems, in this light, unwarranted (Analysis of Mind, 1923, p. 165). We have here only one particular phase of the double-aspect theory of consciousness that has been noted in Chapter XXXI. From this point of view the question that is sometimes raised, as to whether our sense of willing (free will), our desires, are illusions, logical constructs, fictions, or the like (see B. Russell, Analysis of Mind, 1923, p. 32) seems pointless. The question whether we strike a man because we are angry, or whether as William James has put it, we are angry because we strike a man, seems to fall into this category. There are certain conditions in us that are tending to bring about, and that presently do bring about, the blow. Our own particular *way of sensing* these conditions is that which we express by saying that we entertain the emotion of anger, that we have forethought and intent to hit the man. From this "double-aspect" point of view there seems no room for any essential conflict between the standpoint taken, for example, by Bertrand Russell (Analysis of Mind, pp. 32, 280) that *desires* like *forces* are fictitious; and, on the other hand, the standpoint taken of the present writer, in Science Progress, January, 1924, pp. 417, 418, that forces, like desires, may, after all, not be purely fictitious. They may be the subjective, i.e., immediate or directly sensed aspect of certain states that can also become topics of objective, i.e., indirect observation.

TABLE 36

A Classification of the Sciences

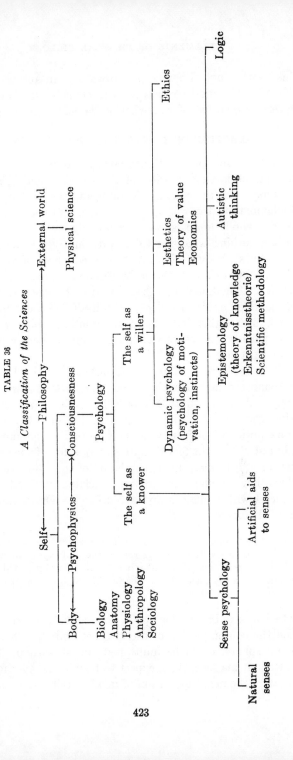

This chart is not of course put forward as in any sense complete, but rather as suggestive of a natural classification, and as setting forth certain relations of somewhat fundamental character.

REACTION OF KNOWLEDGE UPON EMOTIONS

The feature in this chart that chiefly interests us in our present considerations is that division of the topics which arises from the twofold aspect of the Self, the Knower and the Willer.

Fundamentally the world of knowledge and the world of will, of desire, are wholly apart, as we have already had occasion to observe. Logic has nothing whatever to do with motives as such, though it may, of course, busy itself with the consequences of motives. Contrariwise, motives are in themselves unrelated to or independent of knowledge. The knowledge that if I cross the street at this moment I shall be killed or maimed does not in itself determine my action nor even my intent; this depends on my emotional bias, whether I am bent on suicide, or desirous of maintaining as nearly as possible a pleasant existence.

Nevertheless a connection is established between knowledge and will, through the fact that the Knower and the Willer are united in one physical body, so that physical reactions do occur between knowing and willing. That the recognition of a truth is attended with an emotional affect we well know, not only from our own experience, but also from the fervid expression of some of the great pioneers of science. So Kepler, upon completion of the evidence establishing his third law of planetary motion, exclaims jubilantly: "Nothing holds me; I will indulge in my sacred fury." Or we may recall the words of Poincaré:

Science puts us in constant relation with something greater than ourselves; it presents to us a spectacle always renewed and always more vast. Behind what it shows us so grand it makes us divine something still more grand; this spectacle is a joy for us, but it is a joy in which we forget ourselves, and this is morally healthful.

Quotations exhibiting this spirit, this connection in men's minds between the contemplation of the intellect and the affections of the emotional sphere, could be multiplied almost without limit.

What result may we, then, expect to flow in the emotional sphere, from that phenomenal expansion of man's intellectual horizon which modern science has brought, and the still greater revelations that are undoubtedly yet to come? Men have gained much knowledge, but as yet they have scarcely had time to realize what they know, and the grandeur of the new truths.   It is not enough to know; there must be a vivid imagination presenting to the mind's eye for contemplation at once the many facets of the glittering gem.   When men shall have learned not only to know but to appraise the esthetic value of their knowledge, when they shall be filled with the glory of it all, surely a new era must dawn for the poetic arts.   Wordsworth says:

Poetry is the breath and finer spirit of all knowledge; it is the impassioned expression which is in the countenance of all Science. . . . . If the time should ever come when what is now called Science . . . . shall be ready to put on, as it were, a form of flesh and blood, the poet will lend his divine spirit to aid the transfiguration, and will welcome the Being thus produced as a dear and genuine inmate of the household of man.

It is, presumably, with such thoughts as this, that he writes in his Prelude

. . . . The song would speak
Of that interminable building reared
By observation of affinities
In objects where no brotherhood exists
To passive minds . . . .

And Renan, in *L'Avenir de la Science*, shows similar sentiment:

Disons donc sans crainte que, si le merveilleux de la fiction a pu jusqu'ici sembler nécéssaire à la poésie, le merveilleux de la nature, quand il sera devoilé dans toute sa splendeur, constituera une poésie mille fois plus sublime, une poésie qui sera la realité même, qui sera à la fois science et poésie.

We may well ask: If the simple Hebraic myth was competent to inspire a Haydn to compose an Oratorio of the Creation, what tone poem shall adequately celebrate the new meaning, in the mind of the modern astronomer, of the words

The Heavens declare the Glory of God
The Wonders of His power proclaims the firmament.

Thus we are not left wholly without indication as to what may be the fundamental trend of the future evolution of our race.   That the evolution of our intellectual capital is subject to a certain particular kind of orthogenesis we have observed in an earlier chapter.   The esthetic reaction of the new knowledge upon the race should bring with it a corresponding quasi-orthogenetic development in the sphere of esthetics, and through its mediation, also in the closely allied sphere of ethics. "When souls reach a certain clearness of *perception*, they accept a knowledge and *motive* above selfishness." We have noted elsewhere that, physically, no clear line of division can be drawn between the body and the environment. Psychologically too, we saw that the ego is not something that divides the world into separate fields, but is rather of the nature of a standard of reference in terms of which we find it most convenient to describe experience. But our system of coordinate reference frames, from a good servant, has threatened to become a bad master. As Keyser remarks, we have "estranged and objectified the world, and lost the sense that we are of it." It is as if evolution had overshot the mark, as if the race must in some degree retrace its step, and regain something of that impersonal consciousness that now seems to be only the occasional property of a few, who, like Wordsworth, are at times "unable to think of external things as having external existence, and who commune with all that they see as something not apart from, but inherent in their own immaterial nature."[5] Perhaps this transfiguration cannot be achieved but by the race passing through some great purging cataclysm, out of which a remnant may evolve toward a higher goal. It is familiar fact in geology that the species which pass on the stock to later eras of evolution are commonly not the main branches nor the most highly developed members of the evolutionary tree. So, also, it may not be the descendants of the now dominant divisions of our species that shall carry on the torch to light the new era, when "the world shall no longer be beheld as an alien thing, beheld by eyes that are not its own."[6] But this uncertainty cannot be allowed to deter us in such efforts as we may see fit to make to further by our own initiative the progress of the species, according

[5] Compare E. Mach, Die Analyse der Empfindungen, 1903, p. 24; "An einem heiteren Sommertage im Freien erschien mir einmal die Welt sammt meinem Ich als eine zusammenhängende Masse von Empfindungen, nur im Ich stärker zusammenhängend." Also Emerson: " . . . the sense of being which in calm hours rises, we know not how, in the soul, is not diverse from things, but one with them . . . . We first share the life by which things exist, and afterward see them as appearances in nature, and forget that we have shared their cause."

[6] C. J. Keyser, The Human Worth of Rigorous Thinking, 1916, p. 126.

to our best lights. It is not the least of our privileges that there seem to have been given into our hands the means whereby we may in a measure ourselves influence and control the fate and future of our species. It must be admitted that the fraction of the population is small that recognizes or cares anything about this great and golden opportunity for man to have a significant voice in the shaping of the world's destiny. But history has given us cause to be optimistic as to the possibilities of achievement by a small minority of perfervid men. "A little leaven leaveneth the whole lump." In our own day we have seen this principle only too effective in various propaganda not of the most desirable type. If men respond thus readily to guidance of very doubtful competence, those better qualified have at least no *prima facie* grounds for despairing utterly of establishing a body of followers. If enlightened men refuse to exert their influence toward the guidance of affairs according to their best knowledge, they certainly have no right to complain when they see the crowds following after leaders less hesitant, if also less competent. Even sheep have a bellwether. Leadership does not necessarily require intelligence of a high type. To say that the populace does not want the highest type of leader is beside the point. The populace does not pick its leader; it is the leader that picks the populace. However, the writer does not mean to suggest that the man of science, should at the present epoch, proffer his services as a leader in spiritual affairs. His reluctance to do anything of this kind is wholly to be commended. But it would seem that the time is ripe for scientific men at least to consider some degree of concerted action, some degree of systematic communion among those who continue to feel a proper interest in the ethical issue, now that the mythological trappings with which this issue is commonly encumbered, have been fairly effectively relegated to the background in well appointed minds. Such concerted action seems needful, not so much for the virtue of that strength which is in union, as on account of that weakness which is the failing of the isolated individual:

> 'Tis meet
> That noble minds keep ever with their likes
> For who so firm that cannot be seduced?

The writer believes that he is expressing a feeling entertained by many, though not perhaps always clearly apprehended, if he states that the world is ripe for some sort of concerted effort, a binding together in one form or other, of men possessing the scientific outlook and method of thought, combined with a sincere interest in the fulfilment of the great World Purpose. It is perhaps well to call to mind that the face of science is not turned squarely and unhesitatingly in this direction. Not only has the World War shown us all too clearly that the weapons of science are as keen for internecine warfare as for the campaign in the conquest of truth; more than this, there is a certain fashionable cynicism abroad which affects a scientific pose. There are those who, having hitched their wagon to a hog, fare forth proclaiming that the world is nothing but a dung heap; and those who advocate a humoring of the elementary man in us as a health measure. From the standpoint of mental hygiene, stupidity, too, is a rather healthy condition. Yet somehow, even for the sake of our health, most of us would hardly elect to be stupid—that is, if we had any choice in the matter. Cynicism has its uses. But in the end no one, not even the cynic himself, takes it very seriously. The pessimist spends his energy in jeremiads while the optimist is covering the ground with his forward stride. Let us endorse the stand taken by L. Witmer:[7]

What the world needs today is more of the optimism of the progressive and a little less of the pathological fear of the standpatter, more faith in creative evolution, more hope of reaching yet higher levels of achievement, and more of that freedom from prejudice called charity, another name for love—the productive passion.

Evolutionary Value of Nurture and Tradition. One form in which the demon of pessimism puts forth its head is in an overloud emphasis on the futility of the effects of *nurture* as opposed to the elemental force of *nature*.[8] Without committing ourselves to indefensible extremes in the opposite direction, we may put in a strong plea in support of the merits of nurture, merits so plain that their very obviousness has made us in some degree blind to them, and has thus given a weapon into the hands of the type of pessimist of which

[7] *What is Intelligence*, Scientific Monthly, 1922, p. 67.

[8] Compare H. S. Jennings, Heredity and Environment, Sci. Monthly, Sept., 1924, p. 225: "What has gotten into the popular consciousness as Mendelism—still presented in the conventional biological gospels—has been grotesquely inadequate and misleading; its seeming implications as to the trivial rôle of the environment has become null and void."

we speak. Those who so glibly discourse on the futility of efforts to improve man's nature, would they be satisfied to spend their lives among untutored savages? Would they relish the company of unclean slatterns and the vermin-ridden denizen of the slums? Would they care to live under the same roof with persons innocent of the rudiments of propriety in ministering to the natural needs of their bodies? If the benefits of nurture in these lesser occasions are so welcome, why make light of them in their relation to the more serious affairs of life? Such inconsistency is surely inconsistent also with the scientific spirit. In point of fact, tradition, so far from being a negligible factor in shaping the world of men, is one of the most powerful influences for evil, as for good, known to history. The tradition most easily within control is family tradition. In it we have a powerful lever competent to stir great masses into motion slow, perhaps, but none the less effective.

Another reflection which is submitted to the attention of those who make light of the potency of nurture is this: Suppose we took this attitude of *laisser faire* in the realm of science. Suppose we said: "What is the use of teaching the young generation the accumulated wisdom of scientific lore—at bottom they will still remain essentially savages." Can we picture to ourselves with any degree of satisfaction the inevitable effect of such a policy upon the advance of science? The fact is, there is a fundamental error in this emphasis upon the alleged futility of nurture. It is based upon a disregard of the organic unity of the social body. It narrowly views the evolution of man as that of an individual "contained in his skin." The evolution of our race today is something very different from this, as we have had ample opportunity to observe in preceding chapters. It is man plus his "artificial" aids to his life activities that evolves as one unit. These artificial aids most assuredly include traditions of all sorts, whether handed down by word of mouth, deposited in the archives of learned societies, or perpetuated in any other way. And there is no reason that can claim even a show of validity why we should attempt to draw a line of division, and say: "Here, in the province of science, industry and so forth, tradition is one of the processes essentially forming part of the evolution of man; but here, in ethics, tradition merely lends him a superficial veneer—at bottom he remains a savage." Our varied institutions of industry, commerce, law, etc., are no doubt subject to change and even to occasional upheaval. Yet they have a considerable degree of stability, quite comparable with that of the somatic substance of our race; it also is neither unalterable nor wholly immune from danger of extinction in some world-wide cataclysm.

We have every reason, then, not only to anticipate, but to encourage a development of man's emotional and ethical being alongside with and in the light of the advances made in the intellectual sphere. And indications are not lacking that in the emotional sphere, as in the intellectual, an orthogenetic bias is ready to anticipate selective evolution. The trend of selection in the realm of emotions, of instinctive proclivities, of tastes we have already noted: it follows Spencer's hedonistic principle, according to which those races are best adapted for survival, in whom adjustment of agreeable feelings to beneficial action is most perfect. And the principle admits of extension. Not only is it advantageous that we should desire those things that profit us and our species, but it is evidently equally essential that we should not set our hearts upon things impossible of attainment. The man who is forever crying for the moon is not well adapted for existence in this practical world. Thus the things we purpose, we who have stood the test of survival, must, on the whole, or at least in reasonable net balance, be things that come to pass. Evidently the statement can be turned about: the things that come to pass are, in many instances at any rate, things we purpose; what is more important, they are the *general type* of things that we purpose. They have, accordingly, to us a characteristic appearance of purposefulness. And the human mind, contemplating the spectacle of the world's events, is impressed with this appearance of purposefulness, and finds itself constrained, by an inborn bias, by an instinctive intuition, to construe this appearance as the outcome of design.

The fact seems to be that the operation of a fundamental purpose or design in Nature is one of those things that can neither be proved nor disproved. We are, therefore, at liberty, if we so choose to, believe in such a purpose. This is an occasion for the legitimate exercise of faith.

We may, if we *will*, embrace this purpose for our own. Such *will* spells ultimate survival. No better guarantee for the welfare of the race could be furnished, than its essential harmony with Nature. Selection, then, would seem to point the way toward a will in conformity with that general principle which, for want of a better term, we may describe as the Supreme Purpose of the Universe.

But selection alone does not determine the path of evolution. Just as the purchaser in a store is dependent upon the bias of the storekeeper who lays in a stock of assorted goods, so evolution must humor any bias there may be in the variety of types presented for selection. Are men's wills changing? Is there a drift in the general average? If so, whither does it tend? Toward a merging with the Supreme Purpose, or away from it? Have we any instrument competent to discover as much as a hint of an answer to these questions?

Perhaps we have. It is true that the recent world cataclysm has reminded us all too clearly of the potency of knowledge to destroy; of the danger that our orthogenesis be of the fatal type; that man, having grown too clever, may perish by the very perfection of his own weapons. But if the proverbial cat has nine lives, the human race at present has some seventeen hundred million, and the presumption is that even the most disastrous conflict would leave some remnant to carry on. Meanwhile there are not lacking signs on which the optimist may hang his hopes of a happier issue of our orthogenesis. He will point out that since our evolution has been upward in the past, it is reasonable to expect it to continue so in the future. He will point to the rude ancestors, more beast than man, from whom we have ascended. Then, he will say, if you wish to form a conception of the future of our race, consider the foremost, the most enlightened spirits of today, and reflect that these will represent the average of a day that is coming. These men, looking out upon the world, are impressed above all with the essential unity of Nature, and of man with her. For "man is part of Nature, the part that studies the whole." Therefore, as man's eyes are opened by modern science to view the intricacies of atomic architecture, or to fathom the secret places of the stars, what is it but the Universe awakening, like some great giant, to a consciousness of his remoter members?[9] To the cold intellectual realization of this unity of man with the Universe there is an emotional counterpart. A full and intensely vivid realization

[9] This was sensed by Hegel, who held that "the course of history is the process, not simply by which man comes to a consciousness of God, but that by which God comes to a consciousness of himself." (A. K. Rogers, A Student's History of Philosophy, 1921, p. 448). Compare also H. G. Wells, God the Invisible King; and M. Lembat, Science Progress, 1923, p. 112.

of the inspiring truth is undoubtedly accompanied by feeling of
high exaltation. To this we have, among many others, the testimony of Wordsworth

> I felt the sentiment of Being spread
> O'er all that moves and all that seemeth still;
> O'er all that, lost beyond the reach of thought
> And human knowledge; to the human eye
> Invisible, yet liveth to the heart.
> . . . . Wonder not
> If high the transport, great the joy I felt
> Communing of this sort through earth and heaven
> With every sort of creature.

It seems inevitable that a lively sense of this merging of the Self with
the Universe shall hold as one of its constituents a fusion of personal
desires with the Supreme Purpose of the Universe. "No man,"
says Emerson "has a right perception of a truth, who has not been
reacted on by it, so as to be ready to be its martyr."

The relation of knowledge and of ignorance to will is discussed,
from a somewhat different angle, by Bertrand Russell in his book
Our Knowledge of the External World (1914, p. 234). He remarks:

> The apparent indeterminateness of the future . . . . is merely a
> result of our ignorance. It is plain that no desirable kind of free will can be
> dependent simply upon ignorance. . . . . Let us therefore imagine a set
> of beings who know the whole future with absolute certainty, and let us ask
> ourselves whether they could have anything that we should call free will.
> . . . . The beings we are imagining would easily come to know the causal
> connections of volitions and therefore *their volitions would be better calculated
> to satisfy their desires than ours are.*

If the extension of Spencer's hedonistic principle, as sketched
above, applies, and if through orthogenetic bias or otherwise the
human race shall provide the requisite material for selection to
operate upon, then these beings which Bertrand Russell "imagines"
for the sake of his argument, will become something of an actuality
as our evolution culminates. To them the words of Emerson will
apply, that they will be "made of the same stuff of which events are
made. . . . . The mind that is parallel with the laws of nature
will be in the current of events, and strong with their strength."
Their attitude will be biologically sound, for, as Claude Bernard has
said:

It is not by struggling against cosmic conditions that the organism develops and maintains its place; on the contrary, it is by an adaptation to, and agreement with, these conditions. So, the living being does not form an exception to the great natural harmony which makes things adapt themselves to one another: it breaks no concord; it is neither in contradiction to nor struggling against general cosmic forces; far from that, it forms a member of the universal concert of things, and the life of the animal, for example, is only a fragment of the total life of the universe.

Or, to quote a spokesman of our own generation, the closing words of Sir Charles Sherrington's Presidential Address still ring in our ears:

One privilege open to the human intellect is to attempt to comprehend . . . . the *how* of the living creature as a whole. In the biological synthesis of the individual this problem is concerned with mind. It includes examination of man himself as acting under a biological trend and process which is combining individuals into a multi-individual organization, a social organism surely new to the world. Man, viewing this great supra-individual process, can shape his course conformably with it even as an individual, feeling that . . . . to rebel would be to sink lower rather to continue his own evolution upward.

Thus, in the light of modern knowledge, man is beginning to discern more clearly what wise men of all ages have intuitively felt—his essential unity with the Universe; and the unity of his puny efforts with the great trend of all Nature. A race with desires all opposed to Nature could not long endure; he that survives must, for that very fact, be in some measure a collaborator with Nature. With extending knowledge must come awakening consciousness of active partnership with the Cosmos—"When souls reach a certain clearness of perception, they accept a knowledge above selfishness;" and "he that sees through the design must *will* that which must *be*." This is no mere resignation of a man to his fate, though the saying of Anatole France be true "Les grandes âmes se résignent avec une sainte joie." Not even *joyful* resignation is adequate; the state of the fully awakened consciousness is better described by the great physicist Clerk Maxwell, as "an abandoment of wilfulness without extinction of will, but rather by a great development of will whereby, instead of being consciously free and really in subjection to an unknown law, it becomes consciously acting by law, and really free from interference of unrecognized laws."

Such is the outlook to which the development of modern Science seems inevitably to be leading the thoughts of men. This is the goal of evolution, the perfect adjustment of feelings to actions, which guarantees survival: To say with the great Stoic—"O Universe, whatsoever is in harmony with thee, is in harmony with me." The being whose will is so adjusted is Fortune's favorite; all things must bend to his will as they bend to Nature's law. For his will is Nature's law.

SYNOPTIC CHART

OF PHYSICAL BIOLOGY AND ALLIED DISCIPLINES AS TREATED IN THIS WORK

"Ce mage divisa en plusieurs parties ce qui n'avait pas besoin d'être divisé; il prouva méthodiquement tout ce qui était clair; il enseigna tout ce qu'on savait; il se passionna froidement, et sortit suant et hors d'haleine. Toute l'assemblée alors se réveilla et crut avoir assisté a une instruction."—*Voltaire.*

SYNOPTIC CHARTS

Guide to References. The numerals prefixed to the several items on Charts I, II, III, IV refer to the following list, which indicates some of the principal references to such items in this book. In a few instances of points not otherwise covered in this book supplementary references to the literature are given.

ITEM	PAGE	ITEM	PAGE
	CHART I	32	108, 109.
		33	108, 109.
1	28, 29	34	103 et seq.
2	28, 29	35	106, 152.
3	28, 29	36	42, 106, 152.
4	28, 29	37	57 et seq.
5	28, 29	38	143 et seq.
6	57	39	325 et seq.
7	58, 64		
8	58		
9	57		CHART II
10	47, 48		
11	48; Am. Jl. Hygiene vol. 3 Jan. Suppl. p. 96.	40	45, 51.
		41	46, 51.
12	57	42	46, 51.
13	100, 128	43	See items 44 to 56.
14	130	44	Not discussed in this work.
15	130	45	See items 46 to 56
16	101, 130 et seq.; Ann. Natur-phil. 1910 vol. 10 p. 65.	46	Proc. Natl. Acad. Sci. vol. 7 1921 p. 169.
17	130, 132 et seq.	47	143, 259, 276. See also items 48 to 56.
18	101, 115, 117 et seq.		
19	87, 117 et seq.	48	261 (Special Case) 262, 265 (Radioactive equilib-rium). Proc. Natl. Acad. Sci. vol. 7 1921 p. 170.
20	Not discussed in this work.		
21	110 et seq.; 115		
22	110 et seq.		
23	110 et seq.		
24	115, 117.	49	259 et seq.
25	Not treated in this work.	50	See items 53 to 56.
26	128	51	See item 48.
27	103 et seq.; 153, 155.	52	97, 212, 229.
28	103 et seq.	53	44, 45.
29	See items 30 to 34.	54	46, 122 et seq.
30	106, 152 et seq.	55	345 et seq.
31	69 et seq.; see also C. Eijkman, Proc. Amster-dam Acad. Sci. 1912 p. 629; Reichenbach, Zeit-schr. f. Hygiene und Infektions-krankheiten 1911 vol. 69 p. 171.	56	122 et seq.
		57	280 et seq.
		58	45, 58, 59.
		59	See items 60, 61, 62.
		60	Am. Jl. Hygiene vol. 3 Jan. Supply. 1923 p. 8.
		61	60 et seq.

ITEM	PAGE	ITEM	PAGE
62	Am. Jl. Hygiene vol. 3 Jan. Suppl. 1923 p. 25.	100	Not specifically treated in this work. For incidental references see items 105, 106, 107, 117 to 119.
63	See items 64 to 76.		
64	64 et seq.		
65	152 et seq.	101	See items 102 to 119.
66	64 et seq.	102	209, 215, 333.
67	77 et seq.	103	218, 226, 334.
68	79, 82; Am. Jl. Hygiene loc. cit.	104	225; see also item 103
		105	229 to 232, 236.
69	83 et seq., 88 et seq.	106	246, 247.
70	94.	107	252 et seq.; 254.
71	266, 296, 297; see also items 72 to 76.	108	256.
		109	See items 110 to 119.
72	61, 146 to 149.	110	188.
73	Not treated in this work.	111	225 to 228.
74	63.	112	See item 111.
75	63.	113	232 et seq.
76	Not treated in this work.	114	248 et seq.; 250.
		115	255.
		116	Not treated in this work.
	CHART III	117	232 to 255.
		118	234, 248.
77	59, 145.	119	239 to 242.
78	59.	120	Not treated in this work.
79	146, 148, 149.	121	See item 122.
80	See items 81 to 125.	122	180, 238, 279; see also item 119.
81	See items 82 and 84.		
82	See item 83.	123	280 et seq.
83	152 et seq.; 155, 157.	124	300 et seq.
84	144.	125	321.
85	280 et seq.		
86	259 et seq.		CHART IV
87	276 et seq.		
88	161 et seq.	126	331 et seq.
89	163.	127	See items 128 and 129.
90	95, 163.	128	345 et seq., 358.
91	See items 92 to 96.	129	Not treated in this work.
92	See items 93, 94.	130	See items 131, 132.
93	164, 171 et seq., 175, 177	131	336 to 345.
94	Not treated in this work.	132	Not treated in this work.
95	166 et seq.	133	See items 134 et seq.
96	See items 97 to 122.	134	328 to 330, 336.
97	277; see also items 98, 99.	135	336 et seq.
98	173 et seq.; 181.	136	See item 137 et seq.
99	181.		

ITEM	PAGE	ITEM	PAGE
137	See item 138 et seq.		topics see special works on
138	317.		the subject, as, for example, Lefèvre, La Chaleur Animale et Bio-énergétique, 1911.
139	300, 311.		
140	363, 370.		
141	45, 46, 122, 345, 348.		
142 ⎫ 143 ⎭	Jl. Washington Acad. Sci. vol. 2 1912 p. 69.	149	410 (Table); see also item 150.
144	17, 336 et seq.; 362 et seq.; 410 et seq.	150	340, 347, 366, 411.
		151	See items 153, 154.
145	339, 371 et seq.; 410 et seq.	152	339, 346, 381, 412, 414, 415, 472.
146	339, 347 et seq.; 363 et seq.		
147	371 et seq.; 410 et seq.	153	350.
148	Indirectly referred to in the substance of pages 383, 394, 395, 398, 402, 407. For the general energetics of nutrition and related	154	See item 155.
		155	350, 353, 416.
		156 to 163	See Table 34, page 412, and text relating thereto.

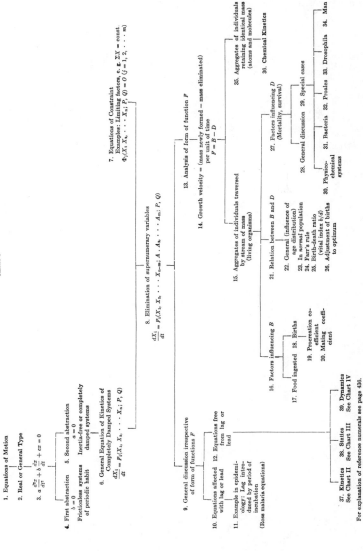

TABULAR SYNOPSIS OF PHYSICAL BIOLOGY

CHART I

TABULAR SYNOPSIS OF PHYSICAL BIOLOGY

CHART II

Kinetics

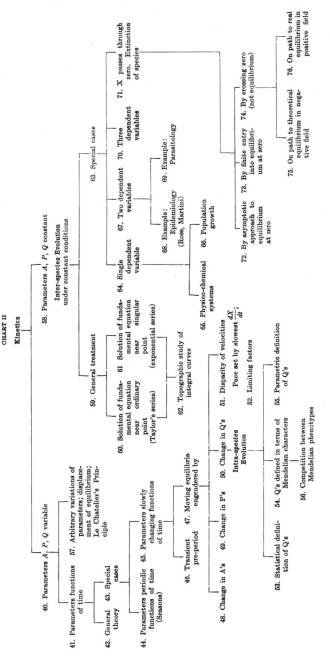

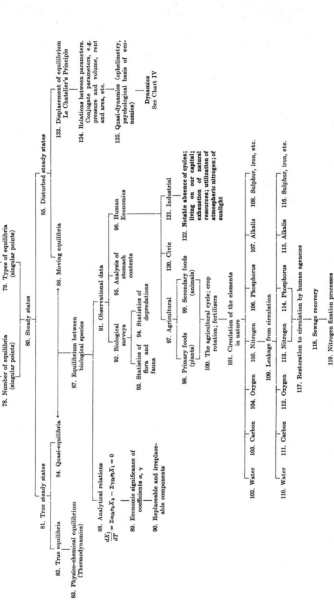

TABULAR SYNOPSIS OF PHYSICAL BIOLOGY

CHART III

Statics

77. Fundamental Equations of Statics
$F_1 = F_2 = \ldots = F_n = 0$

78. Number of equilibria (singular points)

79. Types of equilibria (singular points)

80. Steady states

81. True steady states

82. True equilibria

83. Physico-chemical equilibrium (Thermodynamics)

84. Quasi-equilibria

85. Disturbed steady states

86. Moving equilibria

87. Equilibrium between biological species

88. Analytical relations
$\frac{dX_1}{dT} = \Sigma q_{ik} P_k X_k - \Sigma \gamma_{ik} P_k X_i = 0$

89. Economic significance of coefficients α, γ

90. Replaceable and irreplaceable components

91. Observational data

92. Biological surveys

93. Statistics of flora and fauna

94. Statistics of depredations

95. Analysis of stomach contents

96. Human Economics

97. Agricultural

98. Primary foods (plants)

99. Secondary foods (animals)

100. The agricultural cycle; crop rotation; fertilisers

120. Civic

121. Industrial

122. Notable absence of cycles; living on our capital; exhaustion of natural resources; utilization of atmospheric nitrogen; of sunlight

123. Displacement of equilibrium Le Chatelier's Principle

124. Relations between parameters. Conjugate parameters, e.g. pressure and volume, rent and area, etc.

125. Quasi-dynamics (ophelimetry, psychological basis of economics)

Dynamics
See Chart IV

101. Circulation of the elements in nature

102. Water   103. Carbon   104. Oxygen   105. Nitrogen   106. Phosphorus   107. Alkalis   108. Sulphur, iron, etc.

109. Leakage from circulation

110. Water   111. Carbon   112. Oxygen   113. Nitrogen   114. Phosphorus   115. Alkalis   116. Sulphur, iron, etc.

117. Restoration to circulation by human agencies

118. Sewage recovery

119. Nitrogen fixation processes

TABULAR SYNOPSIS OF PHYSICAL BIOLOGY

CHART IV

Dynamics

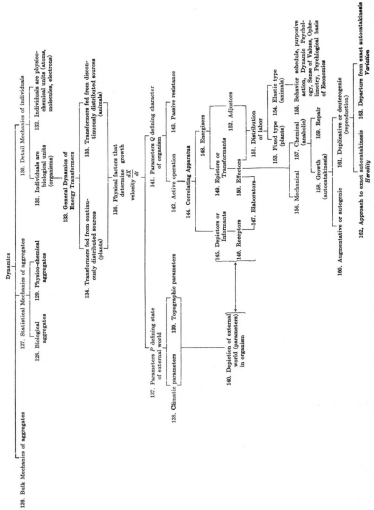

126. Bulk Mechanics of aggregates

127. Statistical Mechanics of aggregates

128. Biological aggregates

129. Physico-chemical aggregates

130. Detail Mechanics of individuals

131. Individuals are biological units (organisms)

132. Individuals are physico-chemical units (atoms, molecules, electrons)

133. **General Dynamics of Energy Transformers**

134. Transformers fed from continuously distributed sources (plants)

135. Transformers fed from discontinuously distributed sources (animals)

136. Physical factors that determine growth velocity $\frac{dX}{dt}$

137. Parameters P defining state of external world

138. Climatic parameters

139. Topographic parameters

140. Depiction of external world (parameters) in organism

141. Parameters Q defining character of organism

142. Active operation

143. Passive resistance

144. Correlating Apparatus

145. Depictors or Informants

146. Receptors

147. Elaborators

148. Energizers

149. Epictors or Transformants

150. Effectors

151. Distribution of labor

152. Adjustors

153. Fixed type (plants)

154. Elastic type (animals)

155. Behavior schedule, purposive action, Dynamic Psychology, Sense of Values, Ophelimetry, Psychological basis of Economics

156. Mechanical

157. Chemical (anabolic)

158. Growth (autocatakinesis)

159. Repair

160. Augmentative or autogenic

161. Duplicative or deuterogenic (reproduction)

162. Approach to exact autocatakinesis *Heredity*

163. Departure from exact autocatakinesis *Variation*

ADDENDA

The following references and notes, which have been omitted from the text through inadvertence or because they came to the author's notice too late, are here appended as a supplement. As stated in the Preface, no attempt at completeness of bibliography has been made. Perhaps, however, the material presented in these pages may be found, by anyone sufficiently interested, to furnish a serviceable base of departure for the gathering of a more exhaustive collation.

Chapter I, page 9, footnote 10. See also L. A. Herrera, Royal Academy of the Lincei, June 15, 1924. Imitation of nervous and cellular tissue, by means of potassium hydroxide, silica and alcohol.

Chapter II, page 36. Compare also A. J. Lotka, Irreversibility, Cosmic and Microcosmic, Jour. Washington Acad. Sci., August, 1924, pp. 352–3. It should perhaps be pointed out that the dissipative processes of nature, as discussed in this chapter, include, of course, both processes irreversible with regard to macroscopic operations, and also processes irreversible in the usual sense, that is, thermodynamically irreversible.

Chapter II, page 44. *Intra-group Evolution*. If the composition or constitution of a group or species of organisms is described in terms of a frequency function, intra-group evolution is exhibited by the fact that the characteristic coefficients in such a function are functions of the time. This point has been referred to by Arne Fisher in Amer. Math. Monthly. March–April issue, 1923, p. 97. Fisher thus writes the normal frequency function in the form

$$y = \frac{1}{2 \pi \varphi_2(t)} e^{[x - \varphi_1(t)]^2 / 2 \varphi_2(t)}$$

Chapter V, page 49 Compare also G. Bohn, La Forme et le Mouvement, Flammarion, 1921, p. 161.

Chapter VII, *Growth of Individual Organism*, page 71. In this connection reference may also be made to the work of Lecomte de Nouy, of the Rockefeller Institute for Medical Research, on the rate of cicatrization of wounds.

Page 72, footnote 9, add the following reference: H. C. Bastian, The Nature and Origin of Living Matter, p. 47.

Chapter VIII. For further discussion of the mathematical analysis of epidemiology and related topics see also R. Ross, Proc. Royal Soc., Ser. *A*, vol. 92, 1916, p. 204; vol. 93, 1917, pp. 212, 225, also; J. Brownlee, Proc. Royal Medical Soc., May, 1918, p. 115.

Chapter XV, Composition of Terrestrial Matter, page 194.   See also V. M. Goldschmidt, Geochemische Verteilungsgesetze der Elemente, Vitenskapsselskapets Skrifter I Mat.- Naturv. Klasse, 1923, no. 3, 1924, nos. 4 and 5; H. S. Washington, Jour. Washington Acad. Sci., 1924, p. 435; L. H. Adams, ibid., p. 459; J. H. Jeans, Nature, vol. 114, 1924, p. 828; H. Jeffreys, The Earth, Cambridge University Press, 1924.

Chapter XV, page 203.   Reference should have been made to Macallum's paper in the Trans. Roy. Soc. Canada, 1908, ii, p. 145.   The marine origin of terrestrial animals was taught in remote antiquity, by Anaximander (610–540 B.C.)

Chapter XXII, page 298.   The rôle of the hands in the evolution of man's intelligence seems to have been clearly recognized by the Greek philosopher Anaxagoras (500–428 B.C.)   "He explained man's intelligence by the power of manipulation that came when the forelimbs were freed from the tasks of locomotion" (W. Durant).

Chapter XXIII, page 300.   Compare also O. Matousek, Geological Laws of Population, Amer. Jour. Physical Anthropology, 1924, vol. 7, p. 389.

Chapter XXV, page 342.   For further details regarding automatic telphone exchanges see also F. A. Ellson, Automatic Telephones (Pitman's Technical Primers, London, 1924); W. Aitken, Automatic Telephone Systems (Ernst Benn, London, 1924)

Page 354.   The influence of diet upon the mode of life was remarked by Aristotle (384–322 B.C.): "Of beasts some are gregarious, and others are solitary—they live in the way which is best adapted to obtain the food of their choice."   Very clearly the characteristics of animals and plants are referred to their respective food sources by La Mettrie in his little book *L'Homme Plante* (1748).   He remarks very pointedly: "Les êtres sans besoins sont aussi sans ésprit."   (See also pages 219 and 366 in Chapters XVII and XXVI.)

Chapter XXVI, pages 265.   For historical data on the introduction of eyeglasses see, for example, R. Greef, Die Erfindung der Augengläser, (A. Ehrlich, Berlin, 1921).

Page 366.   Regarding the modern industrial development, with the use of machinery and, incidentally, with reference to the phonograph and radio concerts of today, the following words of Aristotle have acquired a strangely prophetic significance: "If every instrument should accomplish its own work, obeying or anticipating the will of others, ... if the shuttle should weave, or the plectrum touch the lyre, without a hand to guide them, then chief workmen would not need assistants, nor masters slaves."

Chapter XXVII, page 374.   Regarding the delimitation of the self, and related matters see also E. Mach, Analyse der Empfindungen; K. Pearson, Grammar of Science, 1900, p. 63; B. Bavink, Ergebnisse und Probleme der Naturwissenschaften, pp. 313, 320 et seq.

Page 375.   Add to footnote 7: Compare also the saying of Lamartine: "It is not I who think, but my ideas which think for me."   And a modern writer has remarked that "it is not we who think, thinking is rather something that happens to us."   Accordingly it would be grammatically better advised to employ an impersonal form of verb, and to say, instead of *I think*, rather *it thinks,* just as we say *it thunders.* Language is not altogether devoid of evidence of a vague realization of this. Especially in describing dreams and visions, with their characteristic submergence of the *ego*, we use such terms as *methought, es dünkte mich,* etc.

Chapter XXX, page 395. Poets are good psychologists, in part, no doubt, because by nature introspective; in part, also, because keenly interested in human nature. The relation of emotions and of reason to action is well stated by Pope

> "On life's vast ocean diversely we sail,
> Reason the card, but passion is the gale."

And La Fontaine has it

> "O douce volupté sans qui dès notre enfance
> Le vivre et le mourir nous deviendraient égaux—"

General references. The following references, some of them guides to bibliographic sources, may be regarded essentially as an extension of the footnote 8 on page 366.

Chapter XXVI. M. Schips, Mathematik und Biologie, Teubner, 1922. Contains a bibliography.

H. Przibram, Anwendung Elementarer Mathematik auf Biologische Probleme, Engelmann, Leipzig, 1908. Contains a bibliography.

G. Bohn, La forme et le mouvement, essai de dynamique de la vie. Flammarion, Paris, 1921. Contains a bibliography.

O. Fischer, Physiologische Mechanik, in Encyklopaedie der Mathematischen Wissenschaften, vol. IV, I, II, Heft I, pp. 62–126. The index on the literature of the subject contains a list of 21 textbooks and 421 monographs.

SCIENTIFIC AND TECHNICAL PAPERS
by Alfred J. Lotka

1. Note on the Volume Change on Mixing Two Gases, *Engineering and Mining Journal,* 1907, vol. 83, p. 956.
2. Relation Between Birth Rates and Death Rates, *Science,* 1907, vol. 26, p. 21.
3. Studies on the Mode of Growth of Material Aggregates, *American Journal of Science,* 1907, vol. 24, pp. 199, 375.
4. Some Formulae and Tables for Gas Calculations in the Contact Process for Sulphuric Acid, *Chemical Engineer,* 1909, vol. 9, p. 91.
5. Zur Theorie der periodischen Reaktionen, *Zeitschrift für physikalische Chemie,* 1910, vol. 72, p. 508.
6. Contribution to the Theory of Periodic Reactions, *Journal of Physical Chemistry,* 1910, vol. 14, p. 271.
7. A Problem in Age-Distribution (joint author with F. R. Sharpe), *Philosophical Magazine,* 1911, vol. 21, p. 435.
8. Die Evolution vom Standpunkte der Physik, *Ostwalds Annalen der Naturphilosophie,* 1911, vol. 10, p. 59.
   For English translation see *Scientific American Supplement,* 1913, pp. 345, 354, 379.
9. On the Ratios which the Amounts of Substances in Radioactive Equilibrium Bear to One Another, *Philosophical Magazine,* vol. 22, 1911, p. 353.
10. Quantitative Studies in Epidemiology, *Nature,* 1912, vol. 88, p. 497.
11. Ein Fall von Autokatakinese mit oscillatorischem Verlauf, *Zeitschrift für physiakalische Chemie,* 1912, vol. 80, p. 159.
12. Change of State. Discussion of a General Case, *Physical Review,* 1912, vol. 24, p. 235.
13. Evolution in Discontinuous Systems, *Journal of the Washington Academy of Sciences,* 1912, vol. 2, pp. 2, 49, 66.
14. A Natural Population Norm, *Journal of the Washington Academy of Sciences,* 1913, vol. 3, pp. 241, 289.
15. An Objective Standard of Value Derived from the Principle of Evolution, *Journal of the Washington Academy of Sciences,* 1914, vol. 4, pp. 409, 447, 499.
16. Efficiency as a Factor in Organic Evolution, *Journal of the Washington Academy of Sciences,* 1915, vol. 5, pp. 360, 397.
17. A New Method of Enlarging Photographs Without the Use of a Lens, *Physical Review,* 1916, vol. 7, p. 660; U.S. Patent No. 1,176,384, March 21, 1916.

18. A Contribution to Quantitative Epidemiology, *Journal of the Washington Academy of Sciences*, 1919, vol. 9, p. 73.

19. The Relation Between Birth Rate and Death Rate in a Normal Population, and the Rational Basis of an Empirical Formula for the Mean Length of Life, given by William Farr, *Quarterly Publications of the American Statistical Association*, 1918, vol. 16, p. 121.

20. Evolution and Irreversibility, *Science Progress*, 1920, vol. 14, p. 406.

21. Undamped Oscillations Derived from the Law of Mass Action, *Journal of the American Chemical Society*, 1920, vol. 42, p. 1595.

22. Analytical Note on Certain Rhythmic Relations in Organic Systems, *Proceedings of the National Academy of Sciences*, 1920, vol. 6, p. 410.

23. Contribution to the General Kinetics of Material Transformations, *Proceedings of the American Academy of Arts and Sciences*, 1920, vol. 55, p. 137.

24. Note on Moving Equilibria, *Proceedings of the National Academy of Sciences*, 1921, vol. 7, p. 168.

25. Note on the Economic Conversion Factors of Energy, *Proceedings of the National Academy of Sciences*, 1921, vol. 7, p. 192.

26. A Simple Graphic Contruction for Farr's Relation Between Birth Rate, Death Rate and Mean Length of Life, *Journal of the American Statistical Association*, 1921, vol. 17, p. 998.

27. The General Conditions of Validity of the Principle of Le Chatelier, *Proceedings of the American Academy of Arts and Sciences*, 1922, vol. 57, p. 21.

28. Contribution to the Energetics of Evolution, *Proceedings of the National Academy of Sciences*, 1922, vol. 8, p. 147.

29. Natural Selection as a Physical Principle, *Proceedings of the National Academy of Sciences*, 1922, vol. 8, p. 151.

30. The Stability of the Normal Age Distribution, *Proceedings of the National Academy of Sciences*, 1922, vol. 8, p. 339.

31. Contribution to Quantitative Parasitology, *Journal of the Washington Academy of Sciences*, 1923, vol. 13, p. 152.

32. Martini's Equations for the Epidemiology of Immunizing Diseases, *Nature*, 1923, vol. 111, p. 633.

33. Contributions to the Analysis of Malaria Epidemiology (joint author with F. R. Sharpe), *Supplement to the American Journal of Hygiene*, 1923, vol. 3, p. 1.

34. The Principle of Le Chatelier in Biology and Medicine, *American Journal of Hygiene,* 1923, vol. 3, p. 355.

35. The Intervention of Consciousness in Mechanics, *Science Progress,* 1924, vol. 18, p. 407.

36. Two Models in Statistical Mechanics, *American Mathematical Monthly,* 1924, vol. 31, p. 121.

37. Probability Increase in Shuffling, and the Asymmetry of Time, *Science,* 1924, vol. 59, p. 532.

38. Irreversibility, Cosmic and Microcosmic, *Journal of the Washington Academy of Sciences,* 1924, vol. 14, p. 352.

39. On the True Rate of Natural Increase of a Population (joint author with Louis I. Dublin), *Journal of the American Statistical Association,* 1925, vol. 20, p. 305.

40. The Empirical Elements in Population Forecasts, *Journal of the American Statistical Association,* 1925, vol. 20, p. 569.

41. The Measure of Net Fertility, *Journal of the Washington Academy of Sciences,* 1925, vol. 15, p. 469.

42. Tests for the Significance of Slope Constants, section contained in 'Cancer Mortality Among Insured Wage Earners and Their Families,' *Metropolitan Life Insurance Company,* 1925, p. 79.

43. The Frequency Distribution of Scientific Productivity, *Journal of the Washington Academy of Sciences,* 1926, vol. 16, p. 317.

44. The Progressive Adjustment of Age Distribution to Fecundity, *Journal of the Washington Academy of Sciences,* 1926, vol. 16, p. 505.

45. The Components of Death Curves (joint author with Louis I. Dublin and E. W. Kopf), *American Journal of Hygiene,* 1927, vol. 7, p. 299.

46. The Size of American Families in the Eighteenth Century, *Journal of the American Statistical Association,* 1927, vol. 22, p. 154.

47. The Actuarial Treatment of Official Birth Records, *The Eugenics Review,* 1927, vol. 19, p. 257.

48. Sterility in American Marriages, *Proceedings of the National Academy of Sciences,* 1928, vol. 14, p. 99.

49. The Progeny of a Population Element, *American Journal of Hygiene,* 1928, vol. 8, p. 875.

50. Families of Curves of Pursuit and Their Isochrones, *American Mathematical Monthly,* 1928, vol. 35, p. 421.

51. The Spread of Generations, *Human Biology,* 1929, vol. 1, p. 305.

52. Biometric Functions in a Population Growing in Accordance with a Prescribed Law, *Proceedings of the National Academy of Sciences,* 1929, vol. 15, p. 793.

53. Review of 'The Balance of Births and Deaths, Volume 1, Western and Northern Europe, by R. Kuczynski, Macmillan 1928,' *Journal of the American Statistical Association,* September, 1929, p. 332.

54. A Reply to Dr. Lotka's Review of 'The Balance of Births and Deaths,' by R. Kuczynski. Rejoinder by A. J. Lotka, *Journal of the American Statistical Association,* March 1930, pp. 84, 85.

55. The True Rate of Natural Increase of the Population of the United States. Revision on the Basis of Recent Data (joint author with Louis I. Dublin), *Metron,* 1930, vol. 8, p. 107.

56. Present Outlook for Population Increase (joint author with Louis I. Dublin), *American Sociological Society,* vol. XXIV, No. 2, 1930, p. 106.

57. Some Elementary Properties of Moments of Frequency Distributions, *Journal of the Washington Academy of Sciences,* 1931, vol. 21, p. 17.

58. Orphanhood in Relation to Demographic Factors, A Study in Population Analysis, *Metron,* 1931, vol. 9, p. 37.

59. The Extinction of Families, I, II. *Journal of the Washington Academy of Sciences,* 1931, vol. 21, pp. 377, 453.

60. The Structure of a Growing Population, Paper presented before the Second General Assembly of the International Union for the Scientific Investigation of Population Problems, London 1931, and published in the *Proceedings* (Problems of Population), George Allen & Unwin, 1932. Also published in *Human Biology,* 1931, vol. 3, p. 459.

61. The Average Size of the Family in a Stationary and a Diminishing Population (joint author with Louis I. Dublin), *International Congress for Studies Regarding Population Problems,* Rome, 1931.

62. Contributions to the Mathematical Theory of Capture; Conditions for Capture, *Proceedings of the National Academy of Sciences,* 1932, vol. 18, p. 172.

63. The Growth of Mixed Populations: Two Species Competing for a Common Food Supply, *Journal of the Washington Academy of Sciences,* 1932, vol. 22, p. 461.

64. Zur Dynamik der Bevölkerungsentwicklung, *Allgemeines Statistisches Archiv,* 1932, vol. 22, p. 587; 1933, vol. 23, p. 98.

65. Industrial Replacement, *Skandinavisk Aktuarietidskrift,* 1933, p. 51.

66. Applications de l'analyse au phénomène démographique, *Journal de la Société de Statistique de Paris,* 1933, vol. 74, p. 336.

67. The History of Longevity in the United States (joint author with Louis I. Dublin), *Human Biology,* 1934, vol. 6, p. 43.

68. The Construction of Life Tables by Correlation (joint author with Louis I. Dublin and M. Spiegelman), *Metron,* 1935, vol. 12, p. 121.

69. The Geographic Distribution of Intrinsic Natural Increase in the United States, and an Examination of the Relation Between Several Measures of Net Reproductivity, *Journal of the American Statistical Association,* 1936, vol. 31, p. 273.

70. Modern Trends in the Birth Rate, *The Annals of American Academy of Political and Social Science,* November 1936, vol. 188, p. 1.

71. Population Analysis (Abstract), *Colorado College Publication,* General Series, #208, Studies Series, #21, September 1936.

72. A Historical Error Corrected, *Human Biology,* 1937, vol. 9, p. 104.

73. Uses of the Life Table in Vital Statistics (joint author with Louis I. Dublin), *American Journal of Public Health,* 1937, vol. 27, p. 481.

74. Population Analysis: A Theorem Regarding the Stable Age Distribution, *Journal of the Washington Academy of Sciences,* 1937, vol. 27, p. 299.

75. Some Recent Results in Population Analysis, *Journal of the American Statistical Association,* 1938, vol. 33, p. 164.

76. Quelques résultats récents de l'analyse démographique. *Congrès International de la population,* Paris, 1937, I. Théorie generale de la population, p. 96.

77. Contact Points of Population Study with Related Branches of Science, *The Proceedings of the American Philosophical Society,* 1939, vol. 80, p. 601.

78. A Contribution to the Theory of Self-Renewing Aggregates, with Special Reference to Industrial Replacement, *Annals of Mathematical Statistics,* 1939, vol. X, p. 1.

79. Note on an Integral Equation in Population Analysis, *Annals of Mathematical Statistics,* 1939, vol. X, p. 144.

80. The Theory of Industrial Replacement, A Commentary, *Skandinavisk Aktuarietidskrift*, 1940, p. 1.

81. Sur une équation intégrale de l'analyse démographique et industrielle, *Bulletin de l'Association des Actuaires Suisses*, 1940, vol. 40, p. 1.

82. The Trend of the Birth Rate by Age of Mother and Order of Birth (joint author with Mortimer Spiegelman), *Journal of the American Statistical Association*, 1940, vol. 35, p. 595.

83. The Law of Urban Concentration, *Science*, August 15, 1941, vol. 94, #2433, p. 164.

84. The Progeny of an Entire Population, *Annals of Mathematical Statistics*, 1942, vol. XIII, p. 115.

85. Some Reflections—Statistical and Other—On a Non-Material Universe, *Journal of the American Statistical Association*, March 1943, vol. 38, pp. 1-15.

86. Place of Intrinsic Rate of Natural Increase in Population Analysis, *Proceedings of Eighth American Scientific Congress*, May 1940, vol. VIII.

87. Comparison of Two Methods of Estimating Capitalized Value of Earning Capacity, *Journal of the Washington Academy of Sciences*, vol. 34, #1, January 1944, p. 10.

88. Evolution and Thermodynamics, *Science and Society*, 1944, vol. VIII, #2, p. 161.

89. Trends in Longevity (joint author with L. I. Dublin), *Annals of American Academy of Political and Social Science*, 1945, vol. 237, p. 123.

90. Population Analysis as a Chapter in the Mathematical Theory of Evolution, in testimonial volume *Essays on Growth and Form*, presented to D'Arcy Wentworth Thompson, 1945, University Press, Oxford.

91. The Law of Evolution as a Maximal Principle, *Human Biology*, 1945, vol. 17, p. 167.

92. Evaluation of Some Methods of Measuring Fertility. Paper presented at *International Statistical Congress*, Washington, 1947.

93. Application of Recurrent Series in Renewal Theory. *Annals of Mathematical Statistics*, 1948, vol. 19, p. 190.

94. Physical Aspects of Organic Evolution. *Bulletin of Mathematical Biophysics*, 1948, vol. 10, p. 103.

INDEX OF NAMES

INDEX OF SUBJECTS

A

Abbildung, 363.

Accelerations vanishing with velocities, 29.

Accessibility of raw materials, 206–207.

Accumulators, 328.

Adaptation purely relative, 63.

Adjustors, 339, 381; evolution of, 346; location of, 381; chart, 412; physiological or anatomical, 414; external, 414; economic, 415; internal, 472.

Age and Area theory, 311.

Age distribution, influence on growth, 109; "normal", 110, 114; "stable", 110, 112, 113, 114.

Agriculture, evolution of, 180.

Aggregates, growth, 100; of constant units, 129; of variable units, 130.

Aim, accuracy and versatility of, 338.

Aimed collisions, 337, 409.

Alfalfa weevil, 166.

Anabions, 329.

Animal and plant, distinction, 4–5.

Animals characteristically active, mobile, 336; as catabions, 329.

Annihilation, see extermination, also, extinction of species.

Approximate expression for equilibrium proportions, 267–268.

Aptitudes, influence of special, upon motivation, 399.

Aquatic, life, interspecies equilibrium, 171; aquatic atmosphere, 193.

Aquiculture, 173–181.

Area and rent, 288–305; area as topographic parameter, 301; area and age, see *age*.

Artificial receptors, 364, 440, correlating apparatus, 410, 440.

Assumptions, implicit, 376–377.

Asymmetry of time, 30 et seq., 37.

Atmosphere, 185; losses from, 188; accessions to, 192; aquatic, 193.

Autistic thinking, 410.

Autocatalysis, 72.

Automatic telephone exchange, 342, 440.

Automaton type of behavior schedule, 350.

B

Bacteria, growth of, 69.

Bargain, mutually selfish, 415.

Beef production, 132 et seq; efficiency, 136.

Behavior schedule, 346; rigid or automaton type, 350; elastic type, 350; effect of change in, 350; regulation according to maximum principle, 351; of ideal organism, relation to that of actual, 352; effect of small departure from perfect adjustment, 353; gainful occupations, 416.

Behavior types, 7.

Benign circles, 298, 440.

Biassed movement, exemplified by chess, 343; biassed evolution, 380.

Biochemistry, 317.

Biological basis of economics, 163, 164; surveys, 164.

Biophysics, program of, 49.

Birthrate and deathrate, relation between, 115; in "normal" population, 115; adjustment to optimum, 128; economical and lavish, 131, 132 et seq., 135.

A CATALOGUE OF SELECTED DOVER BOOKS
IN ALL FIELDS OF INTEREST

AMERICA'S OLD MASTERS, James T. Flexner. Four men emerged unexpectedly from provincial 18th century America to leadership in European art: Benjamin West, J. S. Copley, C. R. Peale, Gilbert Stuart. Brilliant coverage of lives and contributions. Revised, 1967 edition. 69 plates. 365pp. of text.

21806-6 Paperbound $3.00

FIRST FLOWERS OF OUR WILDERNESS: AMERICAN PAINTING, THE COLONIAL PERIOD, James T. Flexner. Painters, and regional painting traditions from earliest Colonial times up to the emergence of Copley, West and Peale Sr., Foster, Gustavus Hesselius, Feke, John Smibert and many anonymous painters in the primitive manner. Engaging presentation, with 162 illustrations. xxii + 368pp.

22180-6 Paperbound $3.50

THE LIGHT OF DISTANT SKIES: AMERICAN PAINTING, 1760-1835, James T. Flexner. The great generation of early American painters goes to Europe to learn and to teach: West, Copley, Gilbert Stuart and others. Allston, Trumbull, Morse; also contemporary American painters—primitives, derivatives, academics—who remained in America. 102 illustrations. xiii + 306pp.   22179-2 Paperbound $3.50

A HISTORY OF THE RISE AND PROGRESS OF THE ARTS OF DESIGN IN THE UNITED STATES, William Dunlap. Much the richest mine of information on early American painters, sculptors, architects, engravers, miniaturists, etc. The only source of information for scores of artists, the major primary source for many others. Unabridged reprint of rare original 1834 edition, with new introduction by James T. Flexner, and 394 new illustrations. Edited by Rita Weiss. 6⅝ x 9⅝.

21695-0, 21696-9, 21697-7 Three volumes, Paperbound $15.00

EPOCHS OF CHINESE AND JAPANESE ART, Ernest F. Fenollosa. From primitive Chinese art to the 20th century, thorough history, explanation of every important art period and form, including Japanese woodcuts; main stress on China and Japan, but Tibet, Korea also included. Still unexcelled for its detailed, rich coverage of cultural background, aesthetic elements, diffusion studies, particularly of the historical period. 2nd, 1913 edition. 242 illustrations. lii + 439pp. of text.

20364-6, 20365-4 Two volumes, Paperbound $6.00

THE GENTLE ART OF MAKING ENEMIES, James A. M. Whistler. Greatest wit of his day deflates Oscar Wilde, Ruskin, Swinburne; strikes back at inane critics, exhibitions, art journalism; aesthetics of impressionist revolution in most striking form. Highly readable classic by great painter. Reproduction of edition designed by Whistler. Introduction by Alfred Werner. xxxvi + 334pp.

21875-9 Paperbound $3.00

VISUAL ILLUSIONS: THEIR CAUSES, CHARACTERISTICS, AND APPLICATIONS, Matthew Luckiesh. Thorough description and discussion of optical illusion, geometric and perspective, particularly; size and shape distortions, illusions of color, of motion; natural illusions; use of illusion in art and magic, industry, etc. Most useful today with op art, also for classical art. Scores of effects illustrated. Introduction by William H. Ittleson. 100 illustrations. xxi + 252pp.
21530-X Paperbound $2.00

A HANDBOOK OF ANATOMY FOR ART STUDENTS, Arthur Thomson. Thorough, virtually exhaustive coverage of skeletal structure, musculature, etc. Full text, supplemented by anatomical diagrams and drawings and by photographs of undraped figures. Unique in its comparison of male and female forms, pointing out differences of contour, texture, form. 211 figures, 40 drawings, 86 photographs. xx + 459pp.
5⅜ x 8⅜.
21163-0 Paperbound $3.50

150 MASTERPIECES OF DRAWING, Selected by Anthony Toney. Full page reproductions of drawings from the early 16th to the end of the 18th century, all beautifully reproduced: Rembrandt, Michelangelo, Dürer, Fragonard, Urs, Graf, Wouwerman, many others. First-rate browsing book, model book for artists. xviii + 150pp.
8⅜ x 11¼.
21032-4 Paperbound⋅ $3.50

THE LATER WORK OF AUBREY BEARDSLEY, Aubrey Beardsley. Exotic, erotic, ironic masterpieces in full maturity: Comedy Ballet, Venus and Tannhauser, Pierrot, Lysistrata, Rape of the Lock, Savoy material, Ali Baba, Volpone, etc. This material revolutionized the art world, and is still powerful, fresh, brilliant. With *The Early Work,* all Beardsley's finest work. 174 plates, 2 in color. xiv + 176pp. 8⅛ x 11.
21817-1 Paperbound $3.75

DRAWINGS OF REMBRANDT, Rembrandt van Rijn. Complete reproduction of fabulously rare edition by Lippmann and Hofstede de Groot, completely reedited, updated, improved by Prof. Seymour Slive, Fogg Museum. Portraits, Biblical sketches, landscapes, Oriental types, nudes, episodes from classical mythology—All Rembrandt's fertile genius. Also selection of drawings by his pupils and followers. "Stunning volumes," *Saturday Review.* 550 illustrations. lxxviii + 552pp.
9⅛ x 12¼.
21485-0, 21486-9 Two volumes, Paperbound $10.00

THE DISASTERS OF WAR, Francisco Goya. One of the masterpieces of Western civilization—83 etchings that record Goya's shattering, bitter reaction to the Napoleonic war that swept through Spain after the insurrection of 1808 and to war in general. Reprint of the first edition, with three additional plates from Boston's Museum of Fine Arts. All plates facsimile size. Introduction by Philip Hofer, Fogg Museum.
v + 97pp. 9⅜ x 8¼.
21872-4 Paperbound $2.50

GRAPHIC WORKS OF ODILON REDON. Largest collection of Redon's graphic works ever assembled: 172 lithographs, 28 etchings and engravings, 9 drawings. These include some of his most famous works. All the plates from *Odilon Redon: oeuvre graphique complet,* plus additional plates. New introduction and caption translations by Alfred Werner. 209 illustrations. xxvii + 209pp. 9⅛ x 12¼.
21966-8 Paperbound $5.00

DESIGN BY ACCIDENT; A BOOK OF "ACCIDENTAL EFFECTS" FOR ARTISTS AND DESIGNERS, James F. O'Brien. Create your own unique, striking, imaginative effects by "controlled accident" interaction of materials: paints and lacquers, oil and water based paints, splatter, crackling materials, shatter, similar items. Everything you do will be different; first book on this limitless art, so useful to both fine artist and commercial artist. Full instructions. 192 plates showing "accidents," 8 in color. viii + 215pp. 8⅜ x 11¼. 21942-9 Paperbound $3.75

THE BOOK OF SIGNS, Rudolf Koch. Famed German type designer draws 493 beautiful symbols: religious, mystical, alchemical, imperial, property marks, runes, etc. Remarkable fusion of traditional and modern. Good for suggestions of timelessness, smartness, modernity. Text. vi + 104pp. 6⅛ x 9¼.
20162-7 Paperbound $1.25

HISTORY OF INDIAN AND INDONESIAN ART, Ananda K. Coomaraswamy. An unabridged republication of one of the finest books by a great scholar in Eastern art. Rich in descriptive material, history, social backgrounds; Sunga reliefs, Rajput paintings, Gupta temples, Burmese frescoes, textiles, jewelry, sculpture, etc. 400 photos. viii + 423pp. 6⅜ x 9¾. 21436-2 Paperbound $5.00

PRIMITIVE ART, Franz Boas. America's foremost anthropologist surveys textiles, ceramics, woodcarving, basketry, metalwork, etc.; patterns, technology, creation of symbols, style origins. All areas of world, but very full on Northwest Coast Indians. More than 350 illustrations of baskets, boxes, totem poles, weapons, etc. 378 pp.
20025-6 Paperbound $3.00

THE GENTLEMAN AND CABINET MAKER'S DIRECTOR, Thomas Chippendale. Full reprint (third edition, 1762) of most influential furniture book of all time, by master cabinetmaker. 200 plates, illustrating chairs, sofas, mirrors, tables, cabinets, plus 24 photographs of surviving pieces. Biographical introduction by N. Bienenstock. vi + 249pp. 9⅞ x 12¾. 21601-2 Paperbound $4.00

AMERICAN ANTIQUE FURNITURE, Edgar G. Miller, Jr. The basic coverage of all American furniture before 1840. Individual chapters cover type of furniture—clocks, tables, sideboards, etc.—chronologically, with inexhaustible wealth of data. More than 2100 photographs, all identified, commented on. Essential to all early American collectors. Introduction by H. E. Keyes. vi + 1106pp. 7⅞ x 10¾.
21599-7, 21600-4 Two volumes, Paperbound $11.00

PENNSYLVANIA DUTCH AMERICAN FOLK ART, Henry J. Kauffman. 279 photos, 28 drawings of tulipware, Fraktur script, painted tinware, toys, flowered furniture, quilts, samplers, hex signs, house interiors, etc. Full descriptive text. Excellent for tourist, rewarding for designer, collector. Map. 146pp. 7⅞ x 10¾.
21205-X Paperbound $2.50

EARLY NEW ENGLAND GRAVESTONE RUBBINGS, Edmund V. Gillon, Jr. 43 photographs, 226 carefully reproduced rubbings show heavily symbolic, sometimes macabre early gravestones, up to early 19th century. Remarkable early American primitive art, occasionally strikingly beautiful; always powerful. Text. xxvi + 207pp. 8⅜ x 11¼. 21380-3 Paperbound $3.50

ALPHABETS AND ORNAMENTS, Ernst Lehner. Well-known pictorial source for decorative alphabets, script examples, cartouches, frames, decorative title pages, calligraphic initials, borders, similar material. 14th to 19th century, mostly European. Useful in almost any graphic arts designing, varied styles. 750 illustrations. 256pp. 7 x 10. 21905-4 Paperbound $4.00

PAINTING: A CREATIVE APPROACH, Norman Colquhoun. For the beginner simple guide provides an instructive approach to painting: major stumbling blocks for beginner; overcoming them, technical points; paints and pigments; oil painting; watercolor and other media and color. New section on "plastic" paints. Glossary. Formerly *Paint Your Own Pictures*. 221pp. 22000-1 Paperbound $1.75

THE ENJOYMENT AND USE OF COLOR, Walter Sargent. Explanation of the relations between colors themselves and between colors in nature and art, including hundreds of little-known facts about color values, intensities, effects of high and low illumination, complementary colors. Many practical hints for painters, references to great masters. 7 color plates, 29 illustrations. x + 274pp. 20944-X Paperbound $2.75

THE NOTEBOOKS OF LEONARDO DA VINCI, compiled and edited by Jean Paul Richter. 1566 extracts from original manuscripts reveal the full range of Leonardo's versatile genius: all his writings on painting, sculpture, architecture, anatomy, astronomy, geography, topography, physiology, mining, music, etc., in both Italian and English, with 186 plates of manuscript pages and more than 500 additional drawings. Includes studies for the Last Supper, the lost Sforza monument, and other works. Total of xlvii + 866pp. 7⅞ x 10¾. 22572-0, 22573-9 Two volumes, Paperbound $11.00

MONTGOMERY WARD CATALOGUE OF 1895. Tea gowns, yards of flannel and pillow-case lace, stereoscopes, books of gospel hymns, the New Improved Singer Sewing Machine, side saddles, milk skimmers, straight-edged razors, high-button shoes, spittoons, and on and on . . . listing some 25,000 items, practically all illustrated. Essential to the shoppers of the 1890's, it is our truest record of the spirit of the period. Unaltered reprint of Issue No. 57, Spring and Summer 1895. Introduction by Boris Emmet. Innumerable illustrations. xiii + 624pp. 8½ x 11⅝. 22377-9 Paperbound $6.95

THE CRYSTAL PALACE EXHIBITION ILLUSTRATED CATALOGUE (LONDON, 1851). One of the wonders of the modern world—the Crystal Palace Exhibition in which all the nations of the civilized world exhibited their achievements in the arts and sciences—presented in an equally important illustrated catalogue. More than 1700 items pictured with accompanying text—ceramics, textiles, cast-iron work, carpets, pianos, sleds, razors, wall-papers, billiard tables, beehives, silverware and hundreds of other artifacts—represent the focal point of Victorian culture in the Western World. Probably the largest collection of Victorian decorative art ever assembled—indispensable for antiquarians and designers. Unabridged republication of the Art-Journal Catalogue of the Great Exhibition of 1851, with all terminal essays. New introduction by John Gloag, F.S.A. xxxiv + 426pp. 9 x 12. 22503-8 Paperbound $5.00

A HISTORY OF COSTUME, Carl Köhler. Definitive history, based on surviving pieces of clothing primarily, and paintings, statues, etc. secondarily. Highly readable text, supplemented by 594 illustrations of costumes of the ancient Mediterranean peoples, Greece and Rome, the Teutonic prehistoric period; costumes of the Middle Ages, Renaissance, Baroque, 18th and 19th centuries. Clear, measured patterns are provided for many clothing articles. Approach is practical throughout. Enlarged by Emma von Sichart. 464pp.   21030-8 Paperbound $3.50.

ORIENTAL RUGS, ANTIQUE AND MODERN, Walter A. Hawley. A complete and authoritative treatise on the Oriental rug—where they are made, by whom and how, designs and symbols, characteristics in detail of the six major groups, how to distinguish them and how to buy them. Detailed technical data is provided on periods, weaves, warps, wefts, textures, sides, ends and knots, although no technical background is required for an understanding. 11 color plates, 80 halftones, 4 maps. vi + 320pp. 6⅛ x 9⅛.   22366-3 Paperbound $5.00

TEN BOOKS ON ARCHITECTURE, Vitruvius. By any standards the most important book on architecture ever written. Early Roman discussion of aesthetics of building, construction methods, orders, sites, and every other aspect of architecture has inspired, instructed architecture for about 2,000 years. Stands behind Palladio, Michelangelo, Bramante, Wren, countless others. Definitive Morris H. Morgan translation. 68 illustrations. xii + 331pp.   20645-9 Paperbound $3.00

THE FOUR BOOKS OF ARCHITECTURE, Andrea Palladio. Translated into every major Western European language in the two centuries following its publication in 1570, this has been one of the most influential books in the history of architecture. Complete reprint of the 1738 Isaac Ware edition. New introduction by Adolf Placzek, Columbia Univ. 216 plates. xxii + 110pp. of text. 9½ x 12¾.
                     21308-0 Clothbound $12.50

STICKS AND STONES: A STUDY OF AMERICAN ARCHITECTURE AND CIVILIZATION, Lewis Mumford.One of the great classics of American cultural history. American architecture from the medieval-inspired earliest forms to the early 20th century; evolution of structure and style, and reciprocal influences on environment. 21 photographic illustrations. 238pp.   20202-X Paperbound $2.00

THE AMERICAN BUILDER'S COMPANION, Asher Benjamin. The most widely used early 19th century architectural style and source book, for colonial up into Greek Revival periods. Extensive development of geometry of carpentering, construction of sashes, frames, doors, stairs; plans and elevations of domestic and other buildings. Hundreds of thousands of houses were built according to this book, now invaluable to historians, architects, restorers, etc. 1827 edition. 59 plates. 114pp. 7⅞ x 10¾.
                     22236-5 Paperbound $3.50

DUTCH HOUSES IN THE HUDSON VALLEY BEFORE 1776, Helen Wilkinson Reynolds. The standard survey of the Dutch colonial house and outbuildings, with constructional features, decoration, and local history associated with individual homesteads. Introduction by Franklin D. Roosevelt. Map. 150 illustrations. 469pp. 6⅝ x 9¼.   21469-9 Paperbound $5.00

THE ARCHITECTURE OF COUNTRY HOUSES, Andrew J. Downing. Together with Vaux's *Villas and Cottages* this is the basic book for Hudson River Gothic architecture of the middle Victorian period. Full, sound discussions of general aspects of housing, architecture, style, decoration, furnishing, together with scores of detailed house plans, illustrations of specific buildings, accompanied by full text. Perhaps the most influential single American architectural book. 1850 edition. Introduction by J. Stewart Johnson. 321 figures, 34 architectural designs. xvi + 560pp.

22003-6 Paperbound $4.00

LOST EXAMPLES OF COLONIAL ARCHITECTURE, John Mead Howells. Full-page photographs of buildings that have disappeared or been so altered as to be denatured, including many designed by major early American architects. 245 plates. xvii + 248pp. 7⅞ x 10¾.

21143-6 Paperbound $3.50

DOMESTIC ARCHITECTURE OF THE AMERICAN COLONIES AND OF THE EARLY REPUBLIC, Fiske Kimball. Foremost architect and restorer of Williamsburg and Monticello covers nearly 200 homes between 1620-1825. Architectural details, construction, style features, special fixtures, floor plans, etc. Generally considered finest work in its area. 219 illustrations of houses, doorways, windows, capital mantels. xx + 314pp. 7⅞ x 10¾.

21743-4 Paperbound $4.00

EARLY AMERICAN ROOMS: 1650-1858, edited by Russell Hawes Kettell. Tour of 12 rooms, each representative of a different era in American history and each furnished, decorated, designed and occupied in the style of the era. 72 plans and elevations, 8-page color section, etc., show fabrics, wall papers, arrangements, etc. Full descriptive text. xvii + 200pp. of text. 8⅜ x 11¼.

21633-0 Paperbound $5.00

THE FITZWILLIAM VIRGINAL BOOK, edited by J. Fuller Maitland and W. B. Squire. Full modern printing of famous early 17th-century ms. volume of 300 works by Morley, Byrd, Bull, Gibbons, etc. For piano or other modern keyboard instrument; easy to read format. xxxvi + 938pp. 8⅜ x 11.

21068-5, 21069-3 Two volumes, Paperbound $10.00

KEYBOARD MUSIC, Johann Sebastian Bach. Bach Gesellschaft edition. A rich selection of Bach's masterpieces for the harpsichord: the six English Suites, six French Suites, the six Partitas (Clavierübung part I), the Goldberg Variations (Clavierübung part IV), the fifteen Two-Part Inventions and the fifteen Three-Part Sinfonias. Clearly reproduced on large sheets with ample margins; eminently playable. vi + 312pp. 8⅛ x 11.

22360-4 Paperbound $5.00

THE MUSIC OF BACH: AN INTRODUCTION, Charles Sanford Terry. A fine, nontechnical introduction to Bach's music, both instrumental and vocal. Covers organ music, chamber music, passion music, other types. Analyzes themes, developments, innovations. x + 114pp.

21075-8 Paperbound $1.50

BEETHOVEN AND HIS NINE SYMPHONIES, Sir George Grove. Noted British musicologist provides best history, analysis, commentary on symphonies. Very thorough, rigorously accurate; necessary to both advanced student and amateur music lover. 436 musical passages. vii + 407 pp.

20334-4 Paperbound $2.75

JOHANN SEBASTIAN BACH, Philipp Spitta. One of the great classics of musicology, this definitive analysis of Bach's music (and life) has never been surpassed. Lucid, nontechnical analyses of hundreds of pieces (30 pages devoted to St. Matthew Passion, 26 to B Minor Mass). Also includes major analysis of 18th-century music. 450 musical examples. 40-page musical supplement. Total of xx + 1799pp.
(EUK) 22278-0, 22279-9 Two volumes, Clothbound $17.50

MOZART AND HIS PIANO CONCERTOS, Cuthbert Girdlestone. The only full-length study of an important area of Mozart's creativity. Provides detailed analyses of all 23 concertos, traces inspirational sources. 417 musical examples. Second edition. 509pp.
21271-8 Paperbound $3.50

THE PERFECT WAGNERITE: A COMMENTARY ON THE NIBLUNG'S RING, George Bernard Shaw. Brilliant and still relevant criticism in remarkable essays on Wagner's Ring cycle, Shaw's ideas on political and social ideology behind the plots, role of Leitmotifs, vocal requisites, etc. Prefaces. xxi + 136pp.
(USO) 21707-8 Paperbound $1.75

DON GIOVANNI, W. A. Mozart. Complete libretto, modern English translation; biographies of composer and librettist; accounts of early performances and critical reaction. Lavishly illustrated. All the material you need to understand and appreciate this great work. Dover Opera Guide and Libretto Series; translated and introduced by Ellen Bleiler. 92 illustrations. 209pp.
21134-7 Paperbound $2.00

BASIC ELECTRICITY, U. S. Bureau of Naval Personel. Originally a training course, best non-technical coverage of basic theory of electricity and its applications. Fundamental concepts, batteries, circuits, conductors and wiring techniques, AC and DC, inductance and capacitance, generators, motors, transformers, magnetic amplifiers, synchros, servomechanisms, etc. Also covers blue-prints, electrical diagrams, etc. Many questions, with answers. 349 illustrations. x + 448pp. 6½ x 9¼.
20973-3 Paperbound $3.50

REPRODUCTION OF SOUND, Edgar Villchur. Thorough coverage for laymen of high fidelity systems, reproducing systems in general, needles, amplifiers, preamps, loudspeakers, feedback, explaining physical background. "A rare talent for making technicalities vividly comprehensible," R. Darrell, *High Fidelity*. 69 figures. iv + 92pp.
21515-6 Paperbound $1.35

HEAR ME TALKIN' TO YA: THE STORY OF JAZZ AS TOLD BY THE MEN WHO MADE IT, Nat Shapiro and Nat Hentoff. Louis Armstrong, Fats Waller, Jo Jones, Clarence Williams, Billy Holiday, Duke Ellington, Jelly Roll Morton and dozens of other jazz greats tell how it was in Chicago's South Side, New Orleans, depression Harlem and the modern West Coast as jazz was born and grew. xvi + 429pp.
21726-4 Paperbound $3.00

FABLES OF AESOP, translated by Sir Roger L'Estrange. A reproduction of the very rare 1931 Paris edition; a selection of the most interesting fables, together with 50 imaginative drawings by Alexander Calder. v + 128pp. 6½x9¼.
21780-9 Paperbound $1.50

AGAINST THE GRAIN (A REBOURS), Joris K. Huysmans. Filled with weird images, evidences of a bizarre imagination, exotic experiments with hallucinatory drugs, rich tastes and smells and the diversions of its sybarite hero Duc Jean des Esseintes, this classic novel pushed 19th-century literary decadence to its limits. Full unabridged edition. Do not confuse this with abridged editions generally sold. Introduction by Havelock Ellis. xlix + 206pp. 22190-3 Paperbound $2.50

VARIORUM SHAKESPEARE: HAMLET. Edited by Horace H. Furness; a landmark of American scholarship. Exhaustive footnotes and appendices treat all doubtful words and phrases, as well as suggested critical emendations throughout the play's history. First volume contains editor's own text, collated with all Quartos and Folios. Second volume contains full first Quarto, translations of Shakespeare's sources (Belleforest, and Saxo Grammaticus), Der Bestrafte Brudermord, and many essays on critical and historical points of interest by major authorities of past and present. Includes details of staging and costuming over the years. By far the best edition available for serious students of Shakespeare. Total of xx + 905pp. 21004-9, 21005-7, 2 volumes, Paperbound $7.00

A LIFE OF WILLIAM SHAKESPEARE, Sir Sidney Lee. This is the standard life of Shakespeare, summarizing everything known about Shakespeare and his plays. Incredibly rich in material, broad in coverage, clear and judicious, it has served thousands as the best introduction to Shakespeare. 1931 edition. 9 plates. xxix + 792pp. 21967-4 Paperbound $4.50

MASTERS OF THE DRAMA, John Gassner. Most comprehensive history of the drama in print, covering every tradition from Greeks to modern Europe and America, including India, Far East, etc. Covers more than 800 dramatists, 2000 plays, with biographical material, plot summaries, theatre history, criticism, etc. "Best of its kind in English," New Republic. 77 illustrations. xxii + 890pp. 20100-7 Clothbound $10.00

THE EVOLUTION OF THE ENGLISH LANGUAGE, George McKnight. The growth of English, from the 14th century to the present. Unusual, non-technical account presents basic information in very interesting form: sound shifts, change in grammar and syntax, vocabulary growth, similar topics. Abundantly illustrated with quotations. Formerly Modern English in the Making. xii + 590pp. 21932-1 Paperbound $4.00

AN ETYMOLOGICAL DICTIONARY OF MODERN ENGLISH, Ernest Weekley. Fullest, richest work of its sort, by foremost British lexicographer. Detailed word histories, including many colloquial and archaic words; extensive quotations. Do not confuse this with the Concise Etymological Dictionary, which is much abridged. Total of xxvii + 830pp. 6½ x 9¼. 21873-2, 21874-0 Two volumes, Paperbound $7.90

FLATLAND: A ROMANCE OF MANY DIMENSIONS, E. A. Abbott. Classic of science-fiction explores ramifications of life in a two-dimensional world, and what happens when a three-dimensional being intrudes. Amusing reading, but also useful as introduction to thought about hyperspace. Introduction by Banesh Hoffmann. 16 illustrations. xx + 103pp. 20001-9 Paperbound $1.25

POEMS OF ANNE BRADSTREET, edited with an introduction by Robert Hutchinson. A new selection of poems by America's first poet and perhaps the first significant woman poet in the English language. 48 poems display her development in works of considerable variety—love poems, domestic poems, religious meditations, formal elegies, "quaternions," etc. Notes, bibliography. viii + 222pp.
22160-1 Paperbound $2.50

THREE GOTHIC NOVELS: THE CASTLE OF OTRANTO BY HORACE WALPOLE; VATHEK BY WILLIAM BECKFORD; THE VAMPYRE BY JOHN POLIDORI, WITH FRAGMENT OF A NOVEL BY LORD BYRON, edited by E. F. Bleiler. The first Gothic novel, by Walpole; the finest Oriental tale in English, by Beckford; powerful Romantic supernatural story in versions by Polidori and Byron. All extremely important in history of literature; all still exciting, packed with supernatural thrills, ghosts, haunted castles, magic, etc. xl + 291pp.
21232-7 Paperbound $2.50

THE BEST TALES OF HOFFMANN, E. T. A. Hoffmann. 10 of Hoffmann's most important stories, in modern re-editings of standard translations: Nutcracker and the King of Mice, Signor Formica, Automata, The Sandman, Rath Krespel, The Golden Flowerpot, Master Martin the Cooper, The Mines of Falun, The King's Betrothed, A New Year's Eve Adventure. 7 illustrations by Hoffmann. Edited by E. F. Bleiler. xxxix + 419pp. 21793-0 Paperbound $3.00

GHOST AND HORROR STORIES OF AMBROSE BIERCE, Ambrose Bierce. 23 strikingly modern stories of the horrors latent in the human mind: The Eyes of the Panther, The Damned Thing, An Occurrence at Owl Creek Bridge, An Inhabitant of Carcosa, etc., plus the dream-essay, Visions of the Night. Edited by E. F. Bleiler. xxii + 199pp. 20767-6 Paperbound $1.50

BEST GHOST STORIES OF J. S. LEFANU, J. Sheridan LeFanu. Finest stories by Victorian master often considered greatest supernatural writer of all. Carmilla, Green Tea, The Haunted Baronet, The Familiar, and 12 others. Most never before available in the U. S. A. Edited by E. F. Bleiler. 8 illustrations from Victorian publications. xvii + 467pp. 20415-4 Paperbound $3.00

MATHEMATICAL FOUNDATIONS OF INFORMATION THEORY, A. I. Khinchin. Comprehensive introduction to work of Shannon, McMillan, Feinstein and Khinchin, placing these investigations on a rigorous mathematical basis. Covers entropy concept in probability theory, uniqueness theorem, Shannon's inequality, ergodic sources, the E property, martingale concept, noise, Feinstein's fundamental lemma, Shanon's first and second theorems. Translated by R. A. Silverman and M. D. Friedman. iii + 120pp. 60434-9 Paperbound $2.00

SEVEN SCIENCE FICTION NOVELS, H. G. Wells. The standard collection of the great novels. Complete, unabridged. *First Men in the Moon, Island of Dr. Moreau, War of the Worlds, Food of the Gods, Invisible Man, Time Machine, In the Days of the Comet.* Not only science fiction fans, but every educated person owes it to himself to read these novels. 1015pp. (USO) 20264-X Clothbound $6.00

LAST AND FIRST MEN AND STAR MAKER, TWO SCIENCE FICTION NOVELS, Olaf Stapledon. Greatest future histories in science fiction. In the first, human intelligence is the "hero," through strange paths of evolution, interplanetary invasions, incredible technologies, near extinctions and reemergences. Star Maker describes the quest of a band of star rovers for intelligence itself, through time and space: weird inhuman civilizations, crustacean minds, symbiotic worlds, etc. Complete, unabridged. v + 438pp. (USO) 21962-3 Paperbound $2.50

THREE PROPHETIC NOVELS, H. G. WELLS. Stages of a consistently planned future for mankind. *When the Sleeper Wakes,* and *A Story of the Days to Come,* anticipate *Brave New World* and *1984,* in the 21st Century; *The Time Machine,* only complete version in print, shows farther future and the end of mankind. All show Wells's greatest gifts as storyteller and novelist. Edited by E. F. Bleiler. x + 335pp. (USO) 20605-X Paperbound $2.50

THE DEVIL'S DICTIONARY, Ambrose Bierce. America's own Oscar Wilde— Ambrose Bierce—offers his barbed iconoclastic wisdom in over 1,000 definitions hailed by H. L. Mencken as "some of the most gorgeous witticisms in the English language." 145pp. 20487-1 Paperbound $1.25

MAX AND MORITZ, Wilhelm Busch. Great children's classic, father of comic strip, of two bad boys, Max and Moritz. Also Ker and Plunk (Plisch und Plumm), Cat and Mouse, Deceitful Henry, Ice-Peter, The Boy and the Pipe, and five other pieces. Original German, with English translation. Edited by H. Arthur Klein; translations by various hands and H. Arthur Klein. vi + 216pp.
20181-3 Paperbound $2.00

PIGS IS PIGS AND OTHER FAVORITES, Ellis Parker Butler. The title story is one of the best humor short stories, as Mike Flannery obfuscates biology and English. Also included, That Pup of Murchison's, The Great American Pie Company, and Perkins of Portland. 14 illustrations. v + 109pp. 21532-6 Paperbound $1.25

THE PETERKIN PAPERS, Lucretia P. Hale. It takes genius to be as stupidly mad as the Peterkins, as they decide to become wise, celebrate the "Fourth," keep a cow, and otherwise strain the resources of the Lady from Philadelphia. Basic book of American humor. 153 illustrations. 219pp. 20794-3 Paperbound $2.00

PERRAULT'S FAIRY TALES, translated by A. E. Johnson and S. R. Littlewood, with 34 full-page illustrations by Gustave Doré. All the original Perrault stories— Cinderella, Sleeping Beauty, Bluebeard, Little Red Riding Hood, Puss in Boots, Tom Thumb, etc.—with their witty verse morals and the magnificent illustrations of Doré. One of the five or six great books of European fairy tales. viii + 117pp. 8⅛ x 11. 22311-6 Paperbound $2.00

OLD HUNGARIAN FAIRY TALES, Baroness Orczy. Favorites translated and adapted by author of the *Scarlet Pimpernel.* Eight fairy tales include "The Suitors of Princess Fire-Fly," "The Twin Hunchbacks," "Mr. Cuttlefish's Love Story," and "The Enchanted Cat." This little volume of magic and adventure will captivate children as it has for generations. 90 drawings by Montagu Barstow. 96pp.
(USO) 22293-4 Paperbound $1.95

THE RED FAIRY BOOK, Andrew Lang. Lang's color fairy books have long been children's favorites. This volume includes Rapunzel, Jack and the Bean-stalk and 35 other stories, familiar and unfamiliar. 4 plates, 93 illustrations x + 367pp.

21673-X Paperbound $2.50

THE BLUE FAIRY BOOK, Andrew Lang. Lang's tales come from all countries and all times. Here are 37 tales from Grimm, the Arabian Nights, Greek Mythology, and other fascinating sources. 8 plates, 130 illustrations. xi + 390pp.

21437-0 Paperbound $2.75

HOUSEHOLD STORIES BY THE BROTHERS GRIMM. Classic English-language edition of the well-known tales — Rumpelstiltskin, Snow White, Hansel and Gretel, The Twelve Brothers, Faithful John, Rapunzel, Tom Thumb (52 stories in all). Translated into simple, straightforward English by Lucy Crane. Ornamented with headpieces, vignettes, elaborate decorative initials and a dozen full-page illustrations by Walter Crane. x + 269pp.

21080-4 Paperbound **$2.00**

THE MERRY ADVENTURES OF ROBIN HOOD, Howard Pyle. The finest modern versions of the traditional ballads and tales about the great English outlaw. Howard Pyle's complete prose version, with every word, every illustration of the first edition. Do not confuse this facsimile of the original (1883) with modern editions that change text or illustrations. 23 plates plus many page decorations. xxii + 296pp.

22043-5 Paperbound $2.75

THE STORY OF KING ARTHUR AND HIS KNIGHTS, Howard Pyle. The finest children's version of the life of King Arthur; brilliantly retold by Pyle, with 48 of his most imaginative illustrations. xviii + 313pp. 6⅛ x 9¼.

21445-1 Paperbound $2.50

THE WONDERFUL WIZARD OF OZ, L. Frank Baum. America's finest children's book in facsimile of first edition with all Denslow illustrations in full color. The edition a child should have. Introduction by Martin Gardner. 23 color plates, scores of drawings. iv + 267pp.

20691-2 Paperbound $2.50

THE MARVELOUS LAND OF OZ, L. Frank Baum. The second Oz book, every bit as imaginative as the Wizard. The hero is a boy named Tip, but the Scarecrow and the Tin Woodman are back, as is the Oz magic. 16 color plates, 120 drawings by John R. Neill. 287pp.

20692-0 Paperbound $2.50

THE MAGICAL MONARCH OF MO, L. Frank Baum. Remarkable adventures in a land even stranger than Oz. The best of Baum's books not in the Oz series. 15 color plates and dozens of drawings by Frank Verbeck. xviii + 237pp.

21892-9 Paperbound $2.25

THE BAD CHILD'S BOOK OF BEASTS, MORE BEASTS FOR WORSE CHILDREN, A MORAL ALPHABET, Hilaire Belloc. Three complete humor classics in one volume. Be kind to the frog, and do not call him names . . . and 28 other whimsical animals. Familiar favorites and some not so well known. Illustrated by Basil Blackwell. 156pp.

(USO) 20749-8 Paperbound $1.50

EAST O' THE SUN AND WEST O' THE MOON, George W. Dasent. Considered the best of all translations of these Norwegian folk tales, this collection has been enjoyed by generations of children (and folklorists too). Includes True and Untrue, Why the Sea is Salt, East O' the Sun and West O' the Moon, Why the Bear is Stumpy-Tailed, Boots and the Troll, The Cock and the Hen, Rich Peter the Pedlar, and 52 more. The only edition with all 59 tales. 77 illustrations by Erik Werenskiold and Theodor Kittelsen. xv + 418pp.   22521-6 Paperbound $3.50

GOOPS AND HOW TO BE THEM, Gelett Burgess. Classic of tongue-in-cheek humor, masquerading as etiquette book. 87 verses, twice as many cartoons, show mischievous Goops as they demonstrate to children virtues of table manners, neatness, courtesy, etc. Favorite for generations. viii + 88pp. 6½ x 9¼.
                                        22233-0 Paperbound $1.50

ALICE'S ADVENTURES UNDER GROUND, Lewis Carroll. The first version, quite different from the final *Alice in Wonderland,* printed out by Carroll himself with his own illustrations. Complete facsimile of the "million dollar" manuscript Carroll gave to Alice Liddell in 1864. Introduction by Martin Gardner. viii + 96pp. Title and dedication pages in color.   21482-6 Paperbound $1.25

THE BROWNIES, THEIR BOOK, Palmer Cox. Small as mice, cunning as foxes, exuberant and full of mischief, the Brownies go to the zoo, toy shop, seashore, circus, etc., in 24 verse adventures and 266 illustrations. Long a favorite, since their first appearance in St. Nicholas Magazine. xi + 144pp. 6⅝ x 9¼.
                                        21265-3 Paperbound $1.75

SONGS OF CHILDHOOD, Walter De La Mare. Published (under the pseudonym Walter Ramal) when De La Mare was only 29, this charming collection has long been a favorite children's book. A facsimile of the first edition in paper, the 47 poems capture the simplicity of the nursery rhyme and the ballad, including such lyrics as I Met Eve, Tartary, The Silver Penny. vii + 106pp. (USO) 21972-0 Paperbound
                                                            $2.00

THE COMPLETE NONSENSE OF EDWARD LEAR, Edward Lear. The finest 19th-century humorist-cartoonist in full: all nonsense limericks, zany alphabets, Owl and Pussycat, songs, nonsense botany, and more than 500 illustrations by Lear himself. Edited by Holbrook Jackson. xxix + 287pp.   (USO) 20167-8 Paperbound $2.00

BILLY WHISKERS: THE AUTOBIOGRAPHY OF A GOAT, Frances Trego Montgomery. A favorite of children since the early 20th century, here are the escapades of that rambunctious, irresistible and mischievous goat—Billy Whiskers. Much in the spirit of *Peck's Bad Boy,* this is a book that children never tire of reading or hearing. All the original familiar illustrations by W. H. Fry are included: 6 color plates, 18 black and white drawings. 159pp.   22345-0 Paperbound $2.00

MOTHER GOOSE MELODIES. Faithful republication of the fabulously rare Munroe and Francis "copyright 1833" Boston edition—the most important Mother Goose collection, usually referred to as the "original." Familiar rhymes plus many rare ones, with wonderful old woodcut illustrations. Edited by E. F. Bleiler. 128pp. 4½ x 6⅜.   22577-1 Paperbound $1.00

TWO LITTLE SAVAGES; BEING THE ADVENTURES OF TWO BOYS WHO LIVED AS INDIANS AND WHAT THEY LEARNED, Ernest Thompson Seton. Great classic of nature and boyhood provides a vast range of woodlore in most palatable form, a genuinely entertaining story. Two farm boys build a teepee in woods and live in it for a month, working out Indian solutions to living problems, star lore, birds and animals, plants, etc. 293 illustrations. vii + 286pp.

20985-7 Paperbound $2.50

PETER PIPER'S PRACTICAL PRINCIPLES OF PLAIN & PERFECT PRONUNCIATION. Alliterative jingles and tongue-twisters of surprising charm, that made their first appearance in America about 1830. Republished in full with the spirited woodcut illustrations from this earliest American edition. 32pp. $4\frac{1}{2}$ x $6\frac{3}{8}$.

22560-7 Paperbound $1.00

SCIENCE EXPERIMENTS AND AMUSEMENTS FOR CHILDREN, Charles Vivian. 73 easy experiments, requiring only materials found at home or easily available, such as candles, coins, steel wool, etc.; illustrate basic phenomena like vacuum, simple chemical reaction, etc. All safe. Modern, well-planned. Formerly *Science Games for Children*. 102 photos, numerous drawings. 96pp. $6\frac{1}{8}$ x $9\frac{1}{4}$.

21856-2 Paperbound $1.25

AN INTRODUCTION TO CHESS MOVES AND TACTICS SIMPLY EXPLAINED, Leonard Barden. Informal intermediate introduction, quite strong in explaining reasons for moves. Covers basic material, tactics, important openings, traps, positional play in middle game, end game. Attempts to isolate patterns and recurrent configurations. Formerly *Chess*. 58 figures. 102pp. (USO) 21210-6 Paperbound $1.25

LASKER'S MANUAL OF CHESS, Dr. Emanuel Lasker. Lasker was not only one of the five great World Champions, he was also one of the ablest expositors, theorists, and analysts. In many ways, his Manual, permeated with his philosophy of battle, filled with keen insights, is one of the greatest works ever written on chess. Filled with analyzed games by the great players. A single-volume library that will profit almost any chess player, beginner or master. 308 diagrams. xli x 349pp.

20640-8 Paperbound $2.75

THE MASTER BOOK OF MATHEMATICAL RECREATIONS, Fred Schuh. In opinion of many the finest work ever prepared on mathematical puzzles, stunts, recreations; exhaustively thorough explanations of mathematics involved, analysis of effects, citation of puzzles and games. Mathematics involved is elementary. Translated bv F. Göbel. 194 figures. xxiv + 430pp. 22134-2 Paperbound $3.50

MATHEMATICS, MAGIC AND MYSTERY, Martin Gardner. Puzzle editor for Scientific American explains mathematics behind various mystifying tricks: card tricks, stage "mind reading," coin and match tricks, counting out games, geometric dissections, etc. Probability sets, theory of numbers clearly explained. Also provides more than 400 tricks, guaranteed to work, that you can do. 135 illustrations. xii + 176pp.

20335-2 Paperbound $1.75

MATHEMATICAL PUZZLES FOR BEGINNERS AND ENTHUSIASTS, Geoffrey Mott-Smith. 189 puzzles from easy to difficult—involving arithmetic, logic, algebra, properties of digits, probability, etc.—for enjoyment and mental stimulus. Explanation of mathematical principles behind the puzzles. 135 illustrations. viii + 248pp.
20198-8 Paperbound $1.75

PAPER FOLDING FOR BEGINNERS, William D. Murray and Francis J. Rigney. Easiest book on the market, clearest instructions on making interesting, beautiful origami. Sail boats, cups, roosters, frogs that move legs, bonbon boxes, standing birds, etc. 40 projects; more than 275 diagrams and photographs. 94pp.
20713-7 Paperbound $1.00

TRICKS AND GAMES ON THE POOL TABLE, Fred Herrmann. 79 tricks and games— some solitaires, some for two or more players, some competitive games—to entertain you between formal games. Mystifying shots and throws, unusual caroms, tricks involving such props as cork, coins, a hat, etc. Formerly *Fun on the Pool Table*. 77 figures. 95pp.
21814-7 Paperbound $1.25

HAND SHADOWS TO BE THROWN UPON THE WALL: A SERIES OF NOVEL AND AMUSING FIGURES FORMED BY THE HAND, Henry Bursill. Delightful picturebook from great-grandfather's day shows how to make 18 different hand shadows: a bird that flies, duck that quacks, dog that wags his tail, camel, goose, deer, boy, turtle, etc. Only book of its sort. vi + 33pp. 6½ x 9¼. 21779-5 Paperbound $1.00

WHITTLING AND WOODCARVING, E. J. Tangerman. 18th printing of best book on market. "If you can cut a potato you can carve" toys and puzzles, chains, chessmen, caricatures, masks, frames, woodcut blocks, surface patterns, much more. Information on tools, woods, techniques. Also goes into serious wood sculpture from Middle Ages to present, East and West. 464 photos, figures. x + 293pp.
20965-2 Paperbound $2.00

HISTORY OF PHILOSOPHY, Julián Marias. Possibly the clearest, most easily followed, best planned, most useful one-volume history of philosophy on the market; neither skimpy nor overfull. Full details on system of every major philosopher and dozens of less important thinkers from pre-Socratics up to Existentialism and later. Strong on many European figures usually omitted. Has gone through dozens of editions in Europe. 1966 edition, translated by Stanley Appelbaum and Clarence Strowbridge. xviii + 505pp. 21739-6 Paperbound $3.50

YOGA: A SCIENTIFIC EVALUATION, Kovoor T. Behanan. Scientific but non-technical study of physiological results of yoga exercises; done under auspices of Yale U. Relations to Indian thought, to psychoanalysis, etc. 16 photos. xxiii + 270pp.
20505-3 Paperbound $2.50